# Pure Maths in Practice

## Jean Holderness

Causeway Books

Published by Causeway Press Ltd.,
P.O. Box 13, Ormskirk, Lancs L39 5HP
First published 1986

*British Library Cataloguing in Publication Data*

Holderness, Jean
  Pure maths in practice.
  1. Mathematics—1961–
  I. Title
 510    QA37.2

  ISBN 0-946183-22-8

First impression 1986
Reprinted 1988

Printed in England by
J. W. Arrowsmith Ltd., Bristol

# Preface

**Pure Maths in Practice** book is written for students following a course in Pure Mathematics at Advanced Level, who need to review the syllabus, consolidate basic ideas and practise a variety of questions.

The national common core adopted by the GCE Examination Boards is fully covered in the first 11 chapters, together with a few additional topics. The remaining 4 chapters, covering Complex numbers, Simple differential equations and Coordinate geometry complete the requirements for the syllabuses of the JMB, AEB and Southern boards, and thus the book also covers a great proportion of the work needed for the other examination boards.

The book is planned to help students of varying ability. Each chapter contains bookwork of basic facts with worked examples where appropriate, and then exercises to reinforce these topics. The exercises contain a variety of types of questions, starting with straightforward ones to encourage progress for the less-able students, and also including more challenging ones. The basic work in Algebra, Trigonometry and Calculus is covered in the earlier chapters and developed further in later chapters. To ensure a constant recall of each topic there are miscellaneous revision exercises after every three chapters. These include some multi-choice questions, since occasionally it is useful to try to work more quickly without having to write down every detail of the solution. There are final revision exercises at the end of the book which could be used under timed conditions as practice papers. A formulae checklist is also included, since the formula booklet now made available to most candidates in the examination is unlikely to contain all that may be needed and the other formulae must be learnt. The book includes some suggestions for study and for planning for the examination.

I am grateful to friends, colleagues and also to my publishers for their help and encouragement during the preparation of this book.

Jean Holderness

*To the memory of Agnes Thompson*

# Contents

**To the student:**

# 1 Making Plans

Here are some questions to think about:
1    Do you want to pass 'A' Level Maths?
2    Do you need to pass 'A' Level Maths?
3    If the previous answer is 'Yes', what grade must you achieve?
4    On your present attainment and progress, what grade do you estimate you will get?
5    How much time per week do you spend on studying Pure Maths?
6    How many weeks (or months) are there left before you take your Pure Maths exam?
7    Which parts of the syllabus do you enjoy, or find easy?
8    Which parts of the syllabus do you dislike, or find difficult?

Now, if you have not already done so, you must organise yourself and your work. If you need a certain grade to follow on to the next stage of your career then it is up to you to try to achieve that grade. You may not need to make any extra effort because you have been working conscientiously from the beginning of your course. It may not be possible to make any extra effort because you are doing all you are capable of doing. (In that case, especially if you need to improve, consider whether a different line of approach might help.) But perhaps up to now you have been doing only the minimum, and time is getting on, and you know you could be trying harder and be spending a bit more time on your work.

So analyse your present position and make a plan of action for the future. As well as Pure Maths, you will have work to do in Applied Maths or Mechanics or Statistics, and probably in one or two other subjects, so take these into consideration. Also allow yourself some free time for physical activity and for other interests. Reconsider your plan from time to time to see if it is working or if it needs amending.

**Private study**
In addition to lessons and set homework you should spend some time each week on individual study. Make a plan for this depending on how much time you have available and what you need to learn or practise.

This book has been arranged in an order suitable for revision although you should decide for yourself how you can best use it. Most of the topics in the first 11 chapters of the book should be in your syllabus. The important exceptions are 'starred' and you should consult your own syllabus to see if you need to include these items. You should also check to see which of the topics in Chapters 12–15 are necessary.

The first chapter deals with Algebra and the second with trigonometric functions, because you need to be confident with these for use with most of the other topics. The first two exercises contain revision of elementary algebraic techniques for those who need to begin at this stage.

Perhaps you will decide to work through one chapter every week or every fortnight. Learn the relevant formulae and methods as you go along. Do not do every question in every chapter—leave out the straightforward ones if you want something more challenging, or leave out the longer ones so as to go on to the next topic if that is making the best use of your time.

Make a list of difficulties and try to sort them out. If you can't find the answers yourself then <u>ask</u> someone to help you, either your teacher, another student in your class, a student from another class, or anyone else you know who understands Advanced Level Maths.

Keep a list of what you achieve and you will find it encouraging when after a few weeks you can see you are making real progress.

# 1 Algebra

**Some useful identities:**

$x - y = -(y - x)$

$x^2 + 2xy + y^2 = (x + y)^2$

$x^2 - 2xy + y^2 = (x - y)^2$

$x^2 + y^2$ has no real factors

$x^2 - y^2 = (x + y)(x - y)$

$x^3 + y^3 = (x + y)(x^2 - xy + y^2)$

$x^3 - y^3 = (x - y)(x^2 + xy + y^2)$

## Quadratic Equations

$$ax^2 + bx + c = 0$$

The roots are

$$x = \frac{-b \pm \sqrt{b^2 - 4ac}}{2a}$$

If $b^2 - 4ac > 0$,† the roots are real and unequal.

(If $b^2 - 4ac$ is a perfect square the roots are rational.)

If $b^2 - 4ac = 0$, the roots are real and equal.

If $b^2 - 4ac < 0$, there are no real roots, but there are complex roots.

## Example 1.1

Solve the equation $3x^2 - 5x + 1 = 0$

The roots are $x = \dfrac{-b \pm \sqrt{b^2 - 4ac}}{2a}$ where $a = 3, b = -5, c = 1$

$$= \frac{5 \pm \sqrt{25 - 12}}{6}$$

$$= \frac{5 \pm \sqrt{13}}{6}$$

(These are the exact roots. To 3 significant figures they are 1.43 and 0.232)

---

† When $a$, $b$ and $c$ are real.

**Completing the square**

Since $x^2 + 2ax + a^2 = (x+a)^2$

then $x^2 + 2ax$ will be made into a perfect square by adding $a^2$.

Add (half the coefficient of $x$)$^2$.

## Example 1.2

To complete the square for $x^2 + 6x$, and $x^2 - 5x$

$x^2 + 6x + 9 = (x+3)^2$

$x^2 - 5x + 6\frac{1}{4} = (x - 2\frac{1}{2})^2$

## Example 1.3

Express $2x^2 + 3x + 5$ in the form $2(x+a)^2 + b$

$2(x^2 + \frac{3}{2}x) + 5$

$= 2(x + \frac{3}{4})^2 + 5 - 2 \times \frac{9}{16}$

$= 2(x + \frac{3}{4})^2 + 3\frac{7}{8}$

## Example 1.4

Solve the equation $x^2 - 10x + 6 = 0$

$x^2 - 10x = -6$

Complete the square by adding 25 to both sides

$(x - 5)^2 = 19$

Take the square root of both sides

$x - 5 = \pm\sqrt{19}$

$x = 5 \pm \sqrt{19}$

(To 3 significant figures these roots are 9.36 and 0.641)

## * Relation between the roots and coefficients of a quadratic equation

If the roots are $\alpha$, $\beta$ then the equation can be written as $(x - \alpha)(x - \beta) = 0$

i.e. $x^2 - (\alpha + \beta)x + \alpha\beta = 0$

Comparing with the general equation $ax^2 + bx + c = 0$,

$$\alpha + \beta = -\frac{b}{a}, \qquad \alpha\beta = \frac{c}{a}.$$

If the roots of an equation are known then the equation can be written as

$x^2 - (\text{sum of roots})x + (\text{product of roots}) = 0$.

---

Topics marked * are not included in the national common core and may not be needed for your syllabus.

**Example 1.5**

If the roots of $3x^2 - 5x + 1 = 0$ are $\alpha, \beta$; find the equation whose roots are $\dfrac{\alpha}{\beta}$ and $\dfrac{\beta}{\alpha}$.

$$\alpha + \beta = -\frac{b}{a} = \tfrac{5}{3}, \qquad \alpha\beta = \frac{c}{a} = \tfrac{1}{3}$$

New equation: Sum of roots $= \dfrac{\alpha}{\beta} + \dfrac{\beta}{\alpha}$

$$= \frac{(\alpha + \beta)^2 - 2\alpha\beta}{\alpha\beta}$$

$$= \frac{\frac{25}{9} - \frac{2}{3}}{\frac{1}{3}} = \frac{19}{3}$$

Product of roots $= \dfrac{\alpha}{\beta} \cdot \dfrac{\beta}{\alpha} = 1$

New equation is $x^2 - \tfrac{19}{3}x + 1 = 0$

i.e. $3x^2 - 19x + 3 = 0$

### Checking equations

If to solve an equation you need to square both sides, additional solutions may be introduced which do not satisfy the original equation.

By substitution, check all solutions in the original equation.

**Example 1.6**

Solve the equation $\sqrt{3x + 6} = \sqrt{2x + 5} + 1$

Square both sides

$3x + 6 = 2x + 5 + 2\sqrt{2x + 5} + 1$

$\therefore \qquad x = 2\sqrt{2x + 5}$

Square both sides

$x^2 = 8x + 20$

$\therefore \quad x^2 - 8x - 20 = 0$

$\therefore \quad (x + 2)(x - 10) = 0$

$x = -2$ or $10$

The solution is $x = 10$

($x = -2$ does not satisfy the original equation.)

### * Simultaneous Equations, One Linear and One Quadratic

From the linear equation, find $y$ in terms of $x$.

Substitute this expression for $y$ in the quadratic equation to find the values of $x$.

Use these $x$-values in the linear equation to find the corresponding values of $y$. (In some cases it might be simpler to find $x$ in terms of $y$, etc., for instance, if there is no term in $x^2$.)

**Example 1.7**

Solve the simultaneous equations $2x + 3y = 4$

$$3x^2 + 4y^2 - 7x - 8y + 7xy + 4 = 0$$

From the linear equation, $y = \dfrac{4 - 2x}{3}$

Substitute for $y$ in the quadratic equation

$$3x^2 + 4\left(\frac{4 - 2x}{3}\right)^2 - 7x - 8\left(\frac{4 - 2x}{3}\right) + 7x\left(\frac{4 - 2x}{3}\right) + 4 = 0$$

Multiplying every term by 9 leads to

$$27x^2 + 64 - 64x + 16x^2 - 63x - 96 + 48x + 84x - 42x^2 + 36 = 0$$

$$\therefore \quad x^2 + 5x + 4 = 0$$

$$(x + 1)(x + 4) = 0$$

$$x = -1 \text{ or } x = -4$$

When $x = -1$, $y = \dfrac{4 - 2x}{3} = 2$; when $x = -4$, $y = 4$

The solution is $x = -1$, $y = 2$ or $x = -4$, $y = 4$.

## The Factor Theorem

If a polynomial $f(x)$ is such that $f(a) = 0$, then $f(x)$ has a factor $x - a$.

To show this:

$f(x) = (x - a)Q(x) + R$           where $Q(x)$ is the quotient and R is the remainder when $f(x)$ is divided by $x - a$

$f(a) = (a - a)Q(a) + R$
If $f(a) = 0$, $R = 0$
There is no remainder, so $x - a$ is a factor.

**Example 1.8**

Factorise $6x^3 + 13x^2 + x - 2$

Since the expression starts with $6x^3$ a linear factor involves $x$, $2x$, $3x$ or $6x$.
Since the expression ends with 2 a linear factor involves 1 or 2.
The possible linear factors are $x \pm 1$, $x \pm 2$, $2x \pm 1$, $3x \pm 1$, $3x \pm 2$, $6x \pm 1$.
Test these in turn by finding $f(1)$, $f(-1)$, $f(2)$, $f(-2)$, $f(\frac{1}{2})$, etc.
$f(1) = 6 + 13 + 1 - 2 = 18$. $f(1) \neq 0$ so $x - 1$ is not a factor.
$f(-1) = -6 + 13 - 1 - 2 \neq 0$, so $x + 1$ is not a factor.
$f(2) = 48 + 52 + 2 - 2 \neq 0$, so $x - 2$ is not a factor.

$$f(-2) = -48 + 52 - 2 - 2 = 0, \text{ so } x + 2 \text{ is a factor.}$$

By division, $6x^3 + 13x^2 + x - 2 = (x+2)(6x^2 + x - 1)$
$$= (x+2)(2x+1)(3x-1)$$

## * The Remainder Theorem

If a polynomial $f(x)$ is divided by $x - a$, then the remainder is $f(a)$.

To show this:

$f(x) = (x - a)Q(x) + R$         where $Q(x)$ is the quotient and R is the remainder when $f(x)$ is divided by $x - a$

$f(a) = (a - a)Q(a) + R$
$R = f(a)$

**Example 1.8,** continued.

When the expression $6x^3 + 13x^2 + x - 2$ is divided by $x - 1$, the remainder is $f(1)$, which equals 18.

## Exercise 1.1

1. Factorise the following:

    1   $4x^2 - x - 18$

    2   $6x^2 + 4x - 10$

    3   $4x^2 - 100$

    4   $x^3 - 8$

    5   $x^3 + x^2 - x - 1$

    6   $3x^2 + 14xy + 15y^2$

    7   $6x^2 - 13xy - 8y^2$

    8   $21xy - 12x - 35y + 20$

    9   $x^4 - x^2 - 12$

    10   $27 + y^3$

2. Solve the equations:

    1   $3x(5x - 13) = 0$

    2   $x(x - 3) = 70$

    3   $4x^2 + 4x - 35 = 0$

    4   $2x = 9 - \dfrac{9}{x}$

    5   $\dfrac{1}{x+1} + \dfrac{4}{x+4} = 1$

    6   $\dfrac{x+2}{x-2} - \dfrac{x-6}{x+6} = \dfrac{16}{x}$

    7   $x^4 - 13x^2 + 36 = 0$

    8   $\sqrt{2x+9} = \sqrt{x-4} + 3$

    9   $\sqrt{3x+1} - \sqrt{x-1} = 2$

    10   $\sqrt{8x+4} - 7 = \sqrt{x-3}$

3. Complete these expressions:

    1   $x^2 - 16x + \ldots = (x \ldots)^2$

    2   $x^2 + 4xy + \ldots = (x \ldots)^2$

    3   $2(x^2 + 10x + \ldots) = 2(x \ldots)^2$

    4   $3x^2 - 4x + \ldots = 3(x \ldots)^2$

    5   $x^2 - 7x + \ldots = (x \ldots)^2$

4. Solve these equations, giving solutions correct to 3 significant figures.

    **1** $(x-2)^2 = 17$                         **4** $x(x-3) = 1$

    **2** $(2x+3)^2 = 5$

                                    **5** $x+2 = \dfrac{5}{x}$

    **3** $4x^2 + 7x + 2 = 0$

5. Express in the form $(x+a)^2 + b$:

    **1** $x^2 - 4x + 7$                           **4** $x^2 - 5x$

    **2** $x^2 + 8x - 1$                          **5** $x^2 + x + 1$

    **3** $x^2 + 10x + 50$

6. Express in the form $a(x+b)^2 + c$:

    **1** $2x^2 - 12x + 27$                     **4** $3x^2 - 4x + 2$

    **2** $3x^2 + 12x - 1$                      **5** $5x^2 + 2x$

    **3** $2x^2 - 2x - 3$

7. Solve for $x$ the equations:

    **1** $x^2 - 5ax - 14a^2 = 0$             **4** $x(x+3) = a(a+3)$

    **2** $2x^2 - 13ax + 15a^2 = 0$

                               **5** $\dfrac{x}{x-a} - \dfrac{x}{x+15a} = 1$

    **3** $(x+4)(x-3) = (a-4)(a+3)$

8. Find the possible values of $k$ if these equations have equal roots:

    **1** $2x^2 + (k+4)x + 4(k-2) = 0$        **2** $(1-k)x^2 - 3(1+k)x + 4(1-k) = 0$

9. **1** If the roots of $x^2 + px + q = 0$ are real, show that the roots of $x^2 + (2+p)x + 1 + p + q = 0$ are also real.

    **2** If the roots of $8x(2x-1) + a^2 = 0$ are real and unequal, and $a \neq 0$, show that the equation $4x^2 + a^2(4x+1) = 0$ has no real roots.

10. If $ax^2 + bx + c = 0$, i.e. $x^2 + \dfrac{b}{a}x + \dfrac{c}{a} = 0$, show that

$$x = \frac{-b \pm \sqrt{b^2 - 4ac}}{2a},$$ by using the method of completing the square.

## Exercise 1.2

*This exercise is included to give practice in some basic algebraic techniques.*

1. Solve these simultaneous equations:

    **1** $5x + 3y = 11$                     **2** $3x - 2y = 19$
         $4x + 5y = 1$                        $2x + 3y = 43$

**3** $5x - 7y + 20 = 0$
$3x - 2y + 12 = 0$

**4** $\dfrac{1}{x} + \dfrac{1}{y} = \frac{1}{3}$
$\dfrac{1}{x} - \dfrac{1}{y} = \frac{1}{2}$

**5** $\dfrac{1}{x} + \dfrac{5}{y} = 2$
$\dfrac{4}{x} - \dfrac{3}{y} = 31$

2. Simplify:

**1** $(x+4)^2 - (x-1)(x+3) + (x+2)(x-12)$

**2** $2(x+1)^2 - x(x-2) - (x-4)^2$

**3** $4(x-1)^2 - (2x-1)(2x-5)$

**4** $(x-a)(x-b) - (x-b)(x-c) + (x-c)(x+a)$

**5** $(x+a+b)^2 - (x-a-b)^2$

3. Factorise:

**1** $12x^2 - 36x + 27$

**2** $x^2 - xy - 42y^2$

**3** $28x^2y^2 - 7$

**4** $8x^3 + 1$

**5** $3x^3 - 6x^2 + 3x$

**6** $4xy - 5y - 8xz + 10z$

**7** $(x+y)^3 - x - y$

**8** $6x^4 - 96$

**9** $x^2 - 16xy + 64y^2$

**10** $x^2 + 2x + 1 - a^2$

4. Solve these equations for $x$, in terms of the other letters:

**1** $\dfrac{a}{x} - b = c$

**2** $ax - b = cx - d$

**3** $\dfrac{ax}{b} - c = x$

**4** $\dfrac{1}{x} = \dfrac{1}{a} - \dfrac{1}{b}$

**5** $a = \dfrac{bx^2}{c}$

**6** $a = \dfrac{bx}{c+dx}$

**7** $a = b + c\sqrt{x}$

**8** $x^2 - ax - bx + ab = 0$

**9** $\dfrac{x-a}{x-b} = \dfrac{x-b}{x-c}$

**10** $x^2 + ax + b = 0$

5. Simplify:

**1** $\dfrac{x}{x+y} + \dfrac{y}{x-y}$

**2** $\frac{2}{3}(x+3) - \frac{3}{4}(x-4)$

**3** $\dfrac{x-5}{x-2} - \dfrac{x-3}{x-1}$

**4** $\dfrac{2}{x+2} - \dfrac{x+6}{x^2+6x+8}$

**5** $\dfrac{6}{(x-6)^2} + \dfrac{1}{x-6}$

6.  Simplify:

1  $\dfrac{x^2-4}{x^2-y^2} \times \dfrac{x+y}{2-x}$

2  $\dfrac{x^3+y^3}{x^2+5xy+6y^2} \times \dfrac{x^2+3xy}{x+y}$

3  $\dfrac{3x^2-2x-5}{2x^2+x-3} \div \dfrac{3x-5}{2x+3}$

4  $(x^2-3xy) \div (x^2-9y^2)$

5  $\dfrac{\dfrac{1}{x^2}-\dfrac{1}{y^2}}{\dfrac{1}{x}+\dfrac{1}{y}}$

7.  Solve the equations:

1  $(x-2)^2-(x-3)^2=3$

2  $(x-5)(x-1)-x(x-7)=0$

3  $\frac{5}{3}(1-4x)=2+\frac{3}{2}(1-2x)$

4  $\dfrac{3x-4}{2}-\dfrac{2x-1}{5}=1\frac{1}{2}$

5  $\dfrac{x+1}{x-4}+\dfrac{x-3}{x-7}=2$

6  $(x+1)^2-4=(x-1)^2+2x$

7  $\dfrac{x+10}{x-2}=\dfrac{x+14}{x-1}$

8  $\dfrac{4}{2x-1}-\dfrac{3}{2x+1}=\dfrac{5}{4x^2-1}$

9  $\dfrac{x}{2x-9}=\dfrac{2x-6}{4x-21}$

10  $\dfrac{3}{x+1}+\dfrac{2}{x-2}=\dfrac{21}{x^2-x-2}$

8.  Expand these expressions:

1  $(x^3-x^2+3x-1)(2x-1)$

2  $(2x^3+5x^2+4)(x-2)$

3  $(x^2+2x+3)(x^2-2x+1)$

4  $(x^2-5x+25)(x+5)$

5  $(x^4+x^3+x^2+x+1)(x-1)$

9.  1  Divide $x^3-2x^2+6x-5$ by $x-1$

2  Divide $3x^3-11x^2-6x+8$ by $3x-2$

3  Divide $x^3-27$ by $x-3$

4  Divide $x^4-5x^3-6x^2+7x-18$ by $x+2$

5  Divide $3x^4+2x^3-3x-2$ by $x^2+x+1$

10.  Solve the simultaneous equations:

1  $\begin{aligned} x-y+z&=-2 \\ 2x-3y-z&=-5 \\ 3x-y-4z&=9 \end{aligned}$

2  $\begin{aligned} 3x+2y+z&=2 \\ 4x-3y+z&=-5 \\ 2x+5y-z&=11 \end{aligned}$

3  $\begin{aligned} 2x-y-z&=6 \\ x+2y+3z&=1 \\ 3x-5y-z&=1 \end{aligned}$

4  $\begin{aligned} x+3y+1&=0 \\ y+3z-14&=0 \\ z+4x-13&=0 \end{aligned}$

5  $\begin{aligned} x-2y&=-7 \\ y-3z&=2\frac{1}{2} \\ x+4z&=3 \end{aligned}$

## * Exercise 1.3

1.  Verify these identities, which are useful rearrangements to know:

    1   $\alpha^2 + \beta^2 = (\alpha + \beta)^2 - 2\alpha\beta$

    4   $\dfrac{1}{\alpha} + \dfrac{1}{\beta} = \dfrac{\alpha + \beta}{\alpha\beta}$

    2   $\alpha^3 + \beta^3 = (\alpha + \beta)^3 - 3\alpha\beta(\alpha + \beta)$

    3   $(\alpha - \beta)^2 = (\alpha + \beta)^2 - 4\alpha\beta$

    5   $\dfrac{\alpha}{\beta} + \dfrac{\beta}{\alpha} = \dfrac{(\alpha + \beta)^2 - 2\alpha\beta}{\alpha\beta}$

2.  If the roots of $3x^2 - 7x + 2 = 0$ are $\alpha$, $\beta$, find the value of $\alpha^2 + \beta^2$. Find the equation whose roots are $\alpha^2 + 1$, $\beta^2 + 1$.

3.  If the roots of $x^2 + px + q = 0$ are $\alpha$, $\beta$, find the equation whose roots are $\alpha + \dfrac{1}{\beta}$, $\beta + \dfrac{1}{\alpha}$.

4.  Find the quadratic equation whose roots are the squares of the roots of the equation $ax^2 + bx + c = 0$.

5.  If $\alpha$, $\beta$ are the roots of $x^2 + 5x + 2 = 0$, find the equation with roots $\dfrac{2+\alpha}{\beta}$, $\dfrac{2+\beta}{\alpha}$.

6.  If $\alpha$, $\beta$ are the roots of $x^2 + px + q = 0$, show that the equation with roots $\alpha^3$, $\beta^3$ is $x^2 + p(p^2 - 3q)x + q^3 = 0$.

7.  If one root of $8x^2 + kx - 1 = 0$ is the square of the other, and the roots are real, find the value of $k$.

## * Exercise 1.4

Solve these simultaneous equations:

1.  $y^2 = 8x$
    $5y = 4x - 12$

2.  $xy = 12$
    $y = 4x - 8$

3.  $x^2 + y^2 = 34$
    $x + y = 8$

4.  $x^2 + y^2 - 2x + 6y - 31 = 0$
    $x + y + 1 = 0$

5.  $x^2 + y^2 - 2xy - 9 = 0$
    $3x - 2y = 10$

6.  $3y^2 = x^2 + 8x + 3$
    $x - 3y = 7$

7.  $x^2 - 2xy - y^2 + 1 = 0$
    $2x + y = 1$

8.  $x^2 + y^2 = 17$
    $x - 3y = 11$

9.  $xy = 6$
    $y = 4x + 10$

10. $y^2 = 16x + 12$
    $y = 4x - 12$

## Exercise 1.5

1.  Use the factor theorem to find linear factors of the following expressions and hence factorise completely:

    1   $x^3 - 6x^2 + 11x - 6$

    3   $2x^3 + 3x^2 - 3x - 2$

    5   $x^3 - 10x^2 + 31x - 30$

    2   $x^3 - 5x^2 + 2x + 8$

    4   $6x^3 + 13x^2 - 21x - 18$

2. Show that $2x^3 - 7x^2 - 28x - 12$ is divisible by $x + 2$ and find its other factors.

3. Show that $x^4 - 33x^2 - 28x + 60$ has factors $x + 2$ and $x + 5$ and find its other factors.

4. Use the factor theorem to express $x^3 - 6x^2 + 13x - 10$ as a product of two factors.

5. Show that $x^4 + 2x^3 - 7x^2 - 8x + 12$ has factors $x - 1$ and $x + 3$, and find its other factors. Hence solve the equation $x^4 + 2x^3 - 7x^2 - 8x + 12 = 0$.

6. Find the value of $a$ if $x^4 - 2x^3 + ax^2 + 12x + 36$ has a factor $x + 2$ and show that this is a repeated factor. With this value of $a$, solve the equation
$x^4 - 2x^3 + ax^2 + 12x + 36 = 0$.

7.* Use the remainder theorem to find the remainders when:

    1   $x^3 - 6x^2 + 4$ is divided by $x - 2$

    2   $x^4 - 8x^3 - 2x + 1$ is divided by $x + 1$

    3   $2x^3 - 3x + 1$ is divided by $x - 3$

8.* If $x^3 + bx + 3$ is divided by $x + 2$, the remainder is 7. Find the value of $b$.

9.* If $ax^3 + bx^2 - x$ is divided by $x - 1$, the remainder is 7, and if it is divided by $x + 3$, the remainder is $-33$. Find the values of $a$ and $b$.

## Partial Fractions

There are 4 main types.

**Type 1.** The denominator has linear factors.

**Example 1.9**

Express $\dfrac{5x - 4}{(x+1)(x-2)}$ in partial fractions.

Let $\dfrac{5x - 4}{(x+1)(x-2)} \equiv \dfrac{A}{x+1} + \dfrac{B}{x-2}$

Then $\dfrac{5x - 4}{(x+1)(x-2)} \equiv \dfrac{A(x-2) + B(x+1)}{(x+1)(x-2)}$

$\therefore$  $5x - 4 \equiv A(x-2) + B(x+1)$

This is an identity so it is true for all values of $x$.
Putting $x = -1$ will give the value of $A$ and putting $x = 2$ will give the value of $B$.

Let $x = -1$.      $-9 = -3A$, so $A = 3$
Let $x = 2$.        $6 = 3B$, so $B = 2$

$\therefore$  $\dfrac{5x - 4}{(x+1)(x-2)} \equiv \dfrac{3}{x+1} + \dfrac{2}{x-2}$

**Example 1.10**

Express $\dfrac{4x^2-12}{(x+1)(x-1)(x+3)}$ in partial fractions.

Let $\dfrac{4x^2-12}{(x+1)(x-1)(x+3)} \equiv \dfrac{A}{x+1} + \dfrac{B}{x-1} + \dfrac{C}{x+3}$

Then $4x^2-12 \equiv A(x-1)(x+3) + B(x+1)(x+3) + C(x+1)(x-1)$

Let $x=-1$.　　　$-8=-4A$, so $A=2$
Let $x=1$.　　　$-8=8B$, so $B=-1$
Let $x=-3$.　　　$24=8C$, so $C=3$

$\therefore \dfrac{4x^2-12}{(x+1)(x-1)(x+3)} \equiv \dfrac{2}{x+1} - \dfrac{1}{x-1} + \dfrac{3}{x+3}$

**Type 2.** The denominator has a quadratic factor. This term will have a numerator of the type $Ax+B$.

**Example 1.11**

Express $\dfrac{x^2+5x+3}{(x-1)(x^2+2)}$ in partial fractions.

Let $\dfrac{x^2+5x+3}{(x-1)(x^2+2)} \equiv \dfrac{A}{x-1} + \dfrac{Bx+C}{x^2+2}$

$\therefore \quad x^2+5x+3 \equiv A(x^2+2) + (Bx+C)(x-1)$

Let $x=1$.　　　$9=3A$, so $A=3$
To find $B$ and $C$, compare coefficients of $x^2$, or $x$, or put $x=0$.
Let $x=0$.　　　$3=2A-C$, so $C=3$
Coefficient of $x^2$. $1=A+B$, so $B=-2$
(The coefficient of $x$, $5=C-B$ is useful as a check)

$\therefore \quad \dfrac{x^2+5x+3}{(x-1)(x^2+2)} \equiv \dfrac{3}{x-1} - \dfrac{2x-3}{x^2+2}$

(Note that it is $2x-3$, not $2x+3$ in the numerator because of the minus sign in front of the fraction.)

**Type 3.** There is a repeated linear factor in the denominator. Note how this is expressed in the following example.

**Example 1.12**

Express $\dfrac{6x^2-17x+7}{(x-3)(x-1)^2}$ in partial fractions.

Let $\dfrac{6x^2-17x+7}{(x-3)(x-1)^2} \equiv \dfrac{A}{x-3} + \dfrac{B}{x-1} + \dfrac{C}{(x-1)^2}$

$\dfrac{6x^2-17x+7}{(x-3)(x-1)^2} \equiv \dfrac{A(x-1)^2 + B(x-3)(x-1) + C(x-3)}{(x-3)(x-1)^2}$

(Be careful to use the same denominator on both sides of the identity.)

$\therefore \quad 6x^2 - 17x + 7 \equiv A(x-1)^2 + B(x-3)(x-1) + C(x-3)$

Let $x = 1$. $\qquad\qquad -4 = -2C$, so $C = 2$

Let $x = 3$. $\qquad\qquad 10 = 4A$, so $A = \frac{5}{2}$

To find $B$, compare coefficients of $x^2$, or $x$, or put $x = 0$.

Coefficient of $x^2$. $\qquad\quad 6 = A + B$, so $B = \frac{7}{2}$

$\therefore \quad \dfrac{6x^2 - 17x + 7}{(x-3)(x-1)^2} \equiv \dfrac{5}{2(x-3)} + \dfrac{7}{2(x-1)} + \dfrac{2}{(x-1)^2}$

**Type 4.** The highest power of $x$ in the numerator is equal to, or greater than, the highest power of $x$ in the denominator. By division a quotient and the remaining fraction are obtained.

**Example 1.13**

Express $\dfrac{2x^2 + 3x - 8}{(x+1)(x-2)}$ in partial fractions.

$\dfrac{2x^2 + 3x - 8}{(x+1)(x-2)} = \dfrac{2(x^2 - x - 2) + 5x - 4}{(x+1)(x-2)}$

$\qquad\qquad\qquad = 2 + \dfrac{5x - 4}{(x+1)(x-2)}$

Using the method and result of example 1.9, this is

$2 + \dfrac{3}{x+1} + \dfrac{2}{x-2}$

**Example 1.14**

Express $\dfrac{x^3 + x^2 + x - 8}{(x+1)(x-2)}$ in partial fractions.

By division, $\dfrac{x^3 + x^2 + x - 8}{(x+1)(x-2)} = x + 2 + \dfrac{5x - 4}{(x+1)(x-2)}$

Using the method and result of example 1.9, this is $x + 2 + \dfrac{3}{x+1} + \dfrac{2}{x-2}$

**Exercise 1.6**

Express in partial fractions:

1. $\dfrac{7x+2}{(x-1)(x+2)}$ $\qquad$ 3. $\dfrac{2x}{(x-1)(x-3)}$ $\qquad$ 5. $\dfrac{6}{(x-3)(x-5)}$

2. $\dfrac{3x-3}{(x+1)(x-2)}$ $\qquad$ 4. $\dfrac{3x-7}{(x+1)(x-3)}$ $\qquad$ 6. $\dfrac{2-x}{(x-1)(x+2)}$

7. $\dfrac{x-5}{(2x-1)(x-2)}$

9. $\dfrac{2x^2-x+3}{(x+1)(x-1)(x-2)}$

8. $\dfrac{8x+1}{(2x+1)(x-1)}$

10. $\dfrac{4-5x}{(x-1)(x-2)(2x-1)}$

## Exercise 1.7

Express in partial fractions:

1. $\dfrac{5x^2-x}{(x-1)(x^2+1)}$

6. $\dfrac{4x^3-13x+7}{(2x-1)(x+2)}$

2. $\dfrac{2x^2+5x+6}{(x-2)(x^2+2)}$

7. $\dfrac{20x+15}{(x+2)^2(x-3)}$

3. $\dfrac{x^2-5x+6}{(x+1)(x-1)^2}$

8. $\dfrac{2x^2-5x-4}{(x-2)(x+1)}$

4. $\dfrac{3x^2-23}{(x-3)(x-1)^2}$

9. $\dfrac{4-5x}{(x+1)(x^2-x+1)}$

5. $\dfrac{x^2+2x-1}{x^2+3x+2}$

10. $\dfrac{2x^3-x+3}{x(x+1)(x-1)}$

## Surds

A fraction with a surd in the denominator can have the denominator rationalized.
For a denominator $\sqrt{a}+\sqrt{b}$, multiply the fraction by $\dfrac{\sqrt{a}-\sqrt{b}}{\sqrt{a}-\sqrt{b}}$, to make the denominator
into $(\sqrt{a}+\sqrt{b})(\sqrt{a}-\sqrt{b})$, which becomes $a-b$.

**Example 1.15**
$$\frac{1}{\sqrt{2}}=\frac{1}{\sqrt{2}}\times\frac{\sqrt{2}}{\sqrt{2}}=\frac{\sqrt{2}}{2}$$

**Example 1.16**
$$\frac{1}{4-\sqrt{3}}=\frac{1}{4-\sqrt{3}}\times\frac{4+\sqrt{3}}{4+\sqrt{3}}=\frac{4+\sqrt{3}}{13}$$

**Example 1.17**
Simplify $\sqrt{80}-\sqrt{45}$
$$\sqrt{80}=\sqrt{5\times16}=\sqrt{5}\times\sqrt{16}=4\sqrt{5}$$
$$\sqrt{45}=\sqrt{5\times9}=\sqrt{5}\times\sqrt{9}=3\sqrt{5}$$
$$\sqrt{80}-\sqrt{45}=4\sqrt{5}-3\sqrt{5}=\sqrt{5}$$

## Indices

$$a^m \times a^n = a^{m+n}$$   $$a^0 = 1$$   $$a^{\frac{1}{n}} = \sqrt[n]{a}$$

$$a^m \div a^n = a^{m-n}$$   $$a^{-n} = \frac{1}{a^n}$$   $$a^{\frac{m}{n}} = (\sqrt[n]{a})^m \text{ or } \sqrt[n]{(a^m)}$$

$$(a^m)^n = a^{mn}$$

### Example 1.18

Find the value of $81^{-\frac{3}{4}}$

$$81^{-\frac{3}{4}} = \frac{1}{81^{\frac{3}{4}}} = \frac{1}{(\sqrt[4]{81})^3} = \frac{1}{3^3} = \frac{1}{27}$$

### Example 1.19

Simplify $(ab^3)^{\frac{1}{2}} \times (a^2 c)^{\frac{3}{4}} \times (b^2 c^3)^{-\frac{1}{4}}$

$$a^{\frac{1}{2}} b^{\frac{3}{2}} \cdot a^{\frac{3}{2}} c^{\frac{3}{4}} \cdot b^{-\frac{1}{2}} c^{-\frac{3}{4}} = a^{\frac{1}{2}+\frac{3}{2}} b^{\frac{3}{2}-\frac{1}{2}} c^{\frac{3}{4}-\frac{3}{4}} = a^2 b$$

### Example 1.20

Solve the equation $3^{2x} + 3^{x+2} - 36 = 0$

$\therefore$   $(3^x)^2 + 9 \cdot (3^x) - 36 = 0$     (since $3^{x+2} = 3^x \cdot 3^2 = 9 \cdot 3^x$)

$\therefore$   $(3^x + 12)(3^x - 3) = 0$

$3^x = -12$ (no solution) or $3^x = 3$, $x = 1$.

The solution is $x = 1$.

## Logarithms

### Definition

If $y = a^x$ then $x = \log_a y$

### Rules

$\log_a x + \log_a y = \log_a xy$     Thus $a^{\log_a x} = x$     $\log_a 1 = 0$

$\log_a a = 1$

$\log_a x - \log_a y = \log_a \frac{x}{y}$     $\log_a(a^x) = x$

$\log_a x^k = k \log_a x$     $\log_a \frac{1}{x} = -\log_a x$

Change of base: $\log_a y = \frac{\log_b y}{\log_b a}$

**Logarithms to base e** are called Natural or Napierian logarithms.

The symbol for $\log_e x$ is $\ln x$.

If $y = e^x$ then $x = \ln y$

$e^{\ln x} = \ln(e^x) = x$

$a^x = e^{x \ln a}$

exp $x$ can be used as a symbol for $e^x$.

lg $x$ can be used as a symbol for $\log_{10} x$.

### Example 1.21

Find the approximate value of $\log_{12} 20$.

Using base e, $\log_{12} 20 = \dfrac{\ln 20}{\ln 12} = \dfrac{2.9957}{2.4849} \approx 1.21$

Or using base 10, $\log_{12} 20 = \dfrac{\lg 20}{\lg 12} = \dfrac{1.3010}{1.0792} \approx 1.21$

### Example 1.22

Solve the equation $3 \log_{1000} x - 2 \log_x 10 = 1$

$\dfrac{3 \log_{10} x}{\log_{10} 1000} - \dfrac{2}{\log_{10} x} = 1$

$\therefore \quad (\log_{10} x)^2 - \log_{10} x - 2 = 0 \qquad \text{(since } \log_{10} 1000 = 3)$

$\therefore \quad (\log_{10} x + 1)(\log_{10} x - 2) = 0$

$\log_{10} x = -1 \text{ or } \log_{10} x = 2$

$x = \frac{1}{10} \text{ or } x = 100$

In equations originally involving log. terms, check that all the solutions satisfy the original equations, remembering that $\log x$ only exists if $x$ is positive.

### Exercise 1.8

Simplify:

1. $\dfrac{12}{\sqrt{3}} + 2\sqrt{98} - \dfrac{12}{\sqrt{2}} - \sqrt{48} - \sqrt{128}$

2. $\dfrac{4\sqrt{3} + 3\sqrt{2}}{3\sqrt{2} - 2\sqrt{3}}$

3. $\dfrac{\sqrt{5} + \sqrt{3}}{\sqrt{2} - 1} + \dfrac{\sqrt{5} - \sqrt{3}}{\sqrt{2} + 1}$

4. $9^{\frac{2}{3}} \times 4^{\frac{1}{6}} \times 6^{\frac{2}{3}}$

5. $2^{\frac{1}{2}} \cdot 16^{\frac{1}{8}} + 9^{\frac{7}{8}} \cdot 3^{\frac{1}{4}}$

6. $(9x^{\frac{5}{2}})^{\frac{1}{2}} \times (27x^{\frac{3}{4}})^{-\frac{1}{3}}$

7. $\dfrac{x^{\frac{3}{2}} - y^{\frac{3}{2}}}{x^{\frac{1}{2}} - y^{\frac{1}{2}}}$

8. $\ln \frac{75}{16} - 2 \ln \frac{5}{9} + 5 \ln \frac{2}{3}$

9. $\dfrac{2 \ln 6 - \ln 4}{2 \ln 18 - \ln 12}$

10. $\log_2 9 \cdot \log_3 8$

## Exercise 1.9

1. Find the value of $\dfrac{x^{n+1}}{n+1}$ when $x = 64$ and $n = -\frac{1}{3}$.

2. If $f(x) = \dfrac{x(e^x+1)}{e^x-1}$, show that $f(x) = f(-x)$.

3. Solve $2^{x+1} + 2^{x-1} = 320$.

4. Solve the simultaneous equations $x = 9^{2y+7}$, $3x = 27^{y+4}$.

5. Find the sum of the series $\lg \frac{1}{2} + \lg \frac{2}{3} + \lg \frac{3}{4} + \lg \frac{4}{5} + \ldots + \lg \frac{99}{100}$.

6. Solve $3^{2x} - 4 \cdot (3^x) + 3 = 0$.

7. Solve $6x^{-\frac{3}{4}} = \frac{2}{9}$.

8. If $\ln \dfrac{p-2q}{4} = \frac{1}{2}(\ln p + \ln q)$, show that $p^2 + 4q^2 = 20pq$.

9. Solve $2^{2x+2} + 7 \cdot (2^x) = 2$.

10. If $b = a^3$ and $\log_a d = 4 + \log_a c$, show that $d = abc$.

## Exercise 1.10

1. Simplify $\dfrac{a^{2 \log_a b} - b^{2 \log_b a}}{a^{\log_a b} - b^{\log_b a}}$.

2. Solve $\ln(x^3 + 19) = 3 \ln(x+1)$.

3. Solve $2^{2+2x} - 3 \cdot 2^{x+1} + 2 = 0$.

4. Solve $\lg(x^2 + 6x - 1) - 2 \lg x = 1$.

5. Solve $\log_e x - 6 \log_x e = 1$.

6. Solve the simultaneous equations $x + y = 6e$, $\ln x + \ln y - \ln 8 = 2$.

7. Solve the simultaneous equations $12y^x - y^{2x} = 36$, $36^x = y^8$.

8. Solve the simultaneous equations $y = e^{3+\ln x}$, $x = e^{5-\ln y}$.

9. Solve $\lg 125 - 3 \lg x = \dfrac{\lg 125}{\lg 5}$.

10. If $y = k\, e^{cx^2}$ where $k$ and $c$ are constants, and $y = 4$ when $x = 0$, also $y = 6$ when $x = 1$, find $y$ when $x = 2$.

11. Assuming the laws $a^m \times a^n = a^{m+n}$, $a^m \div a^n = a^{m-n}$, $(a^m)^n = a^{mn}$, show that $a^0 = 1$,

$$a^{-n} = \frac{1}{a^n}, \quad a^{\frac{1}{n}} = \sqrt[n]{a}, \quad a^{\frac{m}{n}} = (\sqrt[n]{a})^m = \sqrt[n]{(a^m)}.$$

12. If $\log_a x = p$ and $\log_a y = q$, use the rules for indices to show that
$\log_a x + \log_a y = \log_a xy$, $\log_a x - \log_a y = \log_a \dfrac{x}{y}$, $\log_a x^k = k \log_a x$.

13. If $y = a^p$, show that $\log_a y = \dfrac{\log_b y}{\log_b a}$.

14. Show that $a^{\log_a x} = \log_a a^x = x$ and $a^x = e^{x \ln a}$.

# 2 Trigonometry

## Circular Measure, Radians

$\theta$ is an angle of 1 radian

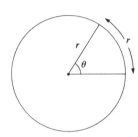

$\pi$ radians $= 180°$

$1 \text{ radian} = \dfrac{180}{\pi} \text{ degrees} \approx 57.3°$

$1 \text{ degree} = \dfrac{\pi}{180} \text{ radians}$

## The Trigonometric Functions

$\sin \theta = \dfrac{y\text{-coordinate}}{r}$

$\cos \theta = \dfrac{x\text{-coordinate}}{r}$

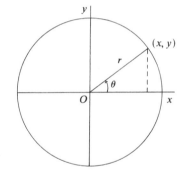

$\tan \theta = \dfrac{\sin \theta}{\cos \theta}$

$\sec \theta = \dfrac{1}{\cos \theta}$

$\operatorname{cosec} \theta = \dfrac{1}{\sin \theta}$

$\cot \theta = \dfrac{1}{\tan \theta} = \dfrac{\cos \theta}{\sin \theta}$

**Positive ratios**

| sin | all |
|-----|-----|
| tan | cos |

To find whether a trig. ratio is positive or negative:
The sign of $\sin \theta$ depends on the $y$-coordinate so $\sin \theta$ is positive in the first and second quadrants and negative in the third and fourth quadrants.

The sign of cos $\theta$ depends on the $x$-coordinate so cos $\theta$ is positive in the first and fourth quadrants and negative in the second and third quadrants.

$\tan \theta = \dfrac{\sin \theta}{\cos \theta}$ so tan $\theta$ is positive in the first and third quadrants where sin $\theta$ and cos $\theta$ have the same sign, and negative in the second and fourth quadrants where sin $\theta$ and cos $\theta$ have opposite signs.

This diagram shows which of these ratios are positive in each of the 4 quadrants.

The signs of cosec $\theta$, sec $\theta$, cot $\theta$ match the signs of sin $\theta$, cos $\theta$, tan $\theta$ respectively.

## Sketch Graphs

$y = \sin x$

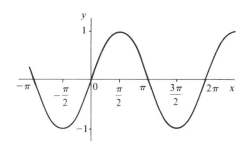

$y = \cos x$

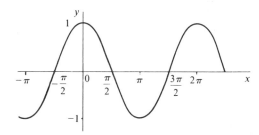

$y = \tan x$

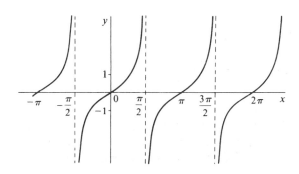

## Some Special Angles

**Equilateral triangle**          **Right-angled isosceles triangle**

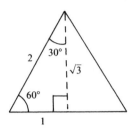          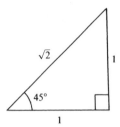

The equilateral triangle gives exact ratios for the angles of 30° and 60°.
The right-angled isosceles triangle gives exact ratios for the angle of 45°.
The ratios for 0°, 90°, 180°, 270°, 360° can be found from the basic definitions.
The ratios for these angles are listed below.

| degrees | 0 | 30 | 45 | 60 | 90 | 180 | 270 | 360 |
|---------|---|----|----|----|----|----|-----|-----|
| radians | 0 | $\dfrac{\pi}{6}$ | $\dfrac{\pi}{4}$ | $\dfrac{\pi}{3}$ | $\dfrac{\pi}{2}$ | $\pi$ | $\dfrac{3\pi}{2}$ | $2\pi$ |
| $\sin x$ | 0 | $\dfrac{1}{2}$ | $\dfrac{1}{\sqrt{2}}$ or $\dfrac{\sqrt{2}}{2}$ | $\dfrac{\sqrt{3}}{2}$ | 1 | 0 | $-1$ | 0 |
| $\cos x$ | 1 | $\dfrac{\sqrt{3}}{2}$ | $\dfrac{1}{\sqrt{2}}$ or $\dfrac{\sqrt{2}}{2}$ | $\dfrac{1}{2}$ | 0 | $-1$ | 0 | 1 |
| $\tan x$ | 0 | $\dfrac{\sqrt{3}}{3}$ or $\dfrac{1}{\sqrt{3}}$ | 1 | $\sqrt{3}$ | $\infty$ | 0 | $\infty$ | 0 |

## Useful Formulae

**Complementary functions**

$\cos\theta = \sin(90° - \theta)$
$\operatorname{cosec}\theta = \sec(90° - \theta)$
$\cot\theta = \tan(90° - \theta)$

**Negative angles**

$\sin(-\theta) = -\sin\theta$
$\cos(-\theta) = \cos\theta$
$\tan(-\theta) = -\tan\theta$

**Pythagoras' theorem**

$\cos^2 A + \sin^2 A = 1$
$\sec^2 A = 1 + \tan^2 A$
$\operatorname{cosec}^2 A = 1 + \cot^2 A$

**Addition formulae**

$\cos(A+B) = \cos A \cos B - \sin A \sin B$
$\cos(A-B) = \cos A \cos B + \sin A \sin B$
$\sin(A+B) = \sin A \cos B + \cos A \sin B$
$\sin(A-B) = \sin A \cos B - \cos A \sin B$

$$\tan(A+B) = \frac{\tan A + \tan B}{1 - \tan A \tan B}$$

$$\tan(A-B) = \frac{\tan A - \tan B}{1 + \tan A \tan B}$$

## Double angles

$$\cos 2A = \cos^2 A - \sin^2 A$$
$$= 2\cos^2 A - 1 \qquad \text{so } \cos^2 A = \tfrac{1}{2} + \tfrac{1}{2}\cos 2A$$
$$= 1 - 2\sin^2 A \qquad \text{so } \sin^2 A = \tfrac{1}{2} - \tfrac{1}{2}\cos 2A$$

$$\sin 2A = 2\sin A \cos A$$

$$\tan 2A = \frac{2\tan A}{1 - \tan^2 A}$$

## Factor formulae

$$\sin A + \sin B = 2\sin\frac{A+B}{2}\cos\frac{A-B}{2} \qquad\qquad \cos A + \cos B = 2\cos\frac{A+B}{2}\cos\frac{A-B}{2}$$

$$\sin A - \sin B = 2\cos\frac{A+B}{2}\sin\frac{A-B}{2} \qquad\qquad \cos A - \cos B = -2\sin\frac{A+B}{2}\sin\frac{A-B}{2}$$

## Product formulae

$$2\sin A \cos B = \sin(A+B) + \sin(A-B)$$
$$2\cos A \cos B = \cos(A+B) + \cos(A-B)$$
$$2\sin A \sin B = \cos(A-B) - \cos(A+B)$$

## General Solutions of Trigonometric Equations

If $\sin\theta = \sin\alpha$
then $\theta =$ any multiple of $2\pi$, $+\alpha$
     or
     any odd multiple of $\pi$, $-\alpha$
i.e. $\theta = n\pi + (-1)^n \alpha$
     where $n$ is an integer.

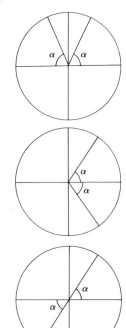

If $\cos\theta = \cos\alpha$
then $\theta =$ any multiple of $2\pi$, $\pm\alpha$
i.e. $\theta = 2n\pi \pm \alpha$

If $\tan\theta = \tan\alpha$
then $\theta =$ any multiple of $\pi$, $+\alpha$
i.e. $\theta = n\pi + \alpha$

## Transformations

$a \cos \theta + b \sin \theta$ can be written in the form $R \cos(\theta - \alpha)$

where $R = \sqrt{a^2 + b^2}$, $\cos \alpha = \dfrac{a}{R}$, $\sin \alpha = \dfrac{b}{R}$.

Since $a \cos \theta + b \sin \theta \equiv R \cos \theta \cos \alpha + R \sin \theta \sin \alpha$

When $\theta = 0$, $a = R \cos \alpha$, $\cos \alpha = \dfrac{a}{R}$.

When $\theta = \dfrac{\pi}{2}$, $b = R \sin \alpha$, $\sin \alpha = \dfrac{b}{R}$.

Squaring and adding gives $R^2 = a^2 + b^2$, $R = \sqrt{a^2 + b^2}$.

$a \cos \theta + b \sin \theta$ can also be written as $R \sin(\theta + \alpha)$

where $R = \sqrt{a^2 + b^2}$, $\cos \alpha = \dfrac{b}{R}$, $\sin \alpha = \dfrac{a}{R}$.

Similarly, if $a \cos \theta - b \sin \theta$ is written as $R \cos(\theta + \alpha)$, then

$R = \sqrt{a^2 + b^2}$, $\cos \alpha = \dfrac{a}{R}$, $\sin \alpha = \dfrac{b}{R}$.

If $a \sin \theta - b \cos \theta$ is written as $R \sin(\theta - \alpha)$, then

$R = \sqrt{a^2 + b^2}$, $\cos \alpha = \dfrac{a}{R}$, $\sin \alpha = \dfrac{b}{R}$.

## The Inverse Trigonometric Functions

$y = \sin^{-1} x$, for $|x| \leq 1$

Range $-\dfrac{\pi}{2} \leq \sin^{-1} x \leq \dfrac{\pi}{2}$

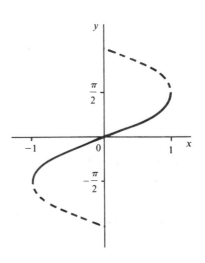

$y = \cos^{-1} x$, for $|x| \leq 1$

Range $0 \leq \cos^{-1} x \leq \pi$

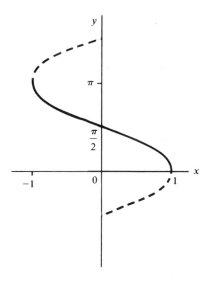

$y = \tan^{-1} x$

Range $-\dfrac{\pi}{2} < \tan^{-1} x < \dfrac{\pi}{2}$

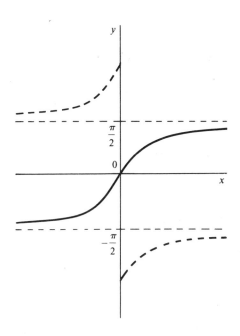

The notation arcsin $x$, arccos $x$, arctan $x$ can be used instead of $\sin^{-1} x$, $\cos^{-1} x$, $\tan^{-1} x$ respectively.

**Examples**

**2.1**   Show that $\cos 3\theta = 4\cos^3\theta - 3\cos\theta$

$\cos 3\theta = \cos(2\theta + \theta)$

$\qquad\quad = \cos 2\theta \cos\theta - \sin 2\theta \sin\theta$          using $\cos(A+B)$ formula

$\qquad\quad = (2\cos^2\theta - 1)\cos\theta - 2\sin\theta\cos\theta\,.\,\sin\theta$     using $\cos 2A$ and $\sin 2A$ formulae

$\qquad\quad = 2\cos^3\theta - \cos\theta - 2\cos\theta(1 - \cos^2\theta)$     using $\sin^2\theta = 1 - \cos^2\theta$

$\qquad\quad = 4\cos^3\theta - 3\cos\theta$

**2.2**   Solve the equation $\sin 3\theta + \sin\theta = \frac{1}{2}\sin 2\theta$

$2\sin 2\theta \cos\theta = \frac{1}{2}\sin 2\theta$          using $\sin A + \sin B$ formula

$\sin 2\theta(2\cos\theta - \frac{1}{2}) = 0$

$\sin 2\theta = 0$ or $\cos\theta = \frac{1}{4}$

For $\sin 2\theta = 0$, one solution is $2\theta = 0°$

The general solution is $2\theta = n\,.\,180° + (-1)^n\,.\,0°$

$\qquad\qquad\qquad\qquad\quad \theta = n\,.\,90°$

For $\cos\theta = \frac{1}{4}$, one solution is $\theta = 75.5°$

The general solution is $\theta = n\,.\,360° \pm 75.5°$

The complete solution is $\theta = n\,.\,90°$ or $n\,.\,360° \pm 75.5°$

For solutions in the range $0° \leqslant \theta \leqslant 360°$ put $n = 0, 1, 2, \ldots$

$\theta = 0°,\ 75.5°,\ 90°,\ 180°,\ 270°,\ 284.5°,\ 360°.$

**2.3**   Solve the equation $\tan 4\theta = \tan\theta$

One solution is $4\theta = \theta$

The general solution is $4\theta = n\pi + \theta$

$\qquad\qquad\qquad\qquad 3\theta = n\pi$

$\qquad\qquad\qquad\qquad \theta = \dfrac{n\pi}{3}$

For solutions in the range $0 \leqslant \theta \leqslant 2\pi$ put $n = 0, 1, 2, \ldots$

$\theta = 0,\ \dfrac{\pi}{3},\ \dfrac{2\pi}{3},\ \pi,\ \dfrac{4\pi}{3},\ \dfrac{5\pi}{3},\ 2\pi.$

**2.4**   Express $\cos\theta + \sqrt{3}\sin\theta$ in the form $R\cos(\theta - \alpha)$, and hence solve the equation $\cos\theta + \sqrt{3}\sin\theta = \sqrt{2}$.

Let $\cos\theta + \sqrt{3}\sin\theta \equiv R\cos(\theta - \alpha)$

Either use formulae to find $R$ and $\alpha$ or continue thus:

$\cos\theta + \sqrt{3}\sin\theta \equiv R\cos\theta\cos\alpha + R\sin\theta\sin\alpha$

Putting $\theta = 0$, $1 = R\cos\alpha$

Putting $\theta = \dfrac{\pi}{2}$, $\sqrt{3} = R\sin\alpha$

Squaring and adding, $1^2 + 3 = R^2$, $R = 2$, $\alpha = \dfrac{\pi}{3}$.

$\therefore\quad \cos\theta + \sqrt{3}\sin\theta \equiv 2\cos\left(\theta - \dfrac{\pi}{3}\right)$

To solve $\cos \theta + \sqrt{3} \sin \theta = \sqrt{2}$

$$2 \cos\left(\theta - \frac{\pi}{3}\right) = \sqrt{2}$$

$$\cos\left(\theta - \frac{\pi}{3}\right) = \frac{1}{\sqrt{2}}$$

One solution is $\theta - \dfrac{\pi}{3} = \dfrac{\pi}{4}$

The general solution is $\theta - \dfrac{\pi}{3} = 2n\pi \pm \dfrac{\pi}{4}$

$$\theta = 2n\pi + \frac{\pi}{12} \text{ or } 2n\pi + \frac{7\pi}{12}$$

The solution in the range $0 < \theta < 2\pi$ is $\theta = \dfrac{\pi}{12}$ or $\dfrac{7\pi}{12}$.

## Exercise 2.1

1. Show that $\dfrac{\cot^2 \theta - \tan^2 \theta}{\operatorname{cosec}^2 \theta - \sec^2 \theta} = 1$.

2. Show that $\cos\left(\theta - \dfrac{\pi}{6}\right) = \sin \theta + \cos\left(\theta + \dfrac{\pi}{6}\right)$.

3. Show that $\dfrac{\cos 6\theta + \cos 4\theta}{\sin 6\theta - \sin 4\theta} = \cot \theta$.

4. Find in surd form the value of $\tan 15°$.

5. Simplify $\cos 2\theta + \tan \theta \sin 2\theta$.

6. If $\sin(\theta + \alpha) = k \cos \theta$, show that $\tan \theta = \dfrac{k - \sin \alpha}{\cos \alpha}$.

7. If $\tan 2\theta = \frac{9}{40}$, find the possible values of $\tan \theta$.

8. Express $2 \cos(\theta + 80°) \cos(\theta + 20°)$ in the form $\cos A + \cos B$. Find its maximum value and the value of $\theta$ between $0°$ and $180°$ for which it has this maximum value.

9. Simplify $\dfrac{(1 + \tan \theta)^2 - \sec^2 \theta}{\tan \theta}$.

10. Show that $\sin \theta + 2 \sin 3\theta + \sin 5\theta = 4 \cos^2 \theta \sin 3\theta$.

11. Show that $\dfrac{1}{1 - \cos \theta} + \dfrac{1}{1 + \cos \theta} = 2 \operatorname{cosec}^2 \theta$.

12. Show that $\cos 10° = \cos 50° + \cos 70°$.

13. Express $\cos 4\theta$ in terms of $\cos 2\theta$ and hence show that $\cos 4\theta = 8 \cos^4 \theta - 8 \cos^2 \theta + 1$.

14. If $C = A + B$, show that $\tan A \tan B \tan C = \tan C - \tan A - \tan B$.

15. Show that $1 + \cos 2\theta + \cos 4\theta + \cos 6\theta = 4 \cos \theta \cos 2\theta \cos 3\theta$.

16. Simplify $\dfrac{\cos 2\theta}{\sin \theta} + \dfrac{\sin 2\theta}{\cos \theta}$.

17. Show that $\cos^2 \theta - \cos^2 5\theta = \sin 4\theta \sin 6\theta$.

18. If $A$, $B$, $C$ are acute angles and $\tan A = \frac{1}{8}$, $\tan B = \frac{2}{9}$ and $\tan C = \frac{14}{5}$,
    1  find the value of $\tan(A + B)$,
    2  show that $A + B + C = \dfrac{\pi}{2}$.

19. Show that $\dfrac{\sin 3\theta}{\sin \theta} = 3 - 4 \sin^2 \theta$.

20. Show that $\cot \theta - \cot 2\theta = \tan \theta + \cot 2\theta = \operatorname{cosec} 2\theta$.

21. Use Pythagoras' theorem and trig. ratios in a
    right-angled triangle to verify that for
    an acute angle $\theta$,
    1  $\cos^2 \theta + \sin^2 \theta = 1$
    2  $\sec^2 \theta = 1 + \tan^2 \theta$.

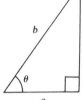

22. Use the addition formulae for $\sin(A + B)$ and $\cos(A + B)$ to verify that
    $$\tan(A + B) = \frac{\tan A + \tan B}{1 - \tan A \tan B}.$$

23. Use the addition formulae to obtain an expression for $\sin(P + Q) + \sin(P - Q)$.
    By putting $A = P + Q$ and $B = P - Q$, verify the formula
    $$\sin A + \sin B = 2 \sin \frac{A + B}{2} \cos \frac{A - B}{2}.$$

## Exercise 2.2

Find the values of the following inverse trig. functions, in the defined ranges.

1.  $\sin^{-1} 0$
2.  $\cos^{-1} 0$
3.  $\sin^{-1} 1$
4.  $\cos^{-1} 1$
5.  $\tan^{-1} 1$
6.  $\sin^{-1} (-1)$

7.  $\cos^{-1} (-1)$
8.  $\tan^{-1} (-1)$
9.  $\sin^{-1}(-\frac{1}{2})$
10. $\cos^{-1} \frac{1}{2}$
11. $\tan^{-1} \sqrt{3}$
12. $\cos^{-1}\left(-\dfrac{\sqrt{3}}{2}\right)$

13. $\sin^{-1}\left(-\dfrac{1}{\sqrt{2}}\right)$
14. $\sec^{-1} (-2)$
15. $\tan^{-1}\left(-\dfrac{\sqrt{3}}{3}\right)$
16. $\cot^{-1} \sqrt{3}$

Find the values of:

17.  $\cos(\sin^{-1}\frac{1}{2})$       19.  $\sin\left[\cos^{-1}\left(-\frac{1}{\sqrt{2}}\right)\right]$

18.  $\tan[\cos^{-1}(-\frac{1}{2})]$       20.  $\tan(\tan^{-1}\sqrt{5})$

Give the general solutions to these equations.

21.  $\sin\theta = \sin\dfrac{\pi}{8}$       24.  $\sin\theta = \dfrac{\sqrt{3}}{2}$

22.  $\cos\theta = \cos\dfrac{2\pi}{5}$       25.  $\tan\theta = 1$

23.  $\tan\theta = \tan\dfrac{\pi}{3}$

## Exercise 2.3

Solve these equations, giving the values of $\theta$ in the stated ranges. Approximate answers in degrees should be given to the nearest 0.1°.

1.   $\sin\theta = -\frac{3}{5}$                           Range $0° < \theta < 360°$

2.   $\cos\theta = \frac{1}{3}$                            Range $0° < \theta < 360°$

3.   $\tan\theta = 4$                             Range $0° < \theta < 360°$

4.   $\sin\theta = \frac{1}{2}$                            General solution, $\theta$ in radians

5.   $\cos\theta = -\dfrac{1}{\sqrt{2}}$                    General solution, $\theta$ in radians

6.   $\tan\theta = -1$                           General solution, $\theta$ in radians

7.   $\sin(\theta + 60°) = \frac{1}{2}$                 Range $-180° < \theta < 180°$

8.   $\cos(\theta - 30°) = \dfrac{1}{\sqrt{2}}$            Range $-180° < \theta < 180°$

9.   $\sin(2\theta + 12°) = \dfrac{\sqrt{3}}{2}$           Range $-180° < \theta < 180°$

10.  $\tan 5\theta = \tan\theta$                     General solution, $\theta$ in radians

11.  $1 + \cos\theta + \cos 2\theta = 0$             General solution, $\theta$ in radians

12.  $\sin 3\theta = \sin\theta$                     General solution, $\theta$ in radians

13.  $9\sin^2\theta = 4\tan^2\theta$                 Range $0° \leqslant \theta \leqslant 180°$

14.  $5\cos\theta + 12\sin\theta = 3.25$             Range $0° < \theta < 360°$

15.  $15\sin\theta - 8\cos\theta = 8$               Range $0° < \theta < 360°$

**Exercise 2.4**

Solve these equations giving the values of $\theta$ in the range $0° < \theta < 360°$, with approximate answers to the nearest $0.1°$.

1.   $\sin \theta = 2 \cos(60° + \theta)$

2.   $\cos(\theta + 45°) = \sqrt{2} \sin \theta$

3.   $\sin \theta + 2 \cos \theta = 1$

4.   $3 \sin 2\theta + \cos^2 \theta = 1$

5.   $4 \cos \theta - 3 \sin \theta - 3 = 0$

6.   $\tan \theta - 3 \cot \theta = 2$

Solve the following equations giving the values of $\theta$ in the range $0 < \theta < 2\pi$.

7.   $\sin \theta - \sqrt{3} \cos \theta = 1$

8.   $\sin \theta + \sin 3\theta = \cos \theta + \cos 3\theta$

9.   $\sin 2\theta + 1 = \sin \theta + 2 \cos \theta$

10.  $\sin \theta + \cos \theta = \dfrac{1}{\sqrt{2}}$

11.  $\cos 4\theta = \cos \theta$

Solve the following equations giving the general solution, $\theta$ in radians.

12.  $\sin \theta + \sin 7\theta = \sin 4\theta$

13.  $2 \sin^2 \theta = 3 - 3 \cos \theta$

14.  $\cos 2\theta + \sin \theta = \sin 3\theta$

15.  $\tan 3\theta = \cot 2\theta$

# 3  Series

## Arithmetic Progression

The sequence is $a,\ a+d,\ a+2d,\ a+3d,\ldots$

$n$th term $= l = a+(n-1)d$

sum of $n$ terms $s_n = \dfrac{n}{2}(a+l) = \dfrac{n}{2}[2a+(n-1)d]$

If 3 numbers $a,\ b,\ c$ are in Arithmetic Progression, then $2b = a+c$.
$b$ is called the Arithmetic mean of $a$ and $c$.

To derive the formula for $s_n$:

$s_n = a+(a+d)+(a+2d)+\ldots+(l-2d)+(l-d)+l$

$s_n = l+(l-d)+(l-2d)+\ldots+(a+2d)+(a+d)+a$      (writing it backwards)

Adding term by term:

$2s_n = (a+l)\times n$

$s_n = \dfrac{n}{2}(a+l)$

Replacing $l$ by $a+(n-1)d$ gives $s_n = \dfrac{n}{2}[2a+(n-1)d]$

## Geometric Progression

The sequence is $a,\ ar,\ ar^2,\ ar^3,\ldots$

$n$th term $= ar^{n-1}$

sum of $n$ terms $s_n = \dfrac{a(1-r^n)}{1-r}$

If $|r|<1$, the series is convergent and has a 'sum to infinity'.

$s_\infty = \dfrac{a}{1-r}$   for $|r|<1$

If 3 numbers $a,\ b,\ c$ are in Geometric Progression then $b^2 = ac$.
$b$ is called the Geometric mean of $a$ and $c$.

To derive the formula for $s_n$:
$$s_n = a + ar + ar^2 + ar^3 + \ldots + ar^{n-1}$$
Multiply each term by $r$
$$rs_n = \quad ar + ar^2 + ar^3 + \ldots + ar^{n-1} + ar^n$$

Subtracting,
$$s_n - rs_n = a - ar^n$$
$$s_n(1-r) = a(1-r^n)$$
$$s_n = \frac{a(1-r^n)}{1-r}$$

If $|r| < 1$, then $r^n \to 0$ as $n \to \infty$ so $s_\infty = \dfrac{a}{1-r}$.

## The Binomial Expansion

$$(1+x)^n = 1 + nx + \frac{n(n-1)}{2!} x^2 + \ldots + \binom{n}{r} x^r + \ldots$$

where $\dbinom{n}{r}$ is defined as $\dfrac{n(n-1)(n-2)\ldots(n-r+1)}{r!}$ and $\dbinom{n}{0}$ is defined as 1.

**If $n$ is a positive integer**, the series terminates with the term $x^n$ and is convergent for all $x$.

$\dbinom{n}{r}$ can be written as $\dfrac{n!}{(n-r)!r!}$      (0! is defined as 1)

The expansion of $(a+x)^n$ is also useful.
$$(a+x)^n = a^n + na^{n-1}x + \frac{n(n-1)}{2!} a^{n-2}x^2 + \ldots + \binom{n}{r} a^{n-r}x^r + \ldots + x^n$$

**If $n$ is not a positive integer**, the series for $(1+x)^n$ is infinite and converges for $|x| < 1$.

## $\Sigma$ notation

Using this notation:
$$a + (a+d) + (a+2d) + \ldots + [a+(n-1)d] = \sum_{r=1}^{n} [a+(r-1)d]$$

$$a + ar + ar^2 + ar^3 + \ldots + ar^{n-1} = \sum_{m=0}^{n-1} ar^m \text{ or } \sum_{m=1}^{n} ar^{m-1}$$

$$(1+x)^n = \sum_{r=0}^{n} \binom{n}{r} x^r \text{ if } n \text{ is a positive integer}$$

$$= \sum_{r=0}^{\infty} \binom{n}{r} x^r \text{ if } n \text{ is not a positive integer and } |x| < 1.$$

**Examples**

**3.1**    In an arithmetical progression $a, \frac{7}{6}a, \frac{4}{3}a, \ldots$ the sum of $2n$ terms is 3 times the sum of $n$ terms. Find the value of $n$.

The first term is $a$, the common difference $d = \frac{1}{6}a$.

$$s_n = \frac{n}{2}[2a + (n-1)d]$$

$$= \frac{n}{2}\left[2a + \frac{a}{6}(n-1)\right]$$

$$= \frac{na}{12}(11 + n)$$

$$s_{2n} = \frac{2n}{2}\left[2a + \frac{a}{6}(2n-1)\right]$$

$$= \frac{na}{6}(11 + 2n)$$

$$S_{2n} = 3s_n$$

$\therefore \quad \dfrac{na}{6}(11 + 2n) = \dfrac{3na}{12}(11 + n) \qquad$ and $n \neq 0, a \neq 0$.

$$22 + 4n = 33 + 3n$$

$$n = 11$$

**3.2**    In a geometric progression the first term is 36 and the sum of the first 3 terms is 52. Find the possible values of the common ratio and for each value find an expression for the sum of the first 6 terms. Find also the sum to infinity if this exists.

$a = 36, \ a + ar + ar^2 = 52.$

$\therefore \quad 36r^2 + 36r - 16 = 0$

$$9r^2 + 9r - 4 = 0$$

$$(3r + 4)(3r - 1) = 0$$

$r = -\frac{4}{3}$ or $\frac{1}{3}$. (These are the values of the common ratio.)

$$s_6 = \frac{a(1 - r^6)}{1 - r}$$

When $r = -\frac{4}{3}, \ a = 36, \ s_6 = \dfrac{36[1 - (-\frac{4}{3})^6]}{1 - (-\frac{4}{3})} = \dfrac{108}{7}\left(1 - \dfrac{4^6}{3^6}\right)$

(Sums of geometric progressions are often left in index form, but this equals $-71\frac{7}{27}$.)

When $r = \frac{1}{3}$ and $a = 36, \ s_6 = \dfrac{36[1 - (\frac{1}{3})^6]}{1 - \frac{1}{3}} = 54\left(1 - \dfrac{1}{3^6}\right) = 53\frac{25}{27}.$

When $r = \frac{1}{3}, \ s_\infty$ exists.

$$s_\infty = \frac{a}{1 - r} = \frac{36}{1 - \frac{1}{3}} = 54.$$

**3.3**    How many terms of the geometric progression $\frac{1}{3}, \frac{1}{2}, \frac{3}{4}, \ldots$ must be taken for the sum to be greater than 3000?

$a = \frac{1}{3}$, $r = \frac{3}{2}$.

$$S_n = \frac{a(1-r^n)}{1-r} = \frac{a(r^n - 1)}{r-1}$$

$\therefore \quad \dfrac{\frac{1}{3}[(\frac{3}{2})^n - 1]}{\frac{3}{2} - 1} > 3000$

$(\frac{3}{2})^n > 4501$

Take logs. of both sides. (Either use base 10 or base e)

$\ln(\frac{3}{2})^n > \ln 4501$

$n \ln \frac{3}{2} > \ln 4501$

$\therefore \quad n > \dfrac{\ln 4501}{\ln \frac{3}{2}} \left( = \dfrac{8.4121}{0.4055} = 20.7 \right)$

21 terms must be taken.

**3.4**    Find the values of $\binom{6}{2}$ and $\binom{6}{4}$. Simplify $(\sqrt{2} + \sqrt{3}x)^6 + (\sqrt{2} - \sqrt{3}x)^6$.

$$\binom{6}{2} = \frac{6!}{4!2!} = \frac{6 \times 5}{2 \times 1} = 15, \qquad \binom{6}{4} = \frac{6!}{2!4!} = 15$$

$$(\sqrt{2} + \sqrt{3}x)^6 = \sqrt{2}^6 + \binom{6}{1}\sqrt{2}^5 \cdot \sqrt{3}x + \binom{6}{2}\sqrt{2}^4(\sqrt{3}x)^2 + \binom{6}{3}\sqrt{2}^3(\sqrt{3}x)^3$$

$$+ \binom{6}{4}\sqrt{2}^2(\sqrt{3}x)^4 + \binom{6}{5}\sqrt{2}(\sqrt{3}x)^5 + (\sqrt{3}x)^6$$

$$(\sqrt{2} - \sqrt{3}x)^6 = \sqrt{2}^6 - \binom{6}{1}\sqrt{2}^5 \cdot \sqrt{3}x + \binom{6}{2}\sqrt{2}^4(\sqrt{3}x)^2 - \binom{6}{3}\sqrt{2}^3(\sqrt{3}x)^3$$

$$+ \binom{6}{4}\sqrt{2}^2(\sqrt{3}x)^4 - \binom{6}{5}\sqrt{2}(\sqrt{3}x)^5 + (\sqrt{3}x)^6$$

$\therefore \quad (\sqrt{2} + \sqrt{3}x)^6 + (\sqrt{2} - \sqrt{3}x)^6 = 2\left[ \sqrt{2}^6 + \binom{6}{2}\sqrt{2}^4(\sqrt{3}x)^2 + \binom{6}{4}\sqrt{2}^2(\sqrt{3}x)^4 + (\sqrt{3}x)^6 \right]$

$$= 16 + 360x^2 + 540x^4 + 54x^6.$$

**3.5**    Find expressions for $\binom{n}{1}$, $\binom{n}{2}$ and $\binom{n}{3}$ when $n = -\frac{3}{2}$. Expand $(1 - 2x)^{-\frac{3}{2}}$ as far as the term in $x^3$. For what values of $x$ is this expansion valid?

$$\binom{n}{1} = -\frac{3}{2}, \qquad \binom{n}{2} = \frac{(-\frac{3}{2})(-\frac{5}{2})}{2!}, \qquad \binom{n}{3} = \frac{(-\frac{3}{2})(-\frac{5}{2})(-\frac{7}{2})}{3!}$$

$$(1 - 2x)^{-\frac{3}{2}} = 1 + (-\frac{3}{2})(-2x) + \frac{(-\frac{3}{2})(-\frac{5}{2})}{2!}(-2x)^2 + \frac{(-\frac{3}{2})(-\frac{5}{2})(-\frac{7}{2})}{3!}(-2x)^3 + \ldots$$

$$= 1 + 3x + \frac{15}{2}x^2 + \frac{35}{2}x^3 + \ldots$$

This expansion is valid when $|-2x| < 1$, i.e. $|x| < \frac{1}{2}$.

**3.6**    Expand $(4-8x)^{-\frac{3}{2}}$, giving the first 3 terms.

This is $4^{-\frac{3}{2}}(1-2x)^{-\frac{3}{2}}$ and $4^{-\frac{3}{2}}=\dfrac{1}{4^{\frac{3}{2}}}=\frac{1}{8}$

Expand $(1-2x)^{-\frac{3}{2}}$ as in the last example.

$$(4-8x)^{-\frac{3}{2}}=\tfrac{1}{8}(1+3x+\tfrac{15}{2}x^2+\ldots)$$
$$=\tfrac{1}{8}+\tfrac{3}{8}x+\tfrac{15}{16}x^2+\ldots$$

(The expansion is valid when $|x|<\frac{1}{2}$.)


## Exercise 3.1

1.  Find the twelth term of the arithmetic progression $12, 7, 2, \ldots$.

2.  Find the sum of 100 terms of the arithmetic progression $-3, 5, 13, \ldots$.

3.  Find the value of $\displaystyle\sum_{r=1}^{20}(3r+1)$.

4.  Find the sum of the multiples of 7 between 100 and 200.

5.  If $x+2$, $x^2$ and $2x+3$ are consecutive terms of an arithmetic progression of increasing terms, find the value of $x$.

6.  Find an expression for the sum of the first $n$ terms of the arithmetic series $8+11+14+ \ldots$. Find the least value of $n$ for which the sum of the first $n$ terms is greater than 1000.

7.  The $n$th term of a series is $\dfrac{2n+1}{4}$. Show that this series is an arithmetic progression.

    Find an expression for the sum of $n$ terms. If this sum is 240, find the value of $n$.

8.  Find in a simplified index form the tenth term of the geometric progression $81, 27, 9, \ldots$.

9.  Find in a simplified index form the sum of 10 terms of the geometric progression $6, -54, 486, \ldots$.

10. Find in a simplified form an expression for $\displaystyle\sum_{r=1}^{9}4(-3)^r$.

11. Find the sum to infinity of the geometric series $\frac{3}{5}-\frac{2}{5}+\frac{4}{15}-\ldots$.

12. If $x+6$, $3x$, $4x+3$ are consecutive positive terms of a geometric progression, find the value of $x$.

13. Find the value of $\displaystyle\sum_{r=1}^{\infty}\tfrac{4}{3}(\tfrac{1}{3})^r$.

14. Find the values of:

   1  $\binom{8}{2}$     2  $\binom{10}{3}$     3  $\binom{9}{4}$     4  $\binom{11}{6}$     5  $\binom{-2}{2}$

   6  $\binom{-2}{3}$     7  $\binom{-1}{4}$     8  $\binom{\frac{1}{3}}{2}$     9  $\binom{\frac{1}{3}}{3}$    10  $\binom{1\frac{1}{2}}{3}$

15. In the expansion of $\left(3x+\dfrac{2}{x}\right)^6$ find the term in $x^2$ and the term independent of $x$.

16. If $y = x + \dfrac{1}{x}$ and $y^3 + ky \equiv x^3 + \dfrac{1}{x^3}$, find the value of $k$.

17. If $(\sqrt{3}-\sqrt{2})^5 \equiv a\sqrt{3}-b\sqrt{2}$, find the values of $a$ and $b$.

18. Expand $\sqrt{1-4x}$ in ascending powers of $x$ as far as the term in $x^3$. For what range of values of $x$ is this expansion valid?

19. Expand $\dfrac{1}{(1+2x)^3}$ in ascending powers of $x$ as far as the term in $x^3$. For what range of values of $x$ is this expansion valid?

20. Expand $\dfrac{1+2x}{1-2x}$ in ascending powers of $x$ as far as the term in $x^3$. For what range of values of $x$ is this expansion valid?

## Exercise 3.2

1. Find an expression for $\displaystyle\sum_{r=1}^{n} \ln a^r$.

2. Find the sum of all the integers between 300 and 400 which are not divisible by 5.

3. Find the series whose sum to $n$ terms is $n(8-3n)$, and show that it is an arithmetic progression.

4. The sum of the first 6 terms of an arithmetic progression of ascending terms is $67\frac{1}{2}$ and the product of the first and sixth terms is 125. Find the first term.

5. Show that $\dfrac{1}{\sqrt{2}}, \dfrac{1}{1+\sqrt{2}}, \dfrac{1}{4+3\sqrt{2}}$ are in arithmetic progression and find the next term of the sequence in the form $\dfrac{1}{a+b\sqrt{2}}$.

6. The first term of a geometric series is 12 and the sum to infinity is 9. Find the common ratio and the sum of the first 5 terms.

7. Find the series whose sum to $n$ terms is $\frac{1}{2}(5^n-1)$ and show that it is a geometric progression.

8. The first term of a geometric progression is 3 and the second term is $3\frac{1}{2}$. Find an expression for the sum of $n$ terms and find the least value of $n$ for which the sum is greater than 9000.

9.  In an infinite geometric progression the sum of all terms after the $n$th is equal to one-quarter of the $n$th term. Find the value of the common ratio.

10. The first, fifth and twenty-first terms of an arithmetic progression are also three consecutive terms of a geometric progression. Find the common ratio of the geometric progression.

11. A geometric progression has a common ratio 3. If the sum of the first $2n$ terms is 82 times the sum of the first $n$ terms, find the value of $n$.

12. In a geometric progression the sum of the first and third terms is 4 times the second term. Find in surd form the possible values of the common ratio.

13. In the expansion of $\left(3x^3 - \dfrac{1}{2x^2}\right)^5$ find the term independent of $x$.

14. In the expansion of $(3+4x)^n$, where $n$ is a positive integer, the coefficient of $x^6$ is two-thirds that of $x^5$. Find the value of $n$.

15. Expand $(1+2x)^{\frac{1}{2}}(1-3x)^{\frac{1}{3}}$ in ascending powers of $x$ as far as the term in $x^2$. For what values of $x$ is this expansion valid?

16. Show that $\left(\dfrac{1+x}{1-x}\right)^n = 1 + 2nx + 2n^2x^2$ if terms in $x^3$ and higher powers of $x$ are neglected.

17. If $(1+ax+bx^2)(1-2x)^{-3}$ is expanded and the coefficients of $x$ and $x^2$ are both zero, find the values of $a$ and $b$.

18. Expand $(1+x-2x^2)^{-1}$ in ascending powers of $x$ as far as the term in $x^2$.

19. Express $\dfrac{1}{(1-x)(1+2x)}$ in partial fractions. Hence expand this expression in ascending powers of $x$ as far as the term in $x^2$, comparing your result with that in question 18. Also give the general term. For what range of values of $x$ is the expansion valid?

20. If $x$ is small enough for terms in $x^3$ to be neglected, show that the expansion of $(1+12x)^{\frac{1}{6}}$ has terms equal to those of the expansion of $\dfrac{1+7x}{1+5x}$. Hence find an approximate value for $\sqrt[6]{1.12}$ as a rational number.

## * The Logarithmic and Exponential Series

$$\ln(1+x) = x - \frac{x^2}{2} + \frac{x^3}{3} - \frac{x^4}{4} + \ldots + (-1)^{r+1}\frac{x^r}{r} + \ldots$$

This series is convergent and valid when $-1 < x \leqslant 1$

$$e^x = 1 + x + \frac{x^2}{2!} + \frac{x^3}{3!} + \ldots + \frac{x^r}{r!} + \ldots$$

This series is convergent and valid for all values of $x$.

Topics marked * are not included in the national common core and may not be needed for your syllabus.

**Example 3.7**

Find the first 4 terms and the general term for these series, and state the values
of $x$ for which each series is valid.

1   $\ln(1-2x)$        2   $\ln(3+x)$        3   $e^{4x}$        4   $e^{1-x}$

1   $\ln(1-2x) = (-2x) - \dfrac{(-2x)^2}{2} + \dfrac{(-2x)^3}{3} - \dfrac{(-2x)^4}{4} + \dots + (-1)^{r+1}\dfrac{(-2x)^r}{r} + \dots$

$= -2x - 2x^2 - \tfrac{8}{3}x^3 - 4x^4 - \dots - \dfrac{2^r}{r}x^r - \dots$

Valid when $-1 < -2x \leqslant 1$, i.e. $1 > 2x \geqslant -1$, i.e. $-\tfrac{1}{2} \leqslant x < \tfrac{1}{2}$

2   $\ln(3+x) = \ln 3\left(1+\dfrac{x}{3}\right) = \ln 3 + \ln\left(1+\dfrac{x}{3}\right)$

$= \ln 3 + \dfrac{x}{3} - \dfrac{\left(\tfrac{x}{3}\right)^2}{2} + \dfrac{\left(\tfrac{x}{3}\right)^3}{3} - \dots + (-1)^{r+1}\dfrac{\left(\tfrac{x}{3}\right)^r}{r} + \dots$

$= \ln 3 + \dfrac{x}{3} - \dfrac{x^2}{18} + \dfrac{x^3}{81} - \dots + (-1)^{r+1}\dfrac{1}{r.3^r}x^r + \dots$

Valid when $-1 < \dfrac{x}{3} \leqslant 1$, i.e. $-3 < x \leqslant 3$

3   $e^{4x} = 1 + 4x + \dfrac{(4x)^2}{2!} + \dfrac{(4x)^3}{3!} + \dots + \dfrac{(4x)^r}{r!} + \dots$

$= 1 + 4x + 8x^2 + \tfrac{32}{3}x^3 + \dots + \dfrac{4^r}{r!}x^r + \dots$

Valid for all values of $x$

4   $e^{1-x} = e^1 e^{-x} = e\left[1 + (-x) + \dfrac{(-x)^2}{2!} + \dfrac{(-x)^3}{3!} + \dots + \dfrac{(-x)^r}{r!} + \dots\right]$

$= e\left(1 - x + \dfrac{x^2}{2} - \dfrac{x^3}{6} + \dots + \dfrac{(-1)^r}{r!}x^r + \dots\right)$

Valid for all values of $x$.

**\* Exercise 3.3**

1.   Find the first 4 terms and the general term for the following series. State the range
of values of $x$ for which each expansion is valid.

1   $\ln(1+3x)$        5   $\ln(2+x)$        9   $\ln\left(1+\dfrac{1}{x}\right)$

2   $\ln(1-x)$         6   $\ln(3-2x)$

3   $e^{2x}$           7   $e^{1+x^2}$       10   $\log_{10}(1+x)$

4   $e^{-3x}$          8   $e^{-x/3}$

2. Find the first 3 terms for the following series:

   1  $\ln(1+x)+\ln(1-2x)$

   2  $\dfrac{e^{2x}-e^{-2x}}{2}$

   3  $\dfrac{\ln(1+x)}{e^x}$

   4  $\dfrac{\ln(1+2x)}{1+2x}$

   5  $\dfrac{1}{(1+x)\,e^x}$

3. By substituting $x=1$ in the expansion of $e^x$, and using your calculator, find the value of e to 4 decimal places.

4. By substituting suitable values of $x$ in the expansion of $e^x$ find the values, in terms of e, of these infinite series:

   1  $1+5+\dfrac{5^2}{2!}+\dfrac{5^3}{3!}+\ldots$

   2  $1-1+\tfrac{1}{2}-\tfrac{1}{6}+\tfrac{1}{24}-\ldots$

   3  $1+\tfrac{1}{2}+\tfrac{1}{8}+\tfrac{1}{48}+\tfrac{1}{384}+\tfrac{1}{3840}+\ldots$

5. Show that the coefficient of $x^r$ in the expansion of $(x^2+x+1)\,e^x$ is $\dfrac{1+r^2}{r!}$.

6. Find the first 3 terms in the expansion of $\ln(1+2x)$ and $\ln(1-3x)$. Show that $\ln(1-x-6x^2)=-x-\tfrac{13}{2}x^2-\tfrac{19}{3}x^3-\ldots$. For what values of $x$ is this expansion valid?

7. Show that $\dfrac{e^6-1}{e^3}=2\left(3+\dfrac{3^3}{3!}+\dfrac{3^5}{5!}+\ldots\right)$.

8. Factorise $1+x^3$. Hence, or otherwise, find the first 6 terms in the expansion of $\ln(1-x+x^2)$.

9. Show that the expansion of $(1-x^2)^{\frac{1}{2}}.(1-x^3)^{\frac{1}{3}}$ is identical to the expansion of $(1-x)\,e^x$ for terms as far as $x^4$.

10. Find the first 3 terms in the expansion of $\ln\dfrac{(1-3x)^2}{(1-2x)^3}$. For what values of $x$ is the expansion valid?

11. Find the first 3 terms in the expansion of $\ln\dfrac{1+x}{1-x}$. By putting $x=0.2$, find the value of $\ln 1.5$ to 3 significant figures.

12. Show that, when $x$ is small enough for $x^4$ and higher powers of $x$ to be neglected, $e^{x(1-x)}+e^{-x}=2+kx^3$, and find the value of $k$.

13. Show that $\ln\left(1+\dfrac{4}{x}+\dfrac{3}{x^2}\right)=\dfrac{3+1}{x}-\dfrac{3^2+1}{2x^2}+\dfrac{3^3+1}{3x^3}-\ldots$ and show that this expansion is valid for $x<-3$ or $x\geq 3$. Substitute in this expansion and use your calculator to find the value of $\ln 1.43$ to 2 significant figures.

# A Revision

## Exercise A1

1. Use the factor theorem to factorise $2x^3 - x^2 - 13x - 6$ and hence solve the equation $2x^3 - x^2 - 13x - 6 = 0$.

2. Show that $\dfrac{x^3 + y^3}{x + y} + \dfrac{x^3 - y^3}{x - y}$, where $x \neq 0$, is always positive.

3. Find the quadratic equation with sum of roots equal to 3 and the sum of squares of the roots equal to 65.

4. Find the possible values of $k$ if the equation $x^2 - 2(k-1)x + 3k + 1 = 0$ has equal roots.

5. Express $\dfrac{3x^2 - 18x + 31}{(x-1)(x-3)^2}$ in partial fractions.

6. Solve the equation $2^{2x} - 9.2^x + 8 = 0$.

7. Simplify $2 \ln 3 + 4 \ln 2 - 2 \ln 12$.

8. If $\dfrac{x^2 + 2x - 2}{(x+2)(x-2)} \equiv A + \dfrac{B}{x+2} + \dfrac{C}{x-2}$, find the values of $A$, $B$ and $C$.

9. The sum of $n$ terms of a series is $2n^2 + 3n$. Show that the series is an arithmetic progression and find the first three terms.

10. The sum of the first three terms of a geometric progression is $\frac{19}{54}$ and the sum to infinity is $\frac{1}{2}$. Find the first term and the common ratio.

11. By expanding, find the value of $(\sqrt{2}+1)^6 + (\sqrt{2}-1)^6$.

12. Expand $(1-2x)^{-\frac{3}{2}}$ as far as the term in $x^3$. For what values of $x$ is the expansion valid?

13. Show that $\sin(\alpha + \beta) \sin(a - \beta) = \cos^2 \beta - \cos^2 \alpha$.

14. If $f(\theta) = \theta \cot \theta$, show that $f(2\theta) = (1 - \tan^2 \theta)f(\theta)$.

15. Solve the equation $\cos(50° + \theta) = 3 \sin(40° + \theta)$ for $0° < \theta < 360°$.

16. Solve the equation $8 \tan \theta \sec \theta - \cot \theta \csc \theta = 0$ for $0° < \theta < 360°$.

17. Solve the equation $\tan^2 \theta - 3 \sec \theta + 3 = 0$ for $0 \leqslant \theta \leqslant 2\pi$.

18. Solve the equation $\sin 2\theta = \cot \theta$ for $0 < \theta < 2\pi$.

19. Solve the equation $\tan 3\theta - \tan \theta = 0$, giving the general solution (in radians).

20. Express $24 \cos \theta + 7 \sin \theta$ in the form $R \cos(\theta - \alpha)$. Solve the equation $24 \cos \theta + 7 \sin \theta = 8$ for $0° < \theta < 360°$.

## Exercise A2

*Select the correct answer to each question.*

1. The value of $\sin 300° + \sin 600°$ is

   **A** $-\sqrt{3}$     **B** $0$     **C** $\sqrt{3}$     **D** $\dfrac{\sqrt{3}-1}{2}$     **E** $-\dfrac{\sqrt{3}+1}{2}$

2. The sum to infinity of the geometric progression $\frac{1}{3}, -\frac{1}{6}, \frac{1}{12}, \ldots$ is

   **A** $-\frac{1}{3}$     **B** $\frac{1}{2}$     **C** $\frac{2}{3}$     **D** $\frac{1}{6}$     **E** $\frac{2}{9}$

3. If $\dfrac{3x^2 + 4x}{(x-2)(x^2+1)} \equiv \dfrac{A}{x-2} + \dfrac{Bx+C}{x^2+1}$, then $A + B + C =$

   **A** $1$     **B** $2$     **C** $3$     **D** $4$     **E** $5$

4. $\cos(2\alpha + \beta) + \cos(2\alpha - \beta) =$

   **A** $2 \cos 2\alpha \cos \beta$     **B** $2 \cos 2\alpha \sin \beta$     **C** $2 \sin 2\alpha \sin \beta$

   **D** $2 \sin 2\alpha \cos \beta$     **E** $-2 \sin 2\alpha \sin \beta$

5. The fourth term in the expansion in ascending powers of $x$ of $\left(\dfrac{x}{2} - \dfrac{2}{x}\right)^8$ is

   **A** $-56x^2$    **B** $-14x^2$     **C** $-70$     **D** $70$     **E** $14x^2$

6. If $3x^3 - 7x^2 + 10x + k$ is exactly divisible by $3x - 1$, then $k$ is

   **A** $-48$    **B** $-4\frac{2}{9}$     **C** $-2\frac{2}{3}$     **D** $2\frac{2}{3}$     **E** $48$

7. $\sin\left(\dfrac{\pi}{2} + \theta\right) - \cos(\pi - \theta)$ simplifies to

   **A** $0$     **B** $2 \cos \theta$     **C** $2 \sin \theta$     **D** $\cos \theta + \sin \theta$

   **E** $\cos \theta - \sin \theta$

8. The roots of $x^2 + 5x - 7 = 0$ are $\alpha$, $\beta$. The equation with roots $\alpha^2$, $\beta^2$ is

   **A** $x^2 - 25x + 49 = 0$     **B** $x^2 + 25x + 49 = 0$     **C** $x^2 + 11x + 49 = 0$

   **D** $x^2 - 11x - 49 = 0$     **E** $x^2 - 39x + 49 = 0$

9. $25^{\frac{2}{3}} \times 4^{\frac{1}{6}} \div 10^{\frac{1}{3}}$ simplifies to

   **A** $5$     **B** $5^4$     **C** $10$     **D** $10^{\frac{1}{2}}$     **E** $\left(\frac{5}{2}\right)^{\frac{1}{3}}$

10. If $\sin A = \frac{4}{5}$ and $\cos B = \frac{12}{13}$ and $A$ and $B$ are both acute angles then $\tan(A - B) =$

    **A** $\frac{11}{7}$     **B** $\frac{33}{16}$     **C** $-\frac{33}{56}$     **D** $\frac{33}{56}$     **E** $\frac{63}{16}$

11. The sum of the first 12 terms of the arithmetic progression with first term 10 is 21. The common difference is

    **A** $-1\frac{1}{2}$    **B** $-\frac{13}{22}$     **C** $-\frac{2}{3}$     **D** $\frac{2}{3}$     **E** $1\frac{1}{2}$

12. $e^{2 \ln x} =$

    A  $2 + x$      B  $2x$          C  $x^2$                D  $\ln x^2$          E  $x e^2$

13. $\dfrac{1 + \cos 2x}{\sin 2x}$ simplifies to

    A   $\tan x$                 B   $\cot x$              C   $1 + \cot 2x$
    D   $1 + \cot x$             E   $-\tan x$

14. The coefficient of $x^3$ in the expansion of $\dfrac{1}{(1 - 2x)^3}$ is

    A   $-160$     B   $-80$          C   $20$               D   $80$              E   $160$

15. If $6 \cos \theta - 5 \sin \theta \equiv R \cos(\theta - \alpha)$, then $\tan \alpha =$
    A   $\sqrt{61}$      B   $\sqrt{11}$          C   $\frac{6}{5}$          D   $\frac{5}{6}$          E   $-\frac{5}{6}$

## Exercise A3

1.  The acute angles $\theta$ and $\phi$ are such that $\tan \theta = \frac{9}{8}$ and $\tan \phi = \frac{1}{17}$. Show that $\theta - \phi = 45°$.

2.  Find the coefficient of $x^3$ in the expansion of $(1 + 2x)(1 - 3x)^6$.

3.  Simplify $\cos^2\left(\theta - \dfrac{\pi}{3}\right) + \sin \theta \sin\left(\theta - \dfrac{2\pi}{3}\right)$.

4.  If $\alpha$, $\beta$ are the roots of the equation $2x^2 - 4x + 1 = 0$, find the equation whose roots are $\alpha^2 + \dfrac{1}{\beta}$, $\beta^2 + \dfrac{1}{\alpha}$.

5.  Find the sum to infinity of the geometric series $\cos^2 \theta + \cos^2 \theta \sin^2 \theta + \cos^2 \theta \sin^4 \theta + \ldots$. For what values of $\theta$ $(0 \leqslant \theta \leqslant 2\pi)$ is this sum incorrect?

6.  Solve the equation $9^x - 3^{x+2} - 3^x + 9 = 0$.

7.  Find the greatest and least values of $\cos\left(x + \dfrac{\pi}{6}\right) \cos\left(x - \dfrac{\pi}{6}\right)$.

8.  Show that, if the equation $x^2 - (3k - 2)x + 2k = 0$ has equal roots, then so has the equation $x^2 + (5k - 2)x + 4k^2 = 0$.

9.  Solve the equation $\sin 2\theta = 2 \cos \theta \sin 3\theta$, giving the general solution (in radians).

10. Show that $\log_b a = \dfrac{\log_c a}{\log_c b}$. Solve the equation $4 \log_x 3 = \log_3 x$.

11. In the arithmetic series $a + (a + d) + (a + 2d) + \ldots + [a + (n-1)d]$, show that the sum of the first $n$ terms, $s_n$, is given by the formula

    $$s_n = \frac{n}{2}[2a + (n-1)d].$$

    In an arithmetic series with $d = \frac{1}{2}$, the sums of $n$ terms, $2n$ terms and $3n$ terms are such that $s_{3n} = s_n + s_{2n} + 900$. Find the value of $n$.

12. Express $6 \sin \theta + 8 \cos \theta$ in the form $R \sin(\theta + \alpha)$. Solve the equation $6 \sin \theta + 8 \cos \theta = 3$, for $0° < \theta < 360°$.

13. Expand $(1 + 6x)^{\frac{2}{3}} - 2(1 - 4x)^{\frac{1}{2}}$ in ascending powers of $x$, giving the first 3 non-zero terms. For what range of values of $x$ is this expansion valid?

14. Express $\dfrac{3x^2 - 8x + 7}{(x-1)(x-2)(x-3)}$ in partial fractions.

15. Use the factor theorem to solve the equation $3x^3 + 3x^2 - x - 1 = 0$. Hence solve the equation $3 \tan^3 \theta + 3 \tan^2 \theta - \tan \theta - 1 = 0$ for $0 < \theta < \pi$.

**To the Student:**

# 2 Improving Your Chances

Check your handwriting and if necessary, improve it. It must be legible, even when you are working quickly. Badly written work means that you confuse 6 with 0 or $b$, 2 with $z$, 5 with $s$, $u$ with $v$, $v$ with $V$. Show minus signs clearly. Do not alter figures, e.g., a 2 into a 3, by overwriting. Cross the 2 out and write 3 nearby. Do not change $+$ into $-$ except by crossing out and re-writing clearly, $+$ is simply ambiguous. Figures and symbols which are not clear cannot be marked as correct.

If you tend to work slowly, try to speed up, because in an examination you must give yourself a reasonable chance of completing the paper to gain good marks. When you are doing a question, concentrate completely on it until you finish it. Learn methods so that when you first read a question you know which approach to use and start on the right method immediately. Do not waste time pressing calculator keys for simple arithmetic which you could do more quickly in your head. By constant repetition you should be able to quote the values of expressions like $\cos 60°$, $\tan^{-1} 1$, $\sqrt{8^2+15^2}$. If you do use your calculator, do not waste time writing down all the 8 given figures in your working if they are not all necessary, and make use of the calculator's memory function so that you do not have to keep re-entering the same numbers.

Make sure that you use brackets correctly. $(2x+3)(x+2)$ does not mean the same thing as $2x+3(x+2)$. Be especially careful with double brackets, and be careful with signs when you remove brackets. Fractions have fraction lines which count as brackets. $\dfrac{2x+3}{x+2}$ is the same as $(2x+3) \div (x+2)$. $\dfrac{2x+3}{x+2}$ is meaningless; you meant to put the line in later using a ruler, and forgot about it!

**You must be confident in using all algebraic techniques.** Learn by your mistakes and do not repeat them. Even if an expression is complicated the normal rules apply, e.g. $\sqrt{(\sin\theta+\cos\theta)^2+(\sin\theta-\cos\theta)^2}$ is an expression of the type $\sqrt{a^2+b^2}$. You know that $\sqrt{a^2+b^2}$ is <u>not</u> $a+b$, so this other expression is not $\sin\theta+\cos\theta+\sin\theta-\cos\theta$. (Work it out properly and the result is $\sqrt{2}$.) Another common mistake is to divide an equation by a factor which could be zero, thus losing one of the solutions. e.g. $x^3+2x^2=9x+18$. If you write this as $x^2(x+2)=9(x+2)$, do not divide by the factor $x+2$, getting $x^2=9$, unless you also note that $x+2$ could be 0, so $x=-2$ is a solution as well as $x=-3$ or 3. (In any case the solution $x=\pm 3$ should be suspect because a cubic equation generally has three roots.) A safer way to solve the equation would be to rearrange it as $x^3+2x^2-9x-18=0$, use the factor theorem to factorise this, ($x+2$ is obviously a factor) and then solve it.

Sketch diagrams can be very useful, even if they are not required as part of an answer. Having found the maximum and minimum points on a curve, a quick sketch of the curve would show whether your answers seem reasonable.

To solve the equation $\sin \theta = \frac{1}{2}$, a sketch like this shows the 2 possible positions for $\theta$, and you can then write down the answer $\theta = 30°, 150°, 390°$, etc., or the general solution $\theta = n \cdot 180° + (-1)^n \cdot 30°$. (Algebraic graphs are introduced in Chapters 5 and 6 and there is a sketchgraph checklist on page 181.)

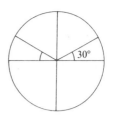

When you have found an answer, consider if it is reasonable, especially if you have pressed calculator keys to get it. $\sqrt{5} - \sqrt{3}$ is '2 and a bit' minus '1 and a bit', so an answer which is not between 0 and 2 cannot be correct. An answer with an awkward number, such as $x = \frac{991}{157}$ might be correct, but it is unlikely. You will probably have made a mistake and it is worth making a check before you continue. Note the instructions in a question about the form of the answer. If an exact answer is wanted, it is no use using approximate numbers from your calculator to get it. If the answer is wanted to 1 significant figure, this is not necessarily the same as answering to 1 decimal place.

# 4 Differentiation (Methods)

Gradient of chord $AB$

$$= \frac{BC}{AC} = \frac{f(x + \delta x) - f(x)}{\delta x}$$

Gradient of tangent at $A$

$$= \text{limit of gradient of chord as } B \to A$$

$$= \underset{\delta x \to 0}{\text{limit}} \frac{f(x + \delta x) - f(x)}{\delta x}$$

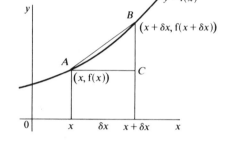

**Definition** $f'(x) = \dfrac{d[f(x)]}{dx} = \underset{\delta x \to 0}{\text{limit}} \dfrac{f(x + \delta x) - f(x)}{\delta x}$

**Instructions to differentiate** may be worded as:

Find $\dfrac{dy}{dx}$

Find the derivative (of $y$ with respect to $x$)

Find the derived function

Find the differential coefficient.

Find the rate of change (of $y$ with respect to $x$)

$f'(x)$ is the symbol for $\dfrac{d[f(x)]}{dx}$

$u'$ is the symbol for $\dfrac{du}{dx}$

$\dot{u}$ is the symbol for $\dfrac{du}{dt}$, where $t$ is time.

**Standard Formulae**

| function | derived function | function | derived function |
|----------|------------------|----------|------------------|
| $x^n$    | $nx^{n-1}$       | $a^x$    | $(\ln a)a^x$     |
| $e^x$    | $e^x$            | $(a > 0)$ |                 |

| function | derived function | function | derived function |
|---|---|---|---|
| $\ln x$ <br> $(x > 0)$ | $\dfrac{1}{x}$ | $\sin^{-1} x$ | $\dfrac{1}{\sqrt{1 - x^2}}$ |
| $\sin x$ <br> $\cos x$ <br> $\tan x$ | $\cos x$ <br> $-\sin x$ <br> $\sec^2 x$ | $\cos^{-1} x$ <br><br> $\tan^{-1} x$ | $-\dfrac{1}{\sqrt{1 - x^2}}$ <br> $\dfrac{1}{1 + x^2}$ |
| $\operatorname{cosec} x$ <br> $\sec x$ <br> $\cot x$ | $-\operatorname{cosec} x \cot x$ <br> $\sec x \tan x$ <br> $-\operatorname{cosec}^2 x$ | | |

## Formulae for Differentiation:

**A product** $\quad \dfrac{d(uv)}{dx} = v\dfrac{du}{dx} + u\dfrac{dv}{dx}$

**A quotient** $\quad \dfrac{d\left(\dfrac{u}{v}\right)}{dx} = \dfrac{v\dfrac{du}{dx} - u\dfrac{dv}{dx}}{v^2}$

**A composite function** $\quad \dfrac{dy}{dx} = \dfrac{dy}{du} \cdot \dfrac{du}{dx}$

**A function defined parametrically**

$$\frac{dy}{dx} = \frac{dy}{dt} \Big/ \frac{dx}{dt}$$

This also gives $\dfrac{dy}{dx} = 1 \Big/ \dfrac{dx}{dy}$

**A function defined implicitly**
Differentiate each term with respect to $x$.

## Differentiation from the definition
## Examples
**4.1.**      To find the derived function of $x^n$

Let $f(x) = x^n$

$$f'(x) = \underset{\delta x \to 0}{\text{limit}} \frac{f(x + \delta x) - f(x)}{\delta x}$$

$$= \underset{\delta x \to 0}{\text{limit}} \frac{(x + \delta x)^n - x^n}{\delta x}$$

$$= \underset{\delta x \to 0}{\text{limit}} \frac{x^n\left(1 + \dfrac{\delta x}{x}\right)^n - x^n}{\delta x}$$

$$= \underset{\delta x \to 0}{\text{limit}} \frac{x^n\left[1 + n\dfrac{\delta x}{x} + \binom{n}{2}\left(\dfrac{\delta x}{x}\right)^2 + \ldots\right] - x^n}{\delta x}$$

$$= \underset{\delta x \to 0}{\text{limit}} \left(nx^{n-1} + \text{terms with powers of } \delta x\right)$$

$$= nx^{n-1}$$

**4.2**      To find the derived function of $\sin x$

Let $f(x) = \sin x$

$$f'(x) = \underset{\delta x \to 0}{\text{limit}}\, \frac{f(x + \delta x) - f(x)}{\delta x}$$

$$= \underset{\delta x \to 0}{\text{limit}}\, \frac{\sin(x + \delta x) - \sin x}{\delta x}$$

$$= \underset{\delta x \to 0}{\text{limit}}\, \frac{2 \cos\left(x + \dfrac{\delta x}{2}\right) \sin \dfrac{\delta x}{2}}{\delta x}$$

$$= \underset{\delta x \to 0}{\text{limit}}\, \cos\left(x + \frac{\delta x}{2}\right) \frac{\sin \dfrac{\delta x}{2}}{\dfrac{\delta x}{2}}$$

$$= \cos x \qquad\qquad\qquad\qquad \text{since } \frac{\sin \dfrac{\delta x}{2}}{\dfrac{\delta x}{2}} \to 1 \text{ as } \delta x \to 0$$

## Differentiation of products, quotients and composite functions

### Examples

**4.3**      $y = (x^2 + x) \ln x$                          let $y = uv$ where $u = x^2 + x$ and $v = \ln x$

$$\frac{dy}{dx} = \ln x \,.\, (2x + 1) + (x^2 + x) \,.\, \frac{1}{x} \qquad\qquad \frac{du}{dx} = 2x + 1 \text{ and } \frac{dv}{dx} = \frac{1}{x}$$

$$= (2x + 1) \ln x + x + 1 \qquad\qquad\qquad \text{Then } \frac{d(uv)}{dx} = v \frac{du}{dx} + u \frac{dv}{dx}$$

**4.4**      $y = \dfrac{\sin x}{x^2}$                          let $y = \dfrac{u}{v}$ where $u = \sin x$ and $v = x^2$

$$\frac{dy}{dx} = \frac{x^2 \cos x - 2x \sin x}{x^4} \qquad\qquad \frac{du}{dx} = \cos x \text{ and } \frac{dv}{dx} = 2x$$

$$= \frac{x \cos x - 2 \sin x}{x^3} \qquad\qquad\qquad \text{Then } \frac{d\left(\dfrac{u}{v}\right)}{dx} = \frac{v \dfrac{du}{dx} - u \dfrac{dv}{dx}}{v^2}$$

**4.5**     $y = e^{\cos x}$                                        let $y = e^u$ where $u = \cos x$

$$\frac{dy}{dx} = -\sin x \cdot e^{\cos x}$$          $$\frac{du}{dx} = -\sin x \text{ and } \frac{dy}{du} = e^u$$

Then $\dfrac{dy}{dx} = \dfrac{dy}{du} \cdot \dfrac{du}{dx}$

## Differentiation of functions defined parametrically

### Example 4.6

$$y = 3t + t^2, \qquad x = t + 5t^2$$

$$\frac{dy}{dt} = 3 + 2t, \qquad \frac{dx}{dt} = 1 + 10t$$

$$\frac{dy}{dx} = \frac{dy}{dt} \bigg/ \frac{dx}{dt} = \frac{3 + 2t}{1 + 10t}$$

## Differentiation of functions defined implicitly

$$\frac{d}{dx}(y^2) = 2y\frac{dy}{dx}$$

$$\frac{d}{dx}(\sin y) = \cos y\frac{dy}{dx}$$

$$\frac{d}{dx}(\sin^{-1} y) = \frac{1}{\sqrt{1 - y^2}}\frac{dy}{dx}$$

and so on . . .

### Example 4.7

$$x^2 + y^2 - xy + 5y + 2x = 10$$

Differentiate with respect to $x$

$$2x + 2y\frac{dy}{dx} - \left(x\frac{dy}{dx} + y \cdot 1\right) + 5\frac{dy}{dx} + 2 = 0$$

$$\frac{dy}{dx} = \frac{y - 2x - 2}{2y - x + 5}$$

### Example 4.8

To show that $\dfrac{d}{dx}(\sin^{-1} x) = \dfrac{1}{\sqrt{1 - x^2}}$

Let $y = \sin^{-1} x$

Then $\sin y = x$

Differentiate with respect to $x$

$$\cos y \frac{dy}{dx} = 1$$

$$\frac{dy}{dx} = \frac{1}{\cos y}$$

$$= \frac{1}{\sqrt{1-x^2}} \qquad \text{since } \cos^2 y = 1 - \sin^2 y$$

$$= 1 - x^2$$
$$\cos y = \sqrt{1-x^2}$$

(A sketch graph of $y = \sin^{-1} x$ shows that in the defined range the gradient is positive so the positive square root is needed.)

## Exercise 4.1

Differentiate with respect to $x$. Simplify your answer if possible.

1. $y = \dfrac{\sqrt{x}}{2} + \dfrac{2}{\sqrt{x}}$

2. $y = \dfrac{3}{x^3} - \dfrac{2}{x^4}$

3. $y = \cos \dfrac{4x}{3}$

4. $y = \ln(x^2 + x - 2)$

5. $y = (x^2 - 2)^4$

6. $y = \text{cosec } 3x$

7. $y = \tan^{-1} 2x$

8. $y = \dfrac{1}{4x - 3}$

9. $y = \ln \sin 3x$

10. $y = \dfrac{1}{(x-4)^2}$

11. $y = e^x \cos x$

12. $y = \cot x (1 - \cos x)$

13. $y = \sqrt{x^2 - 1}$

14. $y = \cos 3x \tan x$

15. $y = x^3 \ln x$

16. $y = x^2 \sin^{-1} x$

17. $y = \dfrac{3x^2 - 2}{x + 1}$

18. $y = \dfrac{\tan x}{x^2}$

19. $y = \dfrac{x}{1 - x}$

20. $y = \dfrac{e^x}{\sin x}$

## Exercise 4.2

For these expressions, find $\dfrac{dy}{dx}$ in terms of $t$.

1. $x = 4t^2, \qquad y = 8t$

2. $x = 5t^2 - 4t, \qquad y = t - t^2$

3. $x = 1 + \dfrac{1}{t}, \qquad y = t + \dfrac{1}{t^2}$

4. $x = \cos^3 t, \qquad y = \sin^3 t$

5. $x = 12t, \qquad y = \dfrac{12}{t}$

For these expressions, find $\dfrac{dy}{dx}$ in terms of $x$ and $y$.

6. $x^2 + 9y^2 = 9$

9. $x^3 + y^3 = 9$

7. $xy^2 = 36$

10. $\sin x + \sin y = 1$

8. $x^2 = 2xy + y^2$

For these expressions, find $\dfrac{dy}{dx}$. Simplify your answer if possible.

11. $y = 4x - 3 \sin 2x$

16. $y = \sqrt{\cos x}$

12. $y = (x^2 + 1)(3x - 5)^2$

17. $y = e^{2x} \tan 3x$

13. $y = \cos^{-1} \frac{1}{2}x$

18. $y = \dfrac{1 + \cos 2x}{1 - \cos 2x}$

14. $y = \tan^3 x$

19. $y = e^{\sin x}$

15. $y = e^{x^2}$

20. $y = \ln \dfrac{1 - x}{1 + x}$

## Exercise 4.3

In questions 1, 2, 3, using the definition for $f'(x)$, show that:

1. $\dfrac{d}{dx}\left(\dfrac{1}{x}\right) = -\dfrac{1}{x^2}$

2. $\dfrac{d}{dx}(\sqrt{x}) = \dfrac{1}{2\sqrt{x}}$

3. $\dfrac{d}{dx}(\cos x) = -\sin x$

4. Using the formula $\tan x = \dfrac{\sin x}{\cos x}$, show that $\dfrac{d}{dx}(\tan x) = \sec^2 x$

5. Show that $\dfrac{d}{dx}(\operatorname{cosec} x) = -\operatorname{cosec} x \cot x$

6. Show that $\dfrac{d}{dx}(\cos^{-1} x) = -\dfrac{1}{\sqrt{1 - x^2}}$, by using $y = \cos^{-1} x$, i.e. $\cos y = x$

7. Show that $\dfrac{d}{dx}(\tan^{-1} x) = \dfrac{1}{1 + x^2}$, by using $y = \tan^{-1} x$

8. By changing $x°$ into radians, find $\dfrac{d}{dx}(\sin x°)$

9.  By changing $\log_2 x$ into base e logarithms, find $\dfrac{d}{dx}(\log_2 x)$

10. Find $\dfrac{d}{dx}(3^x)$ by writing $3^x$ as $e^{x \ln 3}$

Differentiate these expressions with respect to $x$. Simplify your answer if possible.

11. $y = \sqrt{1 - \cos 2x}$

12. $y = \dfrac{1}{\sqrt{x^2 - 4}}$

13. $y = x^2 e^{-3x}$

14. $y = \cos^{-1}(\sin x)$

15. $y = x\sqrt{x^2 + 9}$

16. $y = \sin^{-1}\sqrt{x}$

17. $y = \dfrac{x}{\sqrt{x^2 + 1}}$

18. $y = \ln(x + \sqrt{x^2 + 4})$

In these expressions find $\dfrac{dy}{dx}$ in terms of $x$ and $y$.

19. $\sin^{-1} x + \sin^{-1} y = \dfrac{\pi}{2}$

20. $\sqrt{x} - \sqrt{y} = 5$

# 5 Functions, Inequalities

## Functions

$f(x)$ is a function of $x$ if for every value of $x$ there is one, and only one, value of $f(x)$.

The set of values which $x$ can take is called the **domain** of the function.

The set of values of $f(x)$ mapped onto by $x$ is called the **range** of the function.

If for every value of $f(x)$ there is one and only one value of $x$ this is a one–one mapping.

If for certain values of $f(x)$ there is more than one value of $x$ this is a many–one mapping, e.g. $f(x) = x^2$.

**Notation**

$f(x) = x^3$ may be written as $f: x \mapsto x^3$

**Notation for intervals**

$a \leqslant x \leqslant b$ can be written as the interval $[a, b]$

$a < x < b$ can be written as the interval $(a, b)$

$a < x \leqslant b$ can be written as the interval $(a, b]$

**Notation for certain sets of numbers**

$\mathbb{N}$ the set of positive integers and zero

$\mathbb{Z}$ the set of integers

$\mathbb{Q}$ the set of rational numbers

$\mathbb{R}$ the set of real numbers

$\mathbb{C}$ the set of complex numbers

## The Quadratic Function

The graph of $f(x) = x^2$.
The curve is a parabola.

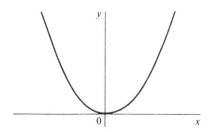

**The general quadratic function** $f(x) = ax^2 + bx + c$

**If $b^2 - 4ac > 0$ then $f(x) = 0$ for** $x = \dfrac{-b \pm \sqrt{b^2 - 4ac}}{2a}$

f(x) has the same sign as *a* outside these roots, and f(x) has the opposite sign to *a* between these roots.

**If $b^2 - 4ac = 0$ then f$(x) = 0$ for $x = -\dfrac{b}{2a}$**

For all other values of $x$, f$(x)$ has the same sign as *a*.

**If $b^2 - 4ac < 0$ then f$(x)$ always has the same sign as *a*.**

**Sketch graphs of $y = f(x)$**

**$a$ positive**

$b^2 - 4ac > 0$

$b^2 - 4ac = 0$

$b^2 - 4ac < 0$

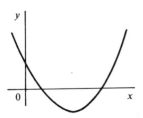
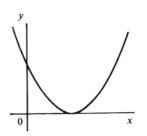
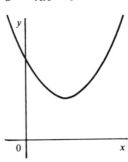

**$a$ negative**

$b^2 - 4ac > 0$

$b^2 - 4ac = 0$

$b^2 - 4ac < 0$

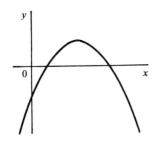
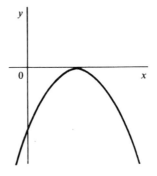
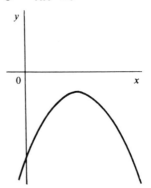

**Example 5.1**

1        $f(x) = x^2 + 8x + 20$

$b^2 - 4ac = 64 - 80 < 0$ and $a > 0$ so f$(x)$ is always positive.
To find the minimum value of f$(x)$, complete the square.
$f(x) = (x+4)^2 + 4$
$(x+4)^2$ is positive except when $x = -4$, when it is 0
So f$(x) = 4$ when $x = -4$ and f$(x) > 4$ when $x \neq -4$
The minimum value of f$(x)$ is 4.

2    $f(x) = x^2 - 6x + 5$

$b^2 - 4ac = 36 - 20 > 0$ so $f(x) = 0$ has real roots.
$f(x) = (x-1)(x-5)$, so $f(x) = 0$ when $x = 1$ or $5$.
For values of $x$ between 1 and 5, $f(x) < 0$
For $x < 1$ or $x > 5$, $f(x) > 0$
To find the minimum value of $x$, complete the square.
$f(x) = (x-3)^2 - 4$
$(x-3)^2$ is positive except when $x = 3$, when it is 0
So $f(x) = -4$ when $x = 3$ and $f(x) > -4$ when $x \neq 3$
The minimum value of $f(x)$ is $-4$.

3    $f(x) = -x^2 + 4x - 4$

$b^2 - 4ac = 16 - 16 = 0$ so $f(x) = 0$ has equal roots.
$f(x) = -(x-2)^2$, so $f(x) = 0$ when $x = 2$
So $f(x)$ is always negative except when $x = 2$ when it is 0
The maximum value of $f(x) = 0$.

**Sketch graphs of $y = f(x)$**

$y = x^2 + 8x + 20$

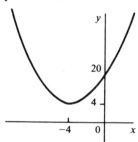

$y = x^2 - 6x + 5$

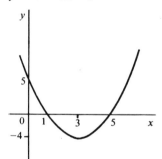

$y = -x^2 + 4x - 4$

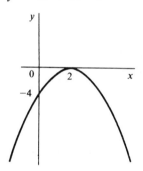

## Polynomials

### The cubic function

$f(x) = x^3$

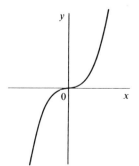

$f(x) = a(x - h)^3$

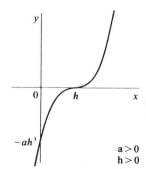

$a > 0$
$h > 0$

**Example 5.2**

1       $f(x) = x^3 - 4x^2 + x + 6$
$$= (x+1)(x-2)(x-3)$$

$f(x) = 0$ when $x = -1$ or 2 or 3
When $x = 0$, $f(x) = 6$
As $x \to \infty$, $f(x)$ behaves like $x^3$
(Maximum points, minimum points and points of inflexion can be found by differentiation, if needed.)

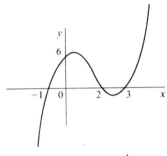

2       $f(x) = x^3 - 3x^2 + 4$
$$= (x+1)(x-2)^2$$

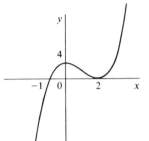

## Rational Functions

The graph of $f(x) = \dfrac{1}{x}$

The axes are asymptotes.†
The curve is a rectangular hyperbola.

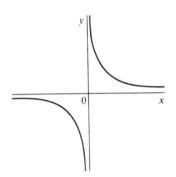

**Rational function** of the type $f(x) = \dfrac{ax + b}{cx + d}$

**Example 5.3**

$$f(x) = \frac{3x - 2}{x + 1}$$

When $x = 0$, $f(x) = -2$
When $x = \frac{2}{3}$, $f(x) = 0$
There is an asymptote at $x = -1$
As $x \to \infty$, $f(x) \to 3$. There is an asymptote at $f(x) = 3$.

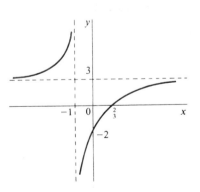

† An asymptote is a line which the curve approaches such that the line touches the curve at infinity.

## The Modular Function $|x|$

$f(x) = |x|$

For $x \geqslant 0$, $f(x) = x$
For $x < 0$, $f(x) = -x$
i.e. the part of the graph of $f(x) = x$ which is below the $x$-axis is reflected in the $x$-axis.

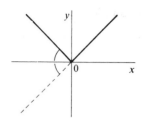

### Example 5.4

$$f(x) = |2x - 3|$$

For $2x - 3 \geqslant 0$, i.e. $x \geqslant 1\frac{1}{2}$, $f(x) = 2x - 3$
For $2x - 3 < 0$, i.e. $x < 1\frac{1}{2}$, $f(x) = -(2x - 3)$

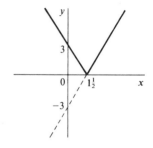

## The Exponential Function and the Logarithmic Function

$f(x) = e^x$

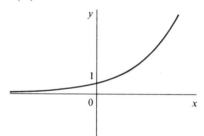

$f(x) = \ln x$

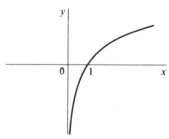

## Symmetry

If a function contains only even powers of $x$, so that $f(x) = f(-x)$, the graph is symmetrical about the $y$-axis.

If a function contains only odd powers of $x$, so that $f(x) = -f(-x)$, the graph is symmetrical about the origin.

If an equation contains only even powers of $y$, the graph is symmetrical about the $x$-axis.

For example:

$y = x^4 - 3x^2 + 2$, $y = \dfrac{1}{x^2}$, are symmetrical about the $y$-axis.

So is $y = \cos x$.

$y = 2x^3 - 8x$, $y = \dfrac{1}{x}$ are symmetrical about the origin.

So are $y = \sin x$ and $y = \tan x$.

$y^2 = x$ is symmetrical about the $x$-axis.

**Periodic functions**

If $f(x+a)=f(x)$, where $a$ is the least value for which this occurs, then $f(x)$ is a periodic function with period $a$.

$f(x)=\sin x$, $f(x)=\cos x$ are periodic functions with period $2\pi$.
$f(x)=\tan x$ is a periodic function with period $\pi$.

## Exercise 5.1

1. Express $x^2+4x+10$ in the form $(x+a)^2+b$. Hence state the minimum value of $x^2+4x+10$ and the value of $x$ at which this occurs.

2. Express $2x^2-5x+3$ in the form $2(x+a)^2+b$. Hence state the minimum value of $2x^2-5x+3$ and the value of $x$ at which this occurs.

3. Express $10x-x^2-4$ in the form $-(x+a)^2+b$. Hence state the maximum value of $10x-x^2-4$ and the value of $x$ at which this occurs.

4. Express $x^2+xy+y^2$ in the form $(x+ay)^2+by^2$ and hence show that this expression is never negative.

5. Express $x^2+y^2-6x+4y+16$ in the form $(x+a)^2+(y+b)^2+c$, and hence show that this expression is always positive. Find its least value, and the values of $x$ and $y$ at which this occurs.

Sketch the graphs of the following functions:

6.  1  $y=x$      2  $y=x^2$      3  $y=x^3$      4  $y=x^4$

7.  1  $y=\dfrac{1}{x}$      2  $y=\dfrac{1}{x^2}$

8.  1  $y=e^x$      2  $y=e^{-x}$      3  $y=2^x$

9.  1  $y=4x^2-4x+1$      2  $y=x^2+8x-20$

     3  $y=x^2-4x+9$      4  $y=4x-x^2$

10.  1  $y=x^2(x+3)$      2  $y=(1-x)(2+x)(3+2x)$

     3  $y=(x-1)(x+3)^2$

11.  1  $y=(x-1)(x+2)(x-3)(x+4)$

     2  $y=x(x-1)^2(x+2)^2$

12.  1  $y=\dfrac{3x}{x-2}$      2  $y=\dfrac{5x+2}{x}$      3  $y=\dfrac{8-x}{4+x}$

13.  1  $y=3+|x|$      2  $y=x+3|x|$      3  $y=|5-x|$

     4  $y=|x^2-9|$

14.  1  $y=\ln(1+x)$      2  $y=1-\ln x$

15. For the following graphs:

(a) $y = 3x^2 + 4$       (b) $y = x^3 - 3x$       (c) $y = |x|$

(d) $y = e^x + e^{-x}$       (e) $y = \sin 2x$       (f) $y = \dfrac{1}{x^2 + 1}$

(g) $y^2 = 2x$       (h) $y = \cos \frac{1}{2}x$       (j) $y^2 = 4x^3$

(k) $x^2 + y^2 = 1$

1   Which graphs are symmetrical about the $y$-axis?
2   Which graphs are symmetrical about the $x$-axis?
3   Which graphs are symmetrical about the origin?

16. State the periods of the following functions:

1   $y = \sin 2x$       2   $y = \cos \frac{1}{2}x$       3   $y = \cot x$

## Composition of Functions

fg is defined as $fg(x) = f[g(x)]$

This only exists when the range of g is a subset of the domain of f
f∘g may be used instead of fg

f.g means $f(x) . g(x)$
f+g means $f(x) + g(x)$

## Examples

**5.5**     If $f(x) = 2^{x-1}$ and $g(x) = 3 + 4x$
$gf(x) = 3 + 4 . 2^{x-1} = 3 + 2^{x+1}$
$fg(x) = 2^{3+4x-1} = 2^{2+4x}$

**5.6**     If $f(x) = \ln x$ and $g(x) = \sin x$,
the range of $g(x)$ is $-1 \le g(x) \le 1$ but the domain of $f(x)$ is $x > 0$, so the composite function fg does not exist.
If the domain of $g(x)$ is restricted e.g. to $0 < x < \pi$, then the range of $g(x)$ is $0 < g(x) \le 1$, and $fg(x) = \ln \sin x$, for $0 < x < \pi$.

## Inverse Functions

If $f(x)$ is a function with a one-one mapping then $f(x)$ can have an inverse function $f^{-1}(x)$ such that $f^{-1}[f(x)] = f[f^{-1}(x)] = x$

It is sometimes possible to obtain an inverse function by reducing the domain of a function, for example $f(x) = \cos x$ has an inverse function if the domain of $x$ is $0 \le x \le \pi$. The inverse function is $f^{-1}(x) = \cos^{-1} x$ with the range $0 \le \cos^{-1} x \le \pi$.

The domain of $f(x)$ is the range of $f^{-1}(x)$ and the range of $f(x)$ is the domain of $f^{-1}(x)$.

On a graph a function and its inverse are symmetrical about the line $y = x$.

To find the inverse function of $y = f(x)$, interchange $x$ and $y$ in the equation.

Rearrange the new equation to get $y$, which is $f^{-1}(x)$, in terms of $x$.

**Example 5.7**

To find the inverse function of $f(x) = \dfrac{3x-2}{x+1}$, i.e. $y = \dfrac{3x-2}{x+1}$

Interchange $x$ and $y$. $\quad x = \dfrac{3y-2}{y+1}$

Rearranging, $\quad xy + x = 3y - 2$

$$y(3 - x) = x + 2$$

$$y = \frac{x+2}{3-x}$$

i.e. $f^{-1}(x) = \dfrac{x+2}{3-x}$

The domain of $f(x)$ is all $x \neq -1$
The range of $f^{-1}(x)$ is all $f^{-1}(x) \neq -1$
The range of $f(x)$ is all $f(x) \neq 3$
The domain of $f^{-1}(x)$ is all $x \neq 3$.

**Other examples of inverse functions**

$e^x$ and $\ln x$

$x^3$ and $x^{\frac{1}{3}}$

$\dfrac{1}{x}$ and itself

$x^2$ and $x^{\frac{1}{2}}$ for $x \geq 0$

$\sin x$ for $-\dfrac{\pi}{2} \leq x \leq \dfrac{\pi}{2}$ and $\sin^{-1} x$

Graph of $y = e^x$, $y = \ln x$, $y = x$

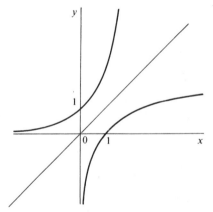

**Inverse of a composite function**

If $h = fg$ then $h^{-1} = g^{-1}f^{-1}$

(A composite function will not have an inverse function unless it has a one–one mapping.)

**Example 5.8**

If $f(x) = 2x - 3$, $g(x) = \cos x$, and $h = fg$,
then $h(x) = 2\cos x - 3$.

For h to have an inverse function, restrict the domain of g, e.g. to $0 \leqslant x \leqslant \pi$, so that the domain of h is also restricted to $0 \leqslant x \leqslant \pi$.

Then $h^{-1}(x) = \cos^{-1}\dfrac{x+3}{2}$

To find $h^{-1}(x)$,

let $y = 2 \cos x - 3$

Interchange $x$ and $y$

$x = 2 \cos y - 3$

$\cos y = \dfrac{x+3}{2}$

$y = \cos^{-1}\dfrac{x+3}{2}$

Since $f^{-1}(x) = \dfrac{x+3}{2}$ and $g^{-1}(x) = \cos^{-1} x$,

$(g^{-1}f^{-1})(x) = \cos^{-1}\dfrac{x+3}{2} = h^{-1}(x)$

## Exercise 5.2

For the following functions $f(x)$ and $g(x)$, find the composite function $h = fg$.

1. $f(x) = e^x$ for all $x$,      $g(x) = 2x+1$
2. $f(x) = \sin 2x$ for all $x$,      $g(x) = |x|$
3. $f(x) = \ln(2+x)$ for $x > -2$,      $g(x) = x^2 - 1$
4. $f(x) = x^2 + 2$ for all $x$,      $g(x) = 3x+1$
5. $f(x) = \dfrac{1}{x+3}$ for all $x \neq -3$,      $g(x) = e^x$

Find the range of the following functions. State or find the inverse function $f^{-1}(x)$, and give its domain and range.

6. $f(x) = \tan x$,      $-\dfrac{\pi}{2} < x < \dfrac{\pi}{2}$

7. $f(x) = \dfrac{x-1}{2x+1}$,    for all $x \neq -\frac{1}{2}$

8. $f(x) = e^{-x}$, for all $x$

9. $f(x) = x^2 + 2$, for $x \geqslant 0$

10. $f(x) = \sin 2x$, $-\dfrac{\pi}{4} \leqslant x \leqslant \dfrac{\pi}{4}$

11. $f(x) = \log_{10} x$, for $x > 0$

12. $f(x) = \dfrac{4}{x}$, for all $x \neq 0$

13. $f(x) = \dfrac{4-x}{x}$, for all $x \neq 0$

14. $f(x) = \sqrt{9 - x^2}$, $0 \leqslant x \leqslant 3$

15. $f(x) = \sqrt{x^2 - 1}$, for $x \geqslant 1$

For the following functions, state or find the inverse function $f^{-1}(x)$, and give its domain and range. On one graph sketch $f(x)$, $f^{-1}(x)$ and the line $y = x$.

16.  $f(x) = x^3$, for all $x$

17.  $f(x) = x^2$, for $x \geq 0$

18.  $f(x) = \sin x$, for $-\dfrac{\pi}{2} \leq x \leq \dfrac{\pi}{2}$

19.  $f(x) = 2^x$, for all $x$

20.  $f(x) = 2x - 5$, for all $x$.

## Exercise 5.3

1.  What is the inverse function $f^{-1}(x)$ if $f(x) = \dfrac{1}{x}$, $(x \neq 0)$? Sketch $y = f(x)$ and the line $y = x$ on one graph.

2.  If $f(x) = \dfrac{2+3x}{x-4}$, $x \neq 4$, find the inverse function $f^{-1}(x)$ and state the domain and range of $f^{-1}(x)$. Show the functions $f(x)$ and $f^{-1}(x)$ on the same graph, or on separate graphs.

3.  If $f(x) = \sqrt{1-x^2}$, $0 \leq x \leq 1$, find the inverse function $f^{-1}(x)$.

4.  Express $\sin x + \cos x$ in the form $R \cos(x - \alpha)$. If $f(x) = \sin x + \cos x$ for $\dfrac{\pi}{4} \leq x \leq \dfrac{3\pi}{4}$, find the inverse function $f^{-1}(x)$ and state its domain.

5.  If $f(x) = 2 + \sqrt{x+1}$ for $x \geq -1$, find the inverse function $f^{-1}(x)$ and state its domain.

6.  If $f(x) = \dfrac{4-x}{2+x}$ for $x \neq -2$ and $g(x) = \dfrac{1}{x}$ for $x \neq 0$, what other restriction must be placed on the domain of $g(x)$ for the composite function $fg$ to exist? With this restriction, find and simplify the function $fg$. For what values of $x$ is $f(x) = fg(x)$?

7.  If $f(x) = 3x + 2$, and $g(x) = \ln x$ for $x > 0$, find the inverse functions $f^{-1}(x)$ and $g^{-1}(x)$. Find the composite function $fg(x)$ and its inverse $(fg)^{-1}(x)$. Verify that $(fg)^{-1}(x) = (g^{-1}f^{-1})(x)$. For the composite function $gf(x)$ to exist, what restriction must be placed on the domain of $f(x)$?

8.  If $f(x) = 4 - x^2$ and $g(x) = 2x + 3$, find the composite functions $fg(x)$ and $gf(x)$. For what values of $x$ is $fg(x) = gf(x)$?

9.  If $f(x) = e^x$ and $g(x) = x^3$, find the composite function $h(x)$ where $h = fg$. Find the inverse function $h^{-1}(x)$ and state its domain.

10.  If $f(x) = \dfrac{x}{3-2x}$ and $x \neq 1\frac{1}{2}$, find the inverse function $f^{-1}(x)$ and state its domain and range. Verify that $ff^{-1}(x) = f^{-1}f(x) = x$.

## Inequalities

**1**    If $x^2 < a^2$ (where $a$ is positive) then $-a < x < a$.
If $x^2 > a^2$ then $x > a$ or $x < -a$.

**2**    If both sides of an inequality are multiplied by a negative number, the inequality sign is reversed.

If both sides of an inequality are multiplied by an unknown number, e.g. $x$, then two cases must be considered.
(i) if $x > 0$, the inequality still holds,
(ii) if $x < 0$, the inequality sign is reversed.

**3**    $a^2 + b^2 \geqslant 2ab$
(Since $(a - b)^2 \geqslant 0$, $a^2 - 2ab + b^2 \geqslant 0$, i.e. $a^2 + b^2 \geqslant 2ab$.
Also since $(a - b)^2 = 0$ only if $a = b$, then $a^2 + b^2 = 2ab$ only if $a = b$.)

## Example 5.9

Find the range of values of $x$ for which $\dfrac{x-1}{x-2} < 5$

If $x - 2 > 0$, the inequality sign does not change when multiplying by $x - 2$.
$x - 1 < 5x - 10$
$x > 2\frac{1}{4}$ (and $x > 2$) i.e. $x > 2\frac{1}{4}$

If $x - 2 < 0$, the inequality sign is reversed when multiplying by $x - 2$.
$x - 1 > 5x - 10$
$x < 2\frac{1}{4}$ and $x < 2$ i.e. $x < 2$

The complete range is $x < 2$ or $x > 2\frac{1}{4}$.

## Graphical methods

## Examples

**5.10**    To find the range of values of $x$ for which $(x - 1)(x + 2)(x - 3) < 0$

Sketch the graph of
$y = (x - 1)(x + 2)\ (x - 3)$
From the graph it can be seen that the
inequality holds for $x < -2$ or $1 < x < 3$

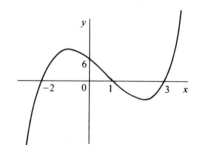

**5.11**   To find the range of values of $x$ for which

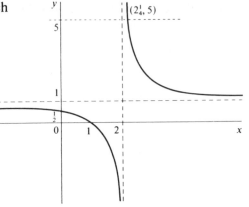

$\dfrac{x-1}{x-2} < 5$. (as in example 5.9)

Sketch the graph of $y = \dfrac{x-1}{x-2}$ and also

solve $\dfrac{x-1}{x-2} = 5$ to find that when $y = 5$,

$x = 2\frac{1}{4}$.

From the graph it can be seen that the inequality holds for $x < 2$ or $x > 2\frac{1}{4}$.

**Example 5.12**

If $y = \dfrac{x^2 - 2x}{2x^2 + 1}$, find the range of possible values of $y$.

Rearrange as a quadratic equation in $x$
$x^2(2y-1) + 2x + y = 0$
This has real roots if '$b^2 - 4ac \geqslant 0$'
$\therefore$   $4 - 4(2y-1)y \geqslant 0$
$2y^2 - y - 1 \leqslant 0$
$(2y+1)(y-1) \leqslant 0$
$-\frac{1}{2} \leqslant y \leqslant 1$

**Exercise 5.4**

Find the range of values of $x$ for which the following inequalities are satisfied.

1.  $(x+1)(x-2)(x-4) \geqslant 0$

2.  $(3-x)(2+x)(1+x) \geqslant 0$

3.  $\dfrac{2x+3}{x} < 1$

4.  $\dfrac{x-4}{x+7} < \frac{1}{2}$

5.  $\dfrac{x-9}{x} < 3$

6.  $|4-x| > 1 - 4x$

7.  $|2x+7| < |31 - 4x|$

8.  $(3x+1)(x-1) > 0$

9.  $(2x+1)(x+2) < 5$

10.  $(x+3)^2 + 1 > 0$

11.  $2x^2 + 3x > 2$

12.  $2x^2 + 7 < 4x$

13.  $x^2 \leqslant 6x - 9$

14.  $3x^2 + 2x \leqslant 1$

15.  $2x^2 - 5x + 4 < 3x^2 - 9x + 8$

16.  Find the range of values of $x$ for which $(x+1)^2 < (x-3)^2 < 16$.

17.  Find the range of possible values of $k$ if the roots of $3x^2 + 3(1-2k)x + 4k^2 - 6k - 1 = 0$ are real.

18. Find the range of possible values of $k$ if the equation $2x^2 + 2(k+5)x + 9(k+1) = 0$ has no real roots.

19. Show that the roots of the equation $x^2 - 2(a+b)x + a^2 - c^2 + 2ab = 0$ are real.

20. Show that $9x^2 + 6kx + k^2 - k + 1$ is positive for all real values of $x$ when $k < 1$.

21. If $y = \dfrac{x^2 + 1}{5x}$, find the range of possible values of $y$.

22. If $y = \dfrac{2x+3}{x^2+4}$, find the range of possible values of $y$.

# 6 Curves and Equations

$ax + by = c$ represents a straight line with gradient $-\dfrac{a}{b}$ and intercept on the $y$-axis $\dfrac{c}{b}$.

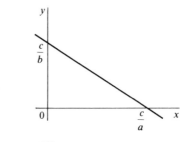

$y = \dfrac{1}{x}$ represents a rectangular hyperbola.

It is symmetrical about the origin.
As $x \to 0$, $y \to \infty$.
As $x \to \infty$, $y \to 0$.
The axes are asymptotes.

A more general form of a rectangular hyperbola is $xy = c^2$.

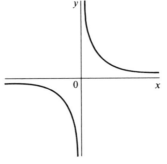

$y = \dfrac{1}{x^2}$.

$y$ is always positive.
As $x \to 0$, $y \to \infty$.
As $x \to \infty$, $y \to 0$.
It is symmetrical about the $y$-axis.

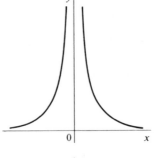

$y^2 = x$ represents a parabola.
$x \geqslant 0$.
It is symmetrical about the $x$-axis.
$y = \sqrt{x}$ is the part of this curve which is in the first quadrant.

A more general form of the parabola is $y^2 = 4ax$.

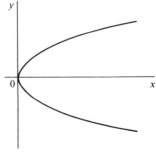

$y^2 = x^3$ is symmetrical about the $x$-axis.
$x \geqslant 0$
$y = x^{\frac{3}{2}}$ is the part of this curve which is in the first quadrant.
This curve is known as a semi-cubical parabola.

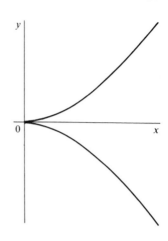

$x^2 + y^2 = r^2$ represents a circle, centre $(0, 0)$, radius $r$.
(It is symmetrical about the $x$ and $y$ axes and the origin.
$|x| \leqslant r$, $|y| \leqslant r$.)

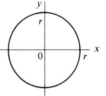

$(x - a)^2 + (y - b)^2 = r^2$ represents a circle centre $(a, b)$ radius $r$.

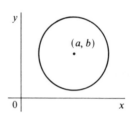

$\dfrac{x^2}{a^2} + \dfrac{y^2}{b^2} = 1$ represents an ellipse, centre $(0, 0)$ with axes from $(-a, 0)$ to $(a, 0)$ and from $(0, -b)$ to $(0, b)$.
It is symmetrical about the $x$ and $y$ axes and the origin.

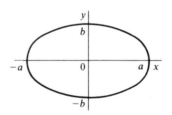

## Parametric Coordinates

The coordinates $x$ and $y$ may be expressed in terms of a parameter $t$ (or $\theta$). Eliminating $t$ between the two equations would give the cartesian equation of the curve.

### Example 6.1

$$x = 3t - 2, \quad y = 2t$$

$t = 0$ gives the point $(-2, 0)$
$t = 1$, gives the point $(1, 2)$
$t = 2$ gives the point $(4, 4)$, and so on.

Eliminating $t$ gives $\dfrac{x+2}{3}=\dfrac{y}{2}$, i.e. $y=\tfrac{2}{3}(x+2)$

This is a straight line, gradient $\tfrac{2}{3}$, intercept $\tfrac{4}{3}$.

**The parabola** $y^2=4ax$ has parametric coordinates $x=at^2$, $y=2at$.

**The rectangular hyperbola** $xy=c^2$ has parametric coordinates $x=ct$, $y=\dfrac{c}{t}$.

**The circle** $(x-a)^2+(y-b)^2=r^2$ has parametric coordinates
$x=a+r\cos t$, $y=b+r\sin t$.

**The ellipse** $\dfrac{x^2}{a^2}+\dfrac{y^2}{b^2}=1$ has parametric coordinates $x=a\cos t$, $y=b\sin t$.

**The curve** $y^2=x^3$ has parametric coordinates $x=t^2$, $y=t^3$.

## Exercise 6.1

Sketch the curves represented by these equations:

1. $y^2=8x$

5. $\dfrac{x^2}{16}+\dfrac{y^2}{9}=1$

2. $xy=36$

6. $3x+4y=12$

3. $(x-4)^2+(y+5)^2=16$

7. $3x^2+4y^2=12$

4. $27y^2=4x^3$

Sketch the curves represented by these parametric equations and give their cartesian equations:

8. $x=2\cos\theta$, $y=\sin\theta$

11. $x=6t^2$, $y=12t$

9. $x=t+5$, $y=4-2t$

12. $x=\cos\theta$, $y=\sin\theta-1$

10. $x=9t^2$, $y=9t^3$

13. $x=4t$, $y=\dfrac{4}{t}$

## Simple Transformations

The transformation $y=f(x)$ to $y=af(x)$ has the effect of altering the $y$-scale by a factor $a$.

The transformation $y=f(x)$ to $y=f(ax)$ has the effect of altering the $x$-scale by a factor $\dfrac{1}{a}$.

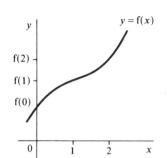
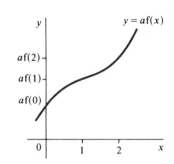
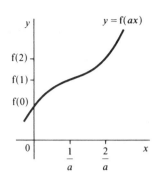

The transformation $y = f(x)$ to $y = f(x) + a$ has the effect of translating the curve by $a$ units in the $y$-direction.

The transformation $y = f(x)$ to $y = f(x - a)$ has the effect of translating the curve by $a$ units in the $x$-direction.

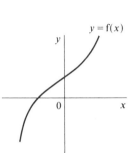
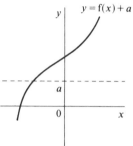
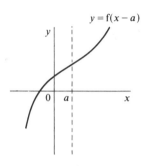

**Example 6.2**

Transformations on the graph of
$y = x^3 - 3x + 2$, i.e. $y = (x - 1)^2(x + 2)$

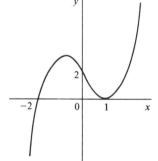

1  $y = 3(x^3 - 3x + 2)$

$y = 3x^3 - 9x + 6$ or $y = 3(x - 1)^2(x + 2)$
The $y$-scale is altered by a factor 3.

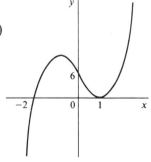

**2**   $y = (2x)^3 - 3.2x + 2$

$y = 8x^3 - 6x + 2$ or
$y = (2x-1)^2(2x+2)$
The $x$-scale is altered by a factor $\frac{1}{2}$.

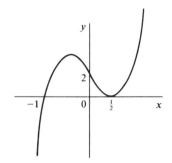

**3**   $y = x^3 - 3x + 2 + 4$

$y = x^3 - 3x + 6$ or
$y = (x-1)^2(x+2) + 4$
The curve is translated 4 units in the $y$-direction.

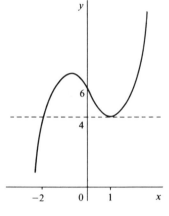

**4**   $y = (x-1)^3 - 3(x-1) + 2$

$y = x^3 - 3x^2 + 4$ or $y = (x-2)^2(x+1)$
The curve is translated 1 unit in the $x$-direction.

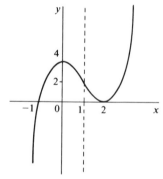

## Exercise 6.2

Sketch these graphs, on the same or adjoining sketches, to show the relationship between the first graph and each of the others.

1.   $y = x^3$, $y = x^3 + 1$, $y = (x-2)^3$

2.   $y = x^2$, $y = 3x^2$, $y = x^2 + 3$, $y = (x+3)^2$

3.   $y = \ln x$, $y = \ln 2x$, $y = \ln(x-2)$, $y = \ln x + 2$, $y = 2\ln x$

4.   $y = x^2$, $y = (x-3)^2$, $y = 2(x-3)^2$, $y = 2(x-3)^2 + 1$

5. $y = e^x$, $y = e^{x-2}$, $y = 2 e^x$, $y = e^{2x}$, $y = e^x + 2$

6. $y = \dfrac{1}{x}$, $y = \dfrac{4}{x}$, $y = \dfrac{1}{x+4}$, $y = 4 + \dfrac{1}{x}$, $y = \dfrac{1}{4x}$

7. $\dfrac{x^2}{25} + \dfrac{y^2}{9} = 1$, $\dfrac{(x-3)^2}{25} + \dfrac{(y+1)^2}{9} = 1$

8. $y = x^2$, $y = (x+1)^2$, $y = 3(x+1)^2$, $y = 3(x+1)^2 + 4$

9. $y = e^x$, $y = e^{-x}$, $y = -e^x$, $y = e^x - 1$

10. $y^2 = 4x$, $y^2 = 4(x-2)$

11. By substituting $X = x - 4$ and $Y = y + 3$ in the equation
    $4x^2 + 9y^2 - 32x + 54y + 109 = 0$,
    identify the curve and sketch it   **1**   referred to axes $X$ and $Y$,   **2**   referred to axes $x$ and $y$.

12. Repeat question 11 for the curve $y^2 - 20x - 4y = 56$ substituting $X = x + 3$ and $Y = y - 2$.

13. Repeat question 11 for the curve $y = x^3 - 6x^2 + 12x - 9$ substituting $X = x - 2$ and $Y = y + 1$.

14. Repeat question 11 for the curve $xy + 3y - 5x = 24$ substituting $X = x + 3$ and $Y = y - 5$.

15. Repeat question 11 for the curve $y^2 + 6y = 8x^3 + 12x^2 + 6x - 8$ substituting $X = x + \frac{1}{2}$ and $Y = y + 3$.

# B   Revision

## Exercise B1

1.  Sketch the graphs of   **1**   $y = 6 - 2|x|$   **2**   $y = |6 - 2x|$.

2.  In a geometric progression, the second term is two-fifths of the sum of the first and third terms. Find the possible values of $r$. If $a = 9$, find the sum to infinity for that value of $r$ for which a sum exists.

3.  Expand $(1 + 4x)^{-\frac{1}{2}}$ in ascending powers of $x$ as far as the term in $x^3$. For what range of values of $x$ is the expansion valid?

4.  Find the range of values of $k$ for which the equation
    $(k - 2)x^2 + 2(2k - 3)x + 5k - 6 = 0$ has real roots.

5.  Sketch the graph of $y = \dfrac{4x}{3 - 2x}$ and state the equations of its asymptotes.

6.  Show that $x^4 - 3x^2 - 4$ is negative only when $|x| < 2$.

7.  Show that $\cos 2\theta - 2 \cos 4\theta + \cos 6\theta = \tan \theta \, (\sin 2\theta - \sin 6\theta)$.

8.  If $\cos 2\theta = \frac{41}{841}$ and $\theta$ is acute, find the value of $\cos \theta$.

9.  Solve the equation $5 \cos \theta = 2 \operatorname{cosec} \theta$ for $0° < \theta < 180°$.

10. Express $8 \cos \theta - 15 \sin \theta$ in the form $R \cos(\theta + \alpha)$, where $R$ is positive and $\alpha$ is an acute angle.

11. If $f(x) = x^4$, using the formula for $f'(x)$ defined as a limit, find $f'(x)$.

12. Differentiate with respect to $x$,   **1**   $y = \dfrac{\tan x}{x^2}$   **2**   $y = x^3 \sin^{-1} x$.

13. Differentiate with respect to $x$,   **1**   $y = e^{x^2}$   **2**   $y = \ln (x^2 + 3)$.

14. Find $\dfrac{dy}{dx}$ in terms of $t$ if,   **1**   $x = a \cos t, \ y = b \sin t$   **2**   $x = 4(1 + t), \ y = 2(2 - t^3)$.

15. Find $\dfrac{dy}{dx}$ in terms of $x$ and $y$ if,   **1**   $xy = 36$   **2**   $x^2 + 3y^2 = 13$.

## Exercise B2

Select the correct answer to each question.

1. If $y = \cos 3x \sin 2x$, $\dfrac{dy}{dx} =$

   **A** $6 \sin 3x \cos 2x$
   **B** $-6 \sin 3x \cos 2x$
   **C** $2 \cos 2x \cos 3x - 3 \sin 2x \sin 3x$
   **D** $-2 \cos 2x \cos 3x + 3 \sin 2x \sin 3x$
   **E** $2 \cos 5x - 3 \sin 5x$

2. The curve with parametric equations $x = 9 \cos t$, $y = 4 \sin t$ has the cartesian equation

   **A** $(x-3)^2 + (y-2)^2 = 1$       **B** $(x-9)^2 + (y-4)^2 = 1$

   **C** $\dfrac{x^2}{3} + \dfrac{y^2}{2} = 1$       **D** $\dfrac{x^2}{9} + \dfrac{y^2}{4} = 1$       **E** $\dfrac{x^2}{81} + \dfrac{y^2}{16} = 1$

3. The complete range of values of $x$ for which $|x-4| < 7x$ is

   **A** $x < 4$     **B** $x > 4$     **C** $x > \frac{1}{2}$     **D** $x > -\frac{2}{3}$     **E** $\frac{1}{2} < x < 4$

4. $\dfrac{\cos 75^\circ + \cos 15^\circ}{\cos 75^\circ - \cos 15^\circ} =$

   **A** $1$       **B** $-\dfrac{1}{\sqrt{3}}$       **C** $-\sqrt{3}$       **D** $\dfrac{1}{\sqrt{3}}$       **E** $\sqrt{3}$

5. If $x+2$ is a factor of $x^3 + kx^2 + 14$, then $k$ is

   **A** $-5\frac{1}{2}$       **B** $-1\frac{1}{2}$       **C** $1\frac{1}{2}$       **D** $2$       **E** $7$

6. If $y = \dfrac{\sqrt{x}}{2} - \dfrac{2}{\sqrt{x}}$ then $\dfrac{dy}{dx} =$

   **A** $\dfrac{x+4}{4x\sqrt{x}}$   **B** $\dfrac{x+4}{4\sqrt{x}}$   **C** $\dfrac{x-4}{4x\sqrt{x}}$   **D** $\dfrac{x-1}{4x\sqrt{x}}$   **E** $\dfrac{1-x}{4\sqrt{x}}$

7. The range of values of $x$ for which the geometric progression

   $1 + \dfrac{1}{1+x} + \dfrac{1}{(1+x)^2} + \ldots$ (where $x \neq -1$) has a sum to infinity is

   **A** $x > 0$ only       **B** $-1 < x < 1$       **C** $x < 1$
   **D** $-2 < x < 0$       **E** $x > 0$ or $x < -2$

8. If $f(x) = \dfrac{1}{x-3}$, where $x \neq 3$, then $f^{-1}(x)$ is

   **A** $\dfrac{1}{x+3}$     **B** $x-3$     **C** $3-x$     **D** $3 - \dfrac{1}{x}$     **E** $3 + \dfrac{1}{x}$

9.   If $y = \tan^{-1} 3x$ then $\dfrac{dy}{dx} =$

   **A**   $-3 \csc^2 3x$          **B**   $-\csc^2 3x$          **C**   $\dfrac{1}{1+9x^2}$

   **D**   $\dfrac{3}{1+9x^2}$          **E**   $\dfrac{1}{3(1+9x^2)}$

10.  If $\dfrac{1}{2^{4x}} = 4^{6-x}$ then $x =$

   **A**   $-6$          **B**   $-2\frac{2}{3}$          **C**   $-2$          **D**   $6$          **E**   $0$ or $6$

11.  The range of values of $x$ for which $x^2 - 5x - 6 < 0$ is

   **A**   $x > 6$ or $x < -1$          **B**   $-1 < x < 6$          **C**   $-6 < x < 1$

   **D**   $-2 < x < 3$          **E**   $x > 1$ or $x < -6$

12.  If $f(x) = x^2 + 2$ and $g(x) = 2 \sin x$ then $gf(x)$ is

   **A**   $2 \sin(x^2 + 2)$          **B**   $2 \sin^2 x + 2$          **C**   $2(x^2 + 2) \sin x$

   **D**   $2 \sin^2(x + 2)$          **E**   $4 \sin^2 x + 2$

13.  If $y = \ln x^4$ then $\dfrac{dy}{dx} =$

   **A**   $\dfrac{1}{4x}$          **B**   $\dfrac{4}{x}$          **C**   $\dfrac{4}{x^3}$          **D**   $\dfrac{1}{4x^3}$          **E**   $\dfrac{1}{x^4}$

14.  The graph of $y = \dfrac{3-x}{3+2x}$ has asymptotes:

   **A**   $x = -1\frac{1}{2}$ only          **B**   $x = -1\frac{1}{2}, y = -\frac{1}{2}$          **C**   $x = -1\frac{1}{2}, y = 1$

   **D**   $x = 3, y = -\frac{1}{2}$          **E**   $x = 3, y = 1$

15.  Which of the following curves is not symmetrical about the $y$-axis?

   **A**   $y = \cos x$          **B**   $y = e^x + e^{-x}$          **C**   $y = |x^3|$

   **D**   $y = (x-1)^2$          **E**   $y = \sin\left(x - \dfrac{\pi}{2}\right)$

## Exercise B3

1.   Find the values of $x$ which satisfy $|x^2 - 7| = 2$.

2.   If $x = a(\theta - \sin \theta)$ and $y = a(1 - \cos \theta)$, show that $\dfrac{dy}{dx} = \cot \dfrac{\theta}{2}$.

3.   If $f(x) = e^{x+2}$, find the inverse function $f^{-1}(x)$. State the domain and range of $f^{-1}(x)$. On one diagram sketch the graphs of $f(x)$ and $f^{-1}(x)$.

4.  If $x = r \cos \theta \cos \phi$, $y = r \cos \theta \sin \phi$ and $z = r \sin \theta$, find an equation connecting $x$ and $y$ in terms of $r$ and $\theta$ only, and hence find an equation connecting $x$, $y$ and $z$ in terms of $r$ only.

5.  Solve the equation $2 \ln(3x+1) - \ln(x+1) = \ln(7x+4)$.

6.  If $\sin x \cos y = 0.7$ and $\cos x \sin y = 0.1$, find the values of $\sin(x+y)$ and $\sin(x-y)$. Hence find the values of $x$ and $y$, in the range $0°$ to $90°$.

7.  If $\alpha$, 10, $\beta$ are 3 numbers in arithmetic progression, and $\alpha$, 6, $\beta$ are 3 numbers in geometric progression, find the equation with roots $\alpha$, $\beta$.

8.  Sketch the curves with equations

    1   $y^2 = x$           2   $(y-3)^2 = x$           3   $(y-3)^2 = x+2$.

9.  Solve the quadratic equation $x^2 + 2x + a = 0$, in terms of $a$. For what range of values of $a$ are the roots real?

10. If $f(x) = kx^2 + 2kx + 2k - 3$, find the range of values of $k$ for which $f(x)$ is always positive.

11. Find the general solution of the equation $2 \cos \theta \cos\left(\dfrac{\pi}{6} - \theta\right) = \sqrt{3}$.

12. Show that the expansion of $(1+8x)^{\frac{3}{4}}$ has terms equal to those of the expansion of $\dfrac{1+7x}{1+x}$, if $x^3$ and higher powers are neglected.

13. When $y = e^{-3t} \cos t$, show that $\dfrac{d^2y}{dt^2} + 6\dfrac{dy}{dt} + 10y = 0$.

14. By substituting $X = x - 3$ and $Y = y - 7$ in the equation $xy - 7x - 3y = 4$, identify the curve and sketch it,   1   referred to axes $X$ and $Y$,   2   referred to axes $x$ and $y$.

15. Express $\dfrac{x^2 + 21x + 50}{(x+4)^2(2x-1)}$ in partial fractions. Hence, if $y = \dfrac{x^2 + 21x + 50}{(x+4)^2(2x-1)}$, find an expression for $\dfrac{dy}{dx}$, and find the value of $\dfrac{dy}{dx}$ when $x = 0$.

**To the Student:**

# 3 Learning Formulae

In your examination you will probably be supplied with a formulae leaflet, so that will reduce the number of formulae you need to know by heart. Look at a copy of the leaflet and find out which formulae are in it, otherwise you may waste time in the exam searching through it in vain for a formula not included, or fail to make use of some formula available to you.

The best way to learn a formula is to be able to derive it, but in a few cases you may simply have to learn it. (If you remember that the signs of $\sin \theta$ and $\cos \theta$ depend on which quadrant $\theta$ is in, and $\sin \theta$ depends on the $y$-coordinate which is positive in the first and second quadrants, $\cos \theta$ depends on the $x$-coordinate which is positive in the first and fourth quadrants, and $\tan \theta = \dfrac{\sin \theta}{\cos \theta}$, then the diagram $\begin{array}{c|c} \sin & \text{all} \\ \hline \tan & \cos \end{array}$ falls into place. Those who prefer a different way invent a sentence such as 'All students take care', giving the initial letters A, S, T, C for 'all, sin, tan, cos'.)

The formulae checklist on page 175 contains most formulae. Go through the list completing each formula, then check your answers from the relevant chapters of the book. Count how many you know, and how many you still need to learn. Write out the correct answers of those you did not know and try to learn them as you write. Make a separate list of their question numbers. After a break, re-do all those you did not know, and you will probably find that you now know some of them. Amend your 'scores'. Write out again those you still do not know, and continue in this way until you eventually know them all.

Now you have to continue to remember them. So check them again, but if you do not want to check them all, choose a random number between 1 and 10 and do every tenth one, e.g. numbers 6, 16, 26, ..., or use some other system to give yourself a quick test.

Of course, learning formulae in isolation will not be very useful. You need to link this with learning methods, so that you know which formulae are needed for the various topics, and how to use them to solve the problems.

# 7 Differentiation (Applications)

**To Find the Gradient of a Curve** (i.e. the gradient of the tangent to the curve).

Find $\dfrac{\mathrm{d}y}{\mathrm{d}x}$, which gives the gradient of the tangent.

Since the tangent and normal are at right angles to each other, the product of their gradients is $-1$, so from the gradient of the tangent the gradient of the normal can be found.

**Stationary Points, Turning Points, Maximum and Minimum Points**

At these points, $\dfrac{\mathrm{d}y}{\mathrm{d}x} = 0$.

If at a point, $\dfrac{\mathrm{d}y}{\mathrm{d}x} = 0$ and $\dfrac{\mathrm{d}^2 y}{\mathrm{d}x^2}$ is positive, it is a minimum point.

If at a point, $\dfrac{\mathrm{d}y}{\mathrm{d}x} = 0$ and $\dfrac{\mathrm{d}^2 y}{\mathrm{d}x^2}$ is negative, it is a maximum point.

$\left( \text{If at a point, } \dfrac{\mathrm{d}y}{\mathrm{d}x} = 0 \text{ and } \dfrac{\mathrm{d}^2 y}{\mathrm{d}x^2} = 0, \text{ there could be a minimum, a maximum, or a point of} \right.$

inflexion. Consider the signs of the gradient $\dfrac{\mathrm{d}y}{\mathrm{d}x}$ on either side of the point to determine

$\left. \text{which.} \right)$

| **Minimum** | **Maximum** | **Point of inflexion** |
|---|---|---|
| gradient changes from negative to 0 to positive | gradient changes from positive to 0 to negative | gradient does not change sign |

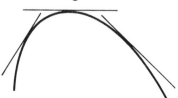
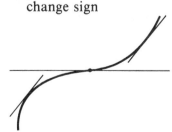

**Curve sketching**

The sign of the gradient, and the coordinates of any maximum or minimum points give additional information useful for sketching the curve.

### Rates of change

The rate of increase of a function $V$ (with respect to time $t$) is given by $\dfrac{dV}{dt}$.

(A negative value would mean that $V$ decreases as $t$ increases.)
If $V$ is a function of $x$ and the rate of change of $x$ (with respect to time $t$) is known
then $\dfrac{dV}{dt} = \dfrac{dV}{dx} \cdot \dfrac{dx}{dt}$

### Small increments and approximations

If $y$ is a function of $x$ then a small change ($\delta x$) in $x$ produces a small change ($\delta y$) in $y$
such that $\delta y \approx \dfrac{dy}{dx} \cdot \delta x$.

### * Other Applications

**Distance ($s$), velocity ($v$) and acceleration ($a$) of a particle moving in a straight line. ($t$ is time.)**

$$v = \frac{ds}{dt}, \quad a = \frac{dv}{dt} = \frac{d^2 s}{dt^2} = v\frac{dv}{ds}$$

If $t$ is in seconds, $s$ in metres, then $v$ is in $ms^{-1}$ and $a$ is in $ms^{-2}$.

**Angular velocity**, the rate of change of an angle with respect to time.
Angular velocity $= \dfrac{d\theta}{dt} = \dot{\theta}$.
If $\theta$ is in radians then angular velocity is in radians . $s^{-1}$.

### Point of inflexion

This is a point at which the curvature of a curve changes.
For a point of inflexion

1   $\dfrac{d^2 y}{dx^2} = 0$   $\left(\text{Note that } \dfrac{dy}{dx} \text{ need not be } 0\right)$

2   $\dfrac{d^2 y}{dx^2}$ changes sign in the region of the point.

$\left(\text{If } \dfrac{d^2 y}{dx^3} \text{ is not 0 then } \textbf{2} \text{ is satisfied,}\right.$

$\left.\text{but if } \dfrac{d^3 y}{dx^3} = 0 \text{ it will be necessary to consider the signs of } \dfrac{d^2 y}{dx^2}.\right)$

---

Topics marked * are not included in the national common core and may not be needed for your syllabus.

**Examples**

**7.1**   Find the equations of the tangent and normal to the curve $y = x + \dfrac{3}{x}$ at the point $(1, 4)$.

$$\frac{dy}{dx} = 1 - \frac{3}{x^2}$$

At the point where $x = 1$, $\dfrac{dy}{dx} = -2$ so the gradient of the tangent is $-2$.

The gradient of the normal is $\tfrac{1}{2}$, since the product of the gradients of tangent and normal is $-1$.

The equation of a line gradient $m$ through $(x_1, y_1)$ is $y - y_1 = m(x - x_1)$.

∴   The equation of the tangent is $y - 4 = -2(x - 1)$, i.e. $2x + y = 6$

The equation of the normal is $y - 4 = \tfrac{1}{2}(x - 1)$, i.e. $2y = x + 7$

**7.2**   Find the equations of the tangent and normal to the ellipse defined by the parametric equations $x = a \cos \theta$, $y = b \sin \theta$ at the point $(a \cos \theta, b \sin \theta)$.

$$y = b \sin \theta \qquad\qquad x = a \cos \theta$$

$$\frac{dy}{d\theta} = b \cos \theta \qquad\qquad \frac{dx}{d\theta} = -a \sin \theta$$

∴   $$\frac{dy}{dx} = \frac{dy}{d\theta} \bigg/ \frac{dx}{d\theta} = -\frac{b \cos \theta}{a \sin \theta}$$

The gradient of the tangent is $-\dfrac{b \cos \theta}{a \sin \theta}$

The gradient of the normal is $\dfrac{a \sin \theta}{b \cos \theta}$

∴   The equation of the tangent is $y - b \sin \theta = -\dfrac{b \cos \theta}{a \sin \theta}(x - a \cos \theta)$

i.e. $bx \cos \theta + ay \sin \theta = ab$

The equation of the normal is $y - b \sin \theta = \dfrac{a \sin \theta}{b \cos \theta}(x - a \cos \theta)$

i.e. $ax \sin \theta - by \cos \theta = (a^2 - b^2) \sin \theta \cos \theta$

**7.3**   Find the turning points on the curve $y = x + \cos 2x$ for $0 \leqslant x \leqslant \pi$, and show whether these are maximum or minimum points.

$$\frac{dy}{dx} = 1 - 2 \sin 2x$$

∴   $\dfrac{dy}{dx} = 0$ when $\sin 2x = \tfrac{1}{2}$, $2x = \dfrac{\pi}{6}$ or $\dfrac{5\pi}{6}$, $x = \dfrac{\pi}{12}$ or $\dfrac{5\pi}{12}$.

$$\frac{d^2y}{dx^2} = -4 \cos 2x$$

When $x = \dfrac{\pi}{12}, \dfrac{d^2y}{dx^2}$ is negative, so there is a maximum point.

The maximum point is $\left(\dfrac{\pi}{12}, \dfrac{\pi}{12} + \dfrac{\sqrt{3}}{2}\right)$.

When $x = \dfrac{5\pi}{12}, \dfrac{d^2y}{dx^2}$ is positive, so there is a minimum point.

The minimum point is $\left(\dfrac{5\pi}{12}, \dfrac{5\pi}{12} - \dfrac{\sqrt{3}}{2}\right)$.

**7.4**    Find the turning points on the curve $y = \dfrac{x}{1+x^2}$ and show whether these are

maximum or minimum points. Sketch the curve.

$$\dfrac{dy}{dx} = \dfrac{(1+x^2).1 - x.2x}{(1+x^2)^2} = \dfrac{1-x^2}{(1+x^2)^2}$$

$\therefore \quad \dfrac{dy}{dx} = 0$ when $x = 1$ or $-1$

$$\dfrac{d^2y}{dx^2} = \dfrac{(1+x^2)^2(-2x) - (1-x^2).2(1+x^2).2x}{(1+x^2)^4} = \dfrac{2x^3 - 6x}{(1+x^2)^3}$$

When $x = 1, \dfrac{d^2y}{dx^2}$ is negative, so there is a maximum point.

When $x = -1, \dfrac{d^2y}{dx^2}$ is positive, so there is a minimum point.

$\therefore$    The maximum point is $(1, \frac{1}{2})$, the minimum point is $(-1, -\frac{1}{2})$.
The only point where the graph crosses the axes is $(0, 0)$.
As $x \to +\infty$, $y \to 0$ from values of $y > 0$.
As $x \to -\infty$, $y \to 0$ from values of $y < 0$.

If $y = f(x), f(-x) = \dfrac{-x}{1+x^2} = -f(x)$, so the graph is symmetrical about the origin.

When $x > 0$, $y > 0$, when $x < 0$, $y < 0$.

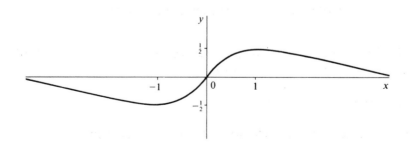

**7.5** If $y = x^2 \ln x$ and $x$ at time $t$ is given by the equation $x = 2t^2 + t$, find the rate of change of $y$ with respect to time, at time $t = 2$.

$$\frac{dy}{dx} = x^2 \cdot \frac{1}{x} + 2x \ln x = x(1 + 2 \ln x)$$

$$\frac{dx}{dt} = 4t + 1$$

$$\therefore \quad \frac{dy}{dt} = \frac{dy}{dx} \cdot \frac{dx}{dt} = x(1 + 2 \ln x)(4t + 1)$$

When $t = 2$, $x = 10$, $\dfrac{dy}{dt} = 90(1 + 2 \ln 10)$

The rate of change of $y$ with respect to time is $90(1 + 2 \ln 10)$.

**7.6** $y$ is connected to $\theta$ by the equation $y = \theta - \frac{1}{2}\sin 2\theta$. If $\theta$ is increased from $\dfrac{\pi}{3}$ to $\left(\dfrac{\pi}{3} + 0.02\right)$, find the approximate increase in $y$.

$$\frac{dy}{d\theta} = 1 - \cos 2\theta$$

When $\theta = \dfrac{\pi}{3}$, $\dfrac{dy}{d\theta} = \frac{3}{2}$

$$\therefore \quad \delta y \approx \frac{dy}{d\theta} \cdot \delta\theta = \frac{3}{2} \times 0.02 = 0.03$$

The approximate increase in $y$ is 0.03

**7.7\*** A particle moves so that its distance $s$ metres travelled in $t$ seconds is given by the equation $s = e^{2t} + 3t - 1$. Find its velocity and acceleration after 2 seconds.

$$v = \frac{ds}{dt} = 2e^{2t} + 3$$

$$a = \frac{dv}{dt} = 4e^{2t}$$

When $t = 2$, $v = 2e^4 + 3$, $a = 4e^4$

The velocity is $(2e^4 + 3)\ \text{ms}^{-1}$, the acceleration is $4e^4\ \text{ms}^{-2}$.

**7.8\*** A wheel turns through an angle $\theta$ radians in $t$ seconds where $\theta = 3t^2 + 2t$. Find its angular velocity after 2 seconds.

$$\text{Angular velocity} = \frac{d\theta}{dt} = 6t + 2$$

$$\therefore \quad \text{When } t = 2, \text{ the angular velocity is 14 radians per second.}$$

**7.9\***    Find the point of inflexion on the curve $y = x\,e^x$.

$$\frac{dy}{dx} = x\,e^x + e^x$$

$$\frac{d^2y}{dx^2} = x\,e^x + 2e^x$$

$\therefore$   $\dfrac{d^2y}{dx^2} = 0$ when $e^x(x+2) = 0$, i.e. $x = -2$

If $x < -2$, $\dfrac{d^2y}{dx^2}$ is negative, if $x > -2$, $\dfrac{d^2y}{dx^2}$ is positive.

$\therefore$   $\dfrac{d^2y}{dx^2}$ changes sign at $x = -2$, so there is a point of inflexion.

$\left(\text{Alternatively, show that } \dfrac{d^3y}{dx^3} = e^x(x+3), \text{ and this is not 0 when } x = -2.\right)$

The point of inflexion is $(-2, -2e^{-2})$.

## Exercise 7.1

1.  Find the equation of the tangent at a point with parameter $t$ on the curve given by the parametric equations $x = 1 - \cos t$, $y = t + \sin t$.

2.  Find the turning points on the curve $y = x^2\,e^{-x}$ and find whether they are maximum or minimum points.

3.  Find the equations of the tangent and normal at the point $(ct, c/t)$ on the rectangular hyperbola with equation $xy = c^2$.

4.  The volume of water in a container is $\frac{1}{18}(x^3 + 3x^2)$ when the depth of water is $x$. The depth at time $t$ after starting to fill it is given by $x = t^2 + 3t$. Find the rate of increase of volume when the depth is 10.

5.  Show that the gradient of the curve $y = \dfrac{9 + 4x}{1 - 2x}$ is always positive. Sketch the curve.

6.  Find the equations of the tangent and normal to the parabola defined by the parametric equations $x = at^2$, $y = 2at$ at the point $(at^2, 2at)$.

7.  Find the stationary points on the curve $y = \dfrac{x^2 + 9}{x}$ and show whether they are maximum or minimum points.

8.  Show that the curves $y = 2 + 3x + \sin x$ and $y = 2e^{2x}$ touch each other where $x = 0$, and find the equation of the common tangent at this point.

9.  In the triangle shown, $y$ and $\theta$ can vary. If $y$ is increased from 3 to 3.01 units, find the approximate decrease in $\theta$ (in radians).

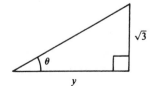

10. Find the turning points on the curve $y = x^3 + 3x^2 - 9x - 27$ and find whether they are maximum or minimum points. Sketch the curve.

11. Find the equations of the tangent and normal to the curve $y^2 = 2x^3$ at the point $(2t^2, 4t^3)$.

12.* Find the points of inflexion on the curve $y = x^4 - 5x^3 + 6x^2$.

13.* A rod moves from a fixed direction such that the angle $\theta$ made with the starting direction at time $t$ is given by $\theta = t^2 - 3t$. What is the angular velocity at time $t = 5$? At what time is the rod instantaneously at rest?

14.* A particle moves along the $x$-axis in such a way that its distance from the origin at time $t$ after starting is given by the equation $x = 4 \cos t + \cos 2t$. Find the time at which the acceleration is first zero and its velocity at that time.

15.* Find the coordinates of the stationary points on the curve $y = x^3 - 9x^2 + 15x + 25$. Find also the point of inflexion and verify that this is halfway between the two stationary points.

## Exercise 7.2

1. Find the stationary points on the curve $y = 3 \sin x + \sin 3x$ for $0 \leqslant x \leqslant \pi/2$, and find whether these are maximum or minimum points.

2. Find $\dfrac{dy}{dx}$ at the point $(-1, 1)$ on the curve $x^3 - 2xy^2 + y^3 = 2$. Find also the equation of the tangent to the curve at this point.

3. The curve $y = e^x(ax^2 + b)$ has a minimum point at $(1, -4e)$. Find the values of $a$ and $b$.

4. A cone has a fixed height $h$ but a variable radius $r$. If the radius is increased by 1% find the approximate % increase in its volume. (Volume of cone $v = \frac{1}{3}\pi r^2 h$.)

5. If $y = (x^2 - x) \ln x$, find the rate of change of $y$ with respect to $x$, and show that as $x$ increases between $\frac{1}{2}$ and 1, $y$ decreases.

6. Find the stationary points on the curve $y = x^4 - 4x^2$, and find whether they are maximum or minimum points. Sketch the curve.

7. $P$ is the point $(t, e^t)$ on the curve $y = e^x$. The tangent at $P$ meets the $x$-axis at $T$ and the ordinate through $P$ meets the $x$-axis at $N$. Find the length of the line $TN$, showing that it is independent of $t$.

8. Show that the function $\sin x - k \tan x$ has no stationary values if $|k| > 1$. If $k = \frac{1}{8}$, find the values of $x$ in the range $0 \leqslant x \leqslant 2\pi$ for which the function has stationary values.

9. The curve $y = ax^3 + bx^2 + cx$ passes through the point $(2, 2)$ and has a minimum point at $(1, -1)$. Find the values of $a$, $b$ and $c$ and find the coordinates of the maximum point.

10. The volume of a spherical balloon is given at time $t$ by $v = 6t + 5$. Find the rate of increase of the radius of the balloon at the time when the radius is 3. (Volume of sphere $v = \frac{4}{3}\pi r^3$.)

11. Find the turning point on the curve $y = x^2 \ln x$ and show whether it is a maximum or minimum point.

12.* A particle moves along a straight line so that its distance $y$ from the origin is given by the equation $y = \dfrac{8 \sin x}{2 - \cos x}$, where the value of $x$ at time $t$ is $\dfrac{\pi}{6}(2t + 1)$. At what time is the velocity of the particle first zero?

13.* Find the points of inflexion on the curve $y = 2x + \cos 2x$ in the range $0 \leqslant x \leqslant \pi$, and find the gradients of the curve at these points.

14.* If an angle $\theta$ changes such that at time $t$, $\theta$ is given by the equation $\theta = \sin t + \cos t$, find the time when the angular velocity is first zero.

15.* A point moves on the positive $x$-axis in such a way that its distance from the origin at time $t$ is $4 \cos t - 3 \sin t + 5t$. Find its distance from the origin when its speed is first zero, and find its acceleration at this time.

# 8 More Trigonometry

**Triangle Formulae**

### Sine rule

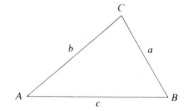

$$\frac{a}{\sin A} = \frac{b}{\sin B} = \frac{c}{\sin C} = 2R$$

($R$ is the radius of the circumcircle of the triangle)

### Cosine rule

$$a^2 = b^2 + c^2 - 2bc \cos A$$

$$\cos A = \frac{b^2 + c^2 - a^2}{2bc}$$

### Area of triangle

$$\text{area} = \tfrac{1}{2}ab \sin C$$

$$\text{area} = \sqrt{s(s-a)(s-b)(s-c)} \text{ where } s = \tfrac{1}{2}(a+b+c)$$

## Circle Formulae

($\theta$ in radians)
length of arc $= r\theta$

area of sector $= \tfrac{1}{2}r^2\theta$

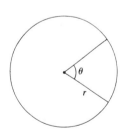

## Angle Between a Line and a Plane

This is the angle ($\theta$) between the line and its projection on the plane.

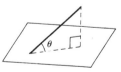

## Angle between two planes

From a point on the line of intersection of the planes, draw two lines, one in each plane, perpendicular to the line of intersection. Find the angle ($\theta$) between these two lines.

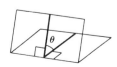

**Angle between two skew lines**

Draw a line parallel to one of the lines, intersecting the second line. Find the angle ($\theta$) between the parallel line and the second line.

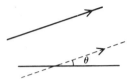

**Examples**

**8.1**    In triangle $ABC$, find the value of $\tan \theta$.

Using the sine rule,

$$\frac{\sin B}{b} = \frac{\sin C}{c}$$

$$\frac{\sin \theta}{4} = \frac{\sin\left(\theta + \frac{\pi}{3}\right)}{5}$$

$$5 \sin \theta = 4\left(\sin \theta \cos \frac{\pi}{3} + \cos \theta \sin \frac{\pi}{3}\right)$$

$$5 \sin \theta = 2 \sin \theta + 2\sqrt{3} \cos \theta$$

$$3 \sin \theta = 2\sqrt{3} \cos \theta$$

$$\tan \theta = \frac{2\sqrt{3}}{3}.$$

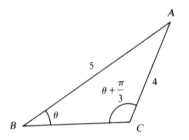

**8.2.**    Find the perimeter and area of a segment $AB$ in the circle centre $O$, where angle $AOB = 2\theta$.

arc $AB = 2r\theta$
chord $AB = 2r \sin \theta$
perimeter $= 2r(\theta + \sin \theta)$.
area of sector $AOB = \frac{1}{2}r^2 . 2\theta$
area of triangle $AOB = \frac{1}{2}r^2 \sin 2\theta$
area of segment $= \frac{1}{2}r^2(2\theta - \sin 2\theta)$.

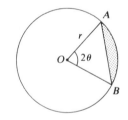

**8.3**    A rectangular box has a square base of edge $x$ and a height $\sqrt{6}x$. Find the angle between a diagonal of the box and the base.

The diagonal is $AC$.
The angle needed is angle $CAB$.
Length $AB = \sqrt{2}x$

$$\tan \angle CAB = \frac{\sqrt{6}x}{\sqrt{2}x} = \sqrt{3}$$

angle $CAB = 60°$.

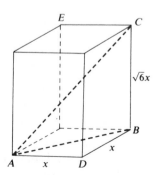

**8.4**    In the previous diagram, find the angle between the skew lines $AB$ and $DC$.

The line $AE$ is parallel to the line $DC$, so find the angle
between $AB$ and $AE$.
In triangle $ABE$,
$AE = EB = \sqrt{7}x$, $AB = \sqrt{2}x$

$$\cos A = \frac{\sqrt{2}x}{2\sqrt{7}x} = \frac{\sqrt{14}}{14}$$

The angle between the lines $AB$ and $DC$ is $\cos^{-1}\dfrac{\sqrt{14}}{14}$.

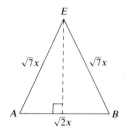

## Exercise 8.1

1.  If $A$, $B$, $C$ are angles of a triangle, show that
    $\sec^2 A + \sec^2 B + 2\sec A \sec B \cos C - (\tan A + \tan B)^2 = 0$.

2.  In triangle $ABC$, express $\sin A$ in terms of $a$, $b$, $c$ and $h$, where $h$ is the length of
    the perpendicular from $A$ to $BC$.

3.  Show that the third side in a triangle with sides $a$, $2a$ and included angle of $120°$
    is the same length as the third side in a triangle with sides $a$, $\sqrt{3}a$ and included
    angle of $150°$.

4.  In the quadrilateral $ABCD$, $AB = 25$ units, $BC = 52$, $CD = 39$ and $DA = 60$. The
    diagonal $AC = 63$. Show that the quadrilateral is cyclic.

5.  In triangle $ABC$, angle $A$ is acute and $\sin A = \frac{3}{5}$. $a = 6$ and $b = 5$. Find the size of
    angle $B$, and find the value of $\sin C$ in surd form.

6.  In triangle $ABC$
    1   show that $a = b \cos C + c \cos B$
    2   if $\theta$ is any angle, show that $a \cos \theta = b \cos(C - \theta) + c \cos(B + \theta)$.

7.  A path $AB$ is in the form of a circular arc of radius $r$ and an angle of $2\theta$ at the
    centre of the circle. If someone walks directly from $A$ to $B$ instead of going along
    the path, find an expression for the fraction of the original distance saved.

8.  A sector of a circle radius $r$, with angle $\theta$ at the centre of the circle, is cut out and
    bent round until the bounding radii coincide, so that a hollow cone is formed. A
    circular base is then added to the cone. Find the total surface area of the cone in
    terms of $r$ and $\theta$.

9.  From a vertex $A$ in an equilateral triangle of side $2a$ an arc is drawn to cut the
    triangle into two parts of equal area. Find the radius of the arc in terms of $a$.

10. $ABCD$ is a tetrahedron with a horizontal base $ABC$. $AD$ is of length $3a$ and makes
    an angle $\alpha$ with the base. $BD$ and $CD$ are each of length $4a$ and angles $DBC$ and
    $DCB$ are each $\alpha$. Find the inclination of the plane $DBC$ to the base.

11. In a pyramid on a horizontal square base each sloping face is inclined at an angle
    $\pi/6$ to the horizontal. Show that a sloping edge is inclined to the horizontal at an
    angle $\alpha$ where $\cot \alpha = \sqrt{6}$.

12. *ABC* is a triangle in a horizontal plane. $AB = d$ units, angle $BAC = \alpha$, angle $ABC = \beta$. At *C* there is a vertical rod *CD* and angle $DAC = \theta$. Find the height of the rod in terms of $d$, $\alpha$, $\beta$, $\theta$.

13. *H* is a point $h$ units vertically above the centre *C* of a horizontal circle of radius $r$ units. *AB* is a chord of the circle subtending angle $\theta$ at *C*. Find the inclination of the plane *ABH* to the horizontal in terms of $r$, $h$, $\theta$.

## Approximations

When $\theta$ is small (and in radians)

$\sin \theta \approx \theta$, $\tan \theta \approx \theta$, $\cos \theta \approx 1 - \frac{1}{2}\theta^2$

## Half-angle formulae

If $t = \tan \frac{1}{2}x$, then

$$\sin x = \frac{2t}{1+t^2}, \quad \cos x = \frac{1-t^2}{1+t^2}, \quad \tan x = \frac{2t}{1-t^2}.$$

Also $\dfrac{dx}{dt} = \dfrac{2}{1+t^2}$

## Examples

**8.5** Find the approximate value, if $\theta$ is small, of $\dfrac{\cos 2\theta - \cos \theta}{\sin^2 \theta}$

$\cos \theta \approx 1 - \frac{1}{2}\theta^2$, $\cos 2\theta \approx 1 - \frac{1}{2}(2\theta)^2$, $\sin \theta \approx \theta$

$$\frac{\cos 2\theta - \cos \theta}{\sin^2 \theta} \approx \frac{1 - 2\theta^2 - (1 - \frac{1}{2}\theta^2)}{\theta^2} = -1\tfrac{1}{2}.$$

**8.6** Express $\dfrac{2 \sin \theta}{1 - \cos \theta}$ in terms of $t$ where $t = \tan \dfrac{\theta}{2}$.

$$\sin \theta = \frac{2t}{1+t^2}, \quad \cos \theta = \frac{1-t^2}{1+t^2}$$

$$\frac{2 \sin \theta}{1 - \cos \theta} = \frac{\dfrac{4t}{1+t^2}}{1 - \dfrac{1-t^2}{1+t^2}} = \frac{4t}{1+t^2-(1-t^2)} = \frac{2}{t}.$$

## Graph of $y = a \cos x + b \sin x$

$a \cos x + b \sin x \equiv R \cos(x - \alpha)$, where $R = \sqrt{a^2 + b^2}$, $\cos \alpha = \dfrac{a}{R}$, $\sin \alpha = \dfrac{b}{R}$.

The graph is a transformation of the graph of $y = \cos x$.

(The graph when $a$ and $b$ are
positive, so that $0 < \alpha < \pi/2$)

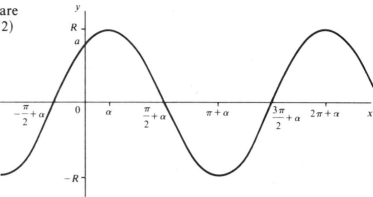

## Example 8.7

Sketch the graph of $y = \cos x - \sqrt{3} \sin x$ for $-\pi \leqslant x \leqslant 2\pi$

Let $\cos x - \sqrt{3} \sin x \equiv R \cos(x + \alpha)$

Then $R = \sqrt{1^2 + \sqrt{3}^2} = 2$, $\cos \alpha = \frac{1}{2}$, $\sin \alpha = \frac{\sqrt{3}}{2}$, $\alpha = \frac{\pi}{3}$

$$y = 2 \cos\left(x + \frac{\pi}{3}\right)$$

The maximum value of $y$ is 2, when $\cos\left(x + \frac{\pi}{3}\right) = 1$, $x = -\frac{\pi}{3}$ or $\frac{5\pi}{3}$

The minimum value of $y$ is $-2$, when $\cos\left(x + \frac{\pi}{3}\right) = -1$, $x = \frac{2\pi}{3}$

$y = 0$ when $\cos\left(x + \frac{\pi}{3}\right) = 0$, $x = \frac{\pi}{6}$ or $\frac{7\pi}{6}$ or $-\frac{5\pi}{6}$

When $x = 0$, $y = 1$.

1   graph of $y = \cos x$

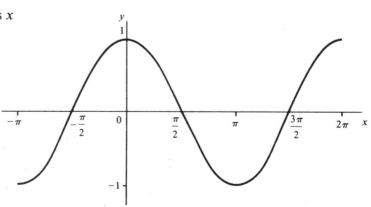

**2**  graph of $y = \cos\left(x + \dfrac{\pi}{3}\right)$

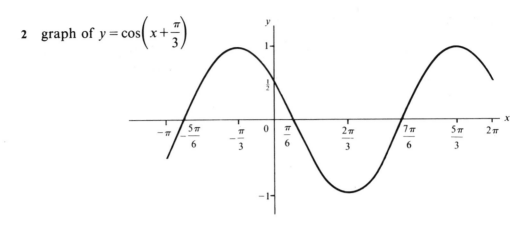

**3**  graph of $y = 2\cos\left(x + \dfrac{\pi}{3}\right)$

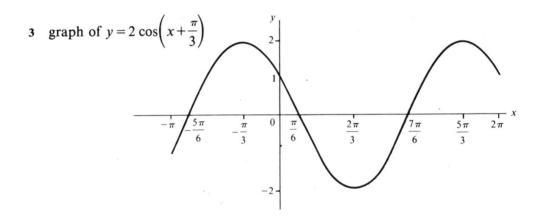

## Inequalities

### Example 8.8

Find the range of values of $x$, where $-\pi < x < \pi$, for which $|\sin x| \geqslant \frac{1}{2}$.

$|\sin x| = \frac{1}{2}$ when $|x| = \dfrac{\pi}{6}$ or $\dfrac{5\pi}{6}$

From a sketch-graph of $y = \sin x$
it can be seen that the inequality
is satisfied for the regions

$-\dfrac{5\pi}{6} \leqslant x \leqslant -\dfrac{\pi}{6}$ and $\dfrac{\pi}{6} \leqslant x \leqslant \dfrac{5\pi}{6}$

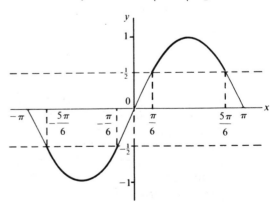

## Exercise 8.2

1. Find the approximate values, if $\theta$ is small, of the following:

   **1** $\dfrac{\sin \theta}{\sin 4\theta}$  **2** $\dfrac{\cos \theta - \cos 3\theta}{\theta^2}$  **3** $\dfrac{\sin 5\theta - \sin 3\theta}{\sin \theta}$  **4** $\dfrac{1 - \cos \theta}{\sin^2 \theta}$.

2. Use the approximation for $\cos \theta$ to find $\theta$ if $\cos \theta = \frac{881}{882}$.

3. If $\cos \theta = \frac{40}{41}$, and $0 < \theta < \dfrac{\pi}{2}$, find the value of $\tan \dfrac{\theta}{2}$.

4. If $\sin \theta = \frac{5}{13}$, and $\dfrac{\pi}{2} < \theta < \pi$, find the value of $\tan \dfrac{\theta}{2}$.

5. Express $\sin \theta$ and $\cos \theta$ in terms of $t$ where $t = \tan \dfrac{\theta}{2}$. Hence solve the equation
   $2 \cos \theta - 5 \sin \theta = 2$ for $0° \leqslant \theta \leqslant 360°$.

6. Solve the equation $\sin \theta + 8 \cos \theta + 8 = 2 \tan \frac{1}{2}\theta$ for $0° < \theta < 360°$.

7. **1** Sketch the graphs of $y = \sin x$ and $y = 2 \sin x$ on the same sketch to show the relationship between them, in the range $0 \leqslant x \leqslant 2\pi$.

   **2** Repeat this for $y = \sin x$ and $y = \sin 2x$

   **3** Repeat for $y = \sin x$ and $y = \sin\left(x + \dfrac{\pi}{4}\right)$

   **4** Repeat for $y = \sin x$ and $y = \sin x + 2$

8. Sketch the graphs of

   **1** $y = \sin \frac{1}{2}x$, for $0 \leqslant x \leqslant 2\pi$

   **2** $y = \tan 2x$, for $0 \leqslant x \leqslant \pi/2$, $x \neq \pi/4$

   **3** $y = 1 - \cos x$, for $0 \leqslant x \leqslant 2\pi$

9. Sketch the graph of $y = \cos x$ for $-\pi \leqslant x \leqslant \pi$, and find the range of values of $x$ for which $|\cos x| < \frac{1}{2}$.

10. Express $\cos x + \sin x$ in the form $R \cos(x - \alpha)$, ($\alpha$ in radians). Sketch the graph of $y = \cos x + \sin x$ for $0 \leqslant x \leqslant 2\pi$. Hence state the solutions of $\cos x + \sin x = 1$ in this range.

## Exercise 8.3

1. The diagram shows a rope stretched between two points $A$, $B$ on the ground and over a circular log with centre $O$ and radius $r$ which touches the ground at the mid-point of $AB$. If the part of the rope in contact with the log subtends an angle $2\theta$ at $O$, find the length of the rope in terms of $r$ and $\theta$.

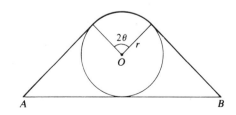

2. A triangle has sides of length 1, 2, $\sqrt{6}$. Show that the size of the largest angle is exactly double the size of the angle opposite the side of length 2.

3. At a point $A$ on a horizontal plane the angle of elevation of the top of a tower due north of $A$ is $\alpha$. At a point $B$ $d$ units due east of $A$ the angle of elevation is $\beta$. Show that the height of the top of the tower above the plane is $\dfrac{d}{\sqrt{\cot^2 \beta - \cot^2 \alpha}}$.

4. **To verify the sine rule**
   In the diagram, find expressions for $h$ in terms of $\sin A$, and $\sin B$. Hence show that
   $$\frac{a}{\sin A} = \frac{b}{\sin B}.$$
   Repeat in a triangle where angle $A$ is obtuse.

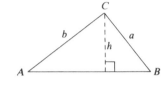

5. **To verify the cosine rule**
   In the diagram, express $a^2$ in terms of $h$, $c$, $p$.
   Express $h^2$ in terms of $b$ and $p$ and hence find $a^2$ in terms of $b$, $c$, $p$.
   Express $p$ in terms of $\cos A$ and hence show that
   $a^2 = b^2 + c^2 - 2bc \cos A.$
   Repeat in a triangle where angle $A$ is obtuse.

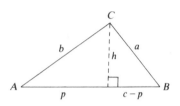

6. **To verify the sine rule**
   In the diagram, $O$ is the centre of the circumcircle of triangle $ABC$ and $CD$ is a diameter (and therefore of length $2R$).
   Which angle is equal to angle $A$?
   What is the size of angle $CBD$?
   Use triangle $CBD$ to show that
   $$2R = \frac{a}{\sin A}.$$
   Repeat in a triangle where angle $A$ is obtuse.

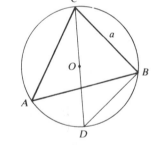

   $\left(\text{In a similar way it can be shown that } 2R = \dfrac{b}{\sin B} \text{ and } 2R = \dfrac{c}{\sin C}\right.$

   $\left.\text{so } \dfrac{a}{\sin A} = \dfrac{b}{\sin B} = \dfrac{c}{\sin C}.\right)$

7. In triangle $ABM$, use the cosine rule to find an expression for $AB^2$.
   In triangle $ACM$, use the cosine rule to find an expression for $AC^2$.
   Hence show that
   $AB^2 + AC^2 = 2AM^2 + 2BM^2.$
   (This is Apollonius' theorem.)
   Find the length of the shortest median in a triangle with sides 5, 7 and 10 units.

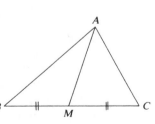

8.  *A, B, C* are 3 points in order on an east–west coastline and distance *AB* = distance *BC* = *k* km. A tower stands north-east of *A*. From point *A* the angle of elevation of the top of the tower is $\alpha$, from *B* the angle of elevation is $\beta$ and from *C* the angle of elevation is $\gamma$.
    Using the theorem of question 7, show that the height of the tower is $\sqrt{2}k(\cot^2\alpha + \cot^2\gamma - 2\cot^2\beta)^{-\frac{1}{2}}$.

9.  Using the cosine rule, show that $1 + \cos C = \dfrac{(a+b+c)(a+b-c)}{2ab}$.

    Putting $a+b+c = 2s$, show that $1 + \cos C = \dfrac{2s(s-c)}{ab}$.

    Find a similar expression for $1 - \cos C$.
    Using the formula *Area of triangle* $= \frac{1}{2}ab\sin C$, and replacing $\sin C$ by $\sqrt{(1+\cos C)(1-\cos C)}$, obtain the formula *Area of triangle* $= \sqrt{s(s-a)(s-b)(s-c)}$ where $s = \frac{1}{2}(a+b+c)$.
    Use this formula to find the area of a triangle with sides 4, 5 and 7 units.

10. By expressing $\sin\theta$ and $\cos\theta$ in terms of $t$ where $t = \tan\frac{1}{2}\theta$, solve the equation $24\sin\theta + 7\cos\theta = 20$, for $0° < \theta < 180°$.
    Compare by solving using the transformation $a\cos\theta + b\sin\theta \equiv R\cos(\theta - \alpha)$.

11. Express $4\sin x + 3\cos x$ in the form $R\sin(x+\alpha)$, ($\alpha$ in degrees).
    Sketch the graph of $y = 4\sin x + 3\cos x$ in the range $0° \leqslant x \leqslant 360°$.
    State the greatest and least values of $y$ and the values of $x$ between $0°$ and $360°$ at which they occur.

12. Sketch the graph of $y = \tan x$ for $-\pi \leqslant x \leqslant \pi$, $|x| \neq \pi/2$, and find the range of values of $x$ for which $|\tan x| < 1$.

13. Sketch the graphs of $y = \sin x$ and $y = 1 - x$, showing that there is only 1 root of the equation $x + \sin x = 1$, and that this root is in the region $0 < x < \pi/4$.
    Use your calculator to verify that this root lies between 0.51 and 0.52.

14. Sketch the graphs of $y = \tan x$ and $y = -x$ for $0 \leqslant x \leqslant \pi$, showing that the first positive root of the equation $x + \tan x = 0$ is in the region $\pi/2 < x < 3\pi/4$.
    Use your calculator to verify that for this root $x \approx 2.03$.

15. In the diagram, *AC* is a tangent to the circle. Find expressions in terms of $r$ and $\theta$ for area of triangle *OBA*, area of sector *OBA*, area of triangle *OAC*.

    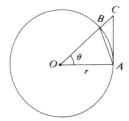

    Hence show that, for $0 < \theta < \dfrac{\pi}{2}$,

    $\sin\theta < \theta < \tan\theta$.

    Derive $1 < \dfrac{\theta}{\sin\theta} < \sec\theta$ and $\cos\theta < \dfrac{\theta}{\tan\theta} < 1$.

    As $\theta \to 0$, $\sec\theta \to 1$ so $\dfrac{\theta}{\sin\theta} \approx 1$, i.e. $\sin\theta \approx \theta$.

    Show similarly that $\tan\theta \approx \theta$.

16.  If $\theta$ is small, use the formula $\cos \theta = (1 - \sin^2 \theta)^{\frac{1}{2}}$, the approximation for $\sin \theta$, and the binomial theorem, to show that $\cos \theta \approx 1 - \frac{1}{2}\theta^2$.

17.  Using the formula for $\tan 2A$, show that $\tan x = \dfrac{2t}{1 - t^2}$,

where $t = \tan \dfrac{x}{2}$.

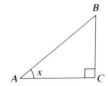

In the right-angled triangle, let $BC = 2t$ units and $AC = 1 - t^2$. Find the length of $AB$.

Hence verify the formulae for $\sin x$ and $\cos x$ in terms of $t$.

# 9   Integration (Methods)

If $f'(x) = \dfrac{d[f(x)]}{dx}$ then $\displaystyle\int f'(x)\,dx = f(x) + c$

$$\int_a^b f'(x)\,dx = f(b) - f(a)$$

## Standard Integrals

| $y$ | $\displaystyle\int y\,dx$ |
|---|---|
| $x^n$ | $\dfrac{x^{n+1}}{n+1}(+c)$ <br> (for $n \neq -1$) |
| $\dfrac{1}{x}$ | $\ln|x|$ |
| $e^x$ | $e^x$ |
| $\cos x$ | $\sin x$ |
| $\sin x$ | $-\cos x$ |
| $\tan x$ | $\ln|\sec x|$ |
| $\operatorname{cosec} x$ | $\ln|\tan \tfrac{1}{2}x|$ |
| $\sec x$ | $\ln|\sec x + \tan x|$ <br> $= \ln\left|\tan\left(\dfrac{\pi}{4} + \tfrac{1}{2}x\right)\right|$ |
| $\cot x$ | $\ln|\sin x|$ |
| $\dfrac{1}{1+x^2}$ | $\tan^{-1} x$ |
| $\dfrac{1}{\sqrt{1-x^2}}$ | $\sin^{-1} x$ |
| $\dfrac{f'(x)}{f(x)}$ | $\ln|f(x)|$ |

## Some other integrals

| $y$ | $\displaystyle\int y\,dx$ |
|---|---|
| $(ax+b)^n$ | $\dfrac{(ax+b)^{n+1}}{a(n+1)}$ <br> (for $n \neq -1$) |
| $\dfrac{1}{ax+b}$ | $\dfrac{1}{a}\ln|ax+b|$ |
| $e^{ax+b}$ | $\dfrac{1}{a}e^{ax+b}$ |
| $\cos(ax+b)$ | $\dfrac{1}{a}\sin(ax+b)$ |
| $\sin(ax+b)$ | $-\dfrac{1}{a}\cos(ax+b)$ |
| $\dfrac{1}{a^2+x^2}$ | $\dfrac{1}{a}\tan^{-1}\dfrac{x}{a}$ |
| $\dfrac{1}{\sqrt{a^2-x^2}}$ | $\sin^{-1}\dfrac{x}{a}$ |
| $\ln x$ | $x\ln x - x$ |
| $\dfrac{1}{a^2-x^2}$ | $\dfrac{1}{2a}\ln\left|\dfrac{a+x}{a-x}\right|$ |
| $\sin^2 x$ | $\tfrac{1}{2}x - \tfrac{1}{4}\sin 2x$ |
| $\cos^2 x$ | $\tfrac{1}{2}x + \tfrac{1}{4}\sin 2x$ |
| $\tan^2 x$ | $\tan x - x$ |
| $\sec^2 x$ | $\tan x$ |

## Methods of integration

1. By using standard forms.
2. By substitution.
3. By partial fractions.
4. Integration by parts. $\displaystyle\int u\frac{dv}{dx}\,dx = uv - \int \frac{du}{dx}v\,dx$

## Integration using standard forms

### Examples

**9.1** $\displaystyle\int \left(5x^5 - 2x + 3 - \frac{6}{x} + \frac{2}{x^2}\right) dx = 5\cdot\frac{x^6}{6} - 2\cdot\frac{x^2}{2} + 3x - 6\ln|x| + 2\cdot\frac{x^{-1}}{-1} + c$

$$= \tfrac{5}{6}x^6 - x^2 + 3x - 6\ln|x| - \frac{2}{x} + c$$

**9.2** Using $\displaystyle\int \frac{f'(x)}{f(x)}\,dx = \ln|f(x)| + c$ 

(Here the numerator $f'(x)$ is the derivative of the denominator $f(x)$.)

$\displaystyle\int \frac{1+e^x}{x+e^x}\,dx = \ln|x+e^x| + c$

(Since the denominator $f(x) = x + e^x$ and its derivative $f'(x) = 1 + e^x$ is the numerator.)

**9.3** $\displaystyle\int_0^{\frac{3}{2}} \frac{1}{\sqrt{9-x^2}}\,dx = \left[\sin^{-1}\frac{x}{3}\right]_0^{\frac{3}{2}}$

$$= \sin^{-1}\tfrac{1}{2} - \sin^{-1} 0$$

$$= \frac{\pi}{6} - 0$$

$$= \frac{\pi}{6}$$

## Integration by substitution

### Examples

**9.4** $\displaystyle\int \frac{3x^2+2}{(x^3+2x)^6}\,dx = \int \frac{1}{z^6}\,dz$

let $z = x^3 + 2x$

then $\dfrac{dz}{dx} = 3x^2 + 2$

i.e. $dz$ can replace $(3x^2+2)\,dx$

$$= \frac{z^{-5}}{-5} + c$$

$$= -\frac{1}{5z^5} + c$$

$$= -\frac{1}{5(x^3+2x)^5} + c$$

**9.5** $\displaystyle\int \frac{1}{x(\ln x)^2}\,dx = \int \frac{1}{z^2}\,dz$      let $z = \ln x$

$$\frac{dz}{dx} = \frac{1}{x}$$

$$= -\frac{1}{z} + c$$

i.e. $dz$ can replace $\dfrac{1}{x}\,dx$

$$= -\frac{1}{\ln x} + c$$

**9.6** $\displaystyle\int_3^{\sqrt{14}} x\sqrt{x^2-5}\,dx = \int_2^3 z \cdot z\,dz$    let $z = \sqrt{x^2-5}$

i.e. $z^2 = x^2 - 5$

$$= \left[\frac{z^3}{3}\right]_2^3$$

$$2z\frac{dz}{dx} = 2x$$

$$= 9 - \tfrac{8}{3} = 6\tfrac{1}{3}$$

so $x\,dx$ can be replaced by $z\,dz$

Changing the limits:

when $x = \sqrt{14}$, $z = 3$

when $x = 3$, $z = 2$

**9.7** $\displaystyle\int_0^{\pi/6} \sin^4 x \cos x\,dx = \int_0^{\frac{1}{2}} z^4\,dz$    For an odd power of $\cos x$ let $z = \sin x$.

(For an odd power of $\sin x$ let $z = \cos x$.)

$$= \left[\frac{z^5}{5}\right]_0^{\frac{1}{2}}$$

let $z = \sin x$

$$= \tfrac{1}{160} - 0 = \tfrac{1}{160}$$

then $\dfrac{dz}{dx} = \cos x$

so $\cos x\,dx$ can be replaced by $dz$

Changing the limits:

when $x = \dfrac{\pi}{6}$, $z = \sin\dfrac{\pi}{6} = \tfrac{1}{2}$

when $x = 0$, $z = \sin 0 = 0$

**Trig. substitutions where the variable $x$ is not changed**

**Examples**

**9.8** $\displaystyle\int \sin^2 x\,dx$      $\cos 2x = 1 - 2\sin^2 x$

so $\sin^2 x = \tfrac{1}{2} - \tfrac{1}{2}\cos 2x$

$$= \int \left(\tfrac{1}{2} - \tfrac{1}{2}\cos 2x\right)\,dx$$

$$= \tfrac{1}{2}x - \tfrac{1}{2} \cdot \frac{\sin 2x}{2} + c$$

$$= \tfrac{1}{2}x - \tfrac{1}{4}\sin 2x + c$$

**9.9**     $\displaystyle\int_0^{\pi/3} \cos \tfrac{1}{2}x \sin \tfrac{3}{2}x \, dx$

Using $2 \sin A \cos B =$
$\sin(A+B) + \sin(A-B)$,
$2 \cos \tfrac{1}{2}x \sin \tfrac{3}{2}x = \sin 2x + \sin x$

$\displaystyle = \int_0^{\pi/3} \tfrac{1}{2}(\sin 2x + \sin x) \, dx$

$\displaystyle = \left[ -\frac{\cos 2x}{4} - \frac{\cos x}{2} \right]_0^{\pi/3}$

$\displaystyle = \left( -\frac{\cos \dfrac{2\pi}{3}}{4} - \frac{\cos \dfrac{\pi}{3}}{2} \right) - \left( -\frac{\cos 0}{4} - \frac{\cos 0}{2} \right)$

$= \tfrac{1}{8} - \tfrac{1}{4} + \tfrac{1}{4} + \tfrac{1}{2} = \tfrac{5}{8}$

## Integration using partial fractions

### Example 9.10

$\displaystyle\int_0^1 \frac{x^2 - 5x - 2}{(4+x^2)(2-x)} \, dx$

Express $\dfrac{x^2 - 5x - 2}{(4+x^2)(2-x)}$ in partial fractions.

$\dfrac{x^2 - 5x - 2}{(4+x^2)(2-x)} = \dfrac{1-2x}{4+x^2} - \dfrac{1}{2-x}$

$\qquad = \dfrac{1}{4+x^2} - \dfrac{2x}{4+x^2} - \dfrac{1}{2-x}$

$\displaystyle\int_0^1 \frac{x^2 - 5x - 2}{(4+x^2)(2-x)} \, dx = \int_0^1 \frac{1}{4+x^2} \, dx - \int_0^1 \frac{2x}{4+x^2} \, dx - \int_0^1 \frac{1}{2-x} \, dx$

$\displaystyle = \left[ \tfrac{1}{2} \tan^{-1} \frac{x}{2} - \ln(4+x^2) + \ln|2-x| \right]_0^1$

$= (\tfrac{1}{2} \tan^{-1} \tfrac{1}{2} - \ln 5 + \ln 1) - (\tfrac{1}{2} \tan^{-1} 0 - \ln 4 + \ln 2)$

$= \tfrac{1}{2} \tan^{-1} \tfrac{1}{2} + \ln \tfrac{2}{5}$

## Integration by parts

$\displaystyle\int u \frac{dv}{dx} \, dx = uv - \int \frac{du}{dx} v \, dx$

### Examples

**9.11**     $\displaystyle\int x \, e^{-x} \, dx = x(-e^{-x}) - \int 1 \cdot (-e^{-x}) \, dx$

let $u = x$

then $\dfrac{du}{dx} = 1$

$\qquad = -x \, e^{-x} - e^{-x} + c$

let $\dfrac{dv}{dx} = e^{-x}$

then $v = -e^{-x}$

**9.12** $\displaystyle\int_1^2 x^2 e^{-x}\,dx$ let $u = x^2$

$$= \left[-x^2 e^{-x}\right]_1^2 - \int_1^2 2x(-e^{-x})\,dx$$ then $\dfrac{du}{dx} = 2x$

$$= \left[-x^2 e^{-x}\right]_1^2 + 2\int_1^2 x e^{-x}\,dx$$ let $\dfrac{dv}{dx} = e^{-x}$

$$= \left[-x^2 e^{-x} - 2x e^{-x} - 2 e^{-x}\right]_1^2$$ then $v = -e^{-x}$

(using the result of example 11)

$$= (-4e^{-2} - 4e^{-2} - 2e^{-2}) - (-e^{-1} - 2e^{-1} - 2e^{-1})$$

$$= 5e^{-1} - 10e^{-2}$$

**9.13**

To show that $\displaystyle\int \ln x\,dx = x \ln x - x + c$ let $u = \ln x$

then $\dfrac{du}{dx} = \dfrac{1}{x}$

$$\int \ln x\,dx = x \ln x - \int \frac{1}{x} \cdot x\,dx$$ let $\dfrac{dv}{dx} = 1$

$$= x \ln x - x + c$$ then $v = x$

**The substitution $t = \tan \dfrac{x}{2}$**

**Example 9.14**

Use the substitution $t = \tan \dfrac{x}{2}$ to find $\displaystyle\int \frac{1}{1 + \sin x}\,dx$

$$\int \frac{1}{1 + \sin x}\,dx$$ let $t = \tan \dfrac{x}{2}$

$$= \int \frac{\dfrac{2}{1 + t^2}}{1 + \dfrac{2t}{1 + t_2}}\,dt$$ then $\dfrac{dt}{dx} = \tfrac{1}{2}\sec^2 \dfrac{x}{2}$

$$= \tfrac{1}{2}\left(1 + \tan^2 \frac{x}{2}\right)$$

$$= \int \frac{2}{1 + t^2 + 2t}\,dt$$ $= \tfrac{1}{2}(1 + t^2)$

$$= \int \frac{2}{(1 + t)^2}\,dt$$ i.e. $\dfrac{dx}{dt} = \dfrac{2}{1 + t^2}$

$$= -\frac{2}{1 + t} + c$$ $\displaystyle\int dx = \int \frac{2}{1 + t^2}\,dt$

$$= -\frac{2}{1 + \tan \dfrac{x}{2}} + c$$

## Exercise 9.1

Find the indefinite integrals.

1. $\displaystyle\int \frac{x+1}{\sqrt{x}}\,dx$

6. $\displaystyle\int \frac{x}{\sqrt{4x^2+3}}\,dx$

2. $\displaystyle\int \frac{1}{\sqrt{25-x^2}}\,dx$

7. $\displaystyle\int \frac{2x+5}{x^2+5x+7}\,dx$

3. $\displaystyle\int (\tan x + \tan^3 x)\,dx$

8. $\displaystyle\int \frac{1}{x^2+5x+6}\,dx$

4. $\displaystyle\int x(x^2+3)^5\,dx$

9. $\displaystyle\int \frac{5x+7}{x^2+2x-3}\,dx$

5. $\displaystyle\int \cos^3 x\,dx$

10. $\displaystyle\int x\sin x\,dx$

Find the value of:

11. $\displaystyle\int_0^{\frac{1}{2}} e^{-2x}\,dx$

16. $\displaystyle\int_1^3 \frac{1}{x^2+3x}\,dx$

12. $\displaystyle\int_0^2 \frac{1}{x^2+4}\,dx$

17. $\displaystyle\int_{\pi/6}^{\pi/3} \cos x \sin 2x\,dx$

13. $\displaystyle\int_\alpha^{\pi/4} \frac{\sec^2 x}{2+3\tan x}\,dx$, where $\tan \alpha = \frac{1}{6}$

18. $\displaystyle\int_{\pi/12}^{\pi/4} \cos^2 x\,dx$

14. $\displaystyle\int_0^1 \frac{2x-3}{1+x^2}\,dx$

19. $\displaystyle\int_0^2 (4-x)\,e^x\,dx$

15. $\displaystyle\int_{\frac{1}{9}}^{\frac{1}{4}} \frac{1}{(1-x)\sqrt{x}}\,dx$

20. $\displaystyle\int_1^2 x\ln x\,dx$

## Exercise 9.2

Find the indefinite integrals.

1. $\displaystyle\int \frac{2x}{(x+2)^2}\,dx$

6. $\displaystyle\int \cos(2x+3)\,dx$

2. $\displaystyle\int \sec^2(3x-2)\,dx$

7. $\displaystyle\int \frac{e^x}{(e^x+3)^2}\,dx$

3. $\displaystyle\int e^{4x-3}\,dx$

8. $\displaystyle\int \sec x \tan x\,dx$

4. $\displaystyle\int \frac{1}{1-x}\,dx$

9. $\displaystyle\int x^2 \ln x\,dx$

5. $\displaystyle\int \frac{1}{x^2+16}\,dx$

10. $\displaystyle\int \frac{1}{(x-2)(x-1)}\,dx$

Find the value of:

11. $\displaystyle\int_0^{\pi/3} \sin x \cos^3 x \, dx$

16. $\displaystyle\int_0^2 \frac{1}{\sqrt{16-x^2}} \, dx$

12. $\displaystyle\int_1^2 \frac{\ln x}{x} \, dx$

17. $\displaystyle\int_{\pi/4}^{\pi/2} \operatorname{cosec}^2 x \, dx$

13. $\displaystyle\int_0^{\pi/2} \sin 3x \, dx$

18. $\displaystyle\int_{\frac{3}{4}}^1 \sqrt{1-x} \, dx$

14. $\displaystyle\int_0^1 x \, e^{-2x} \, dx$

19. $\displaystyle\int_{-1}^3 (x-3)(x+1)^3 \, dx$

15. $\displaystyle\int_{\pi/6}^{\pi/4} \cot x \, dx$

20. $\displaystyle\int_1^{1\frac{1}{3}} \frac{1}{4-x^2} \, dx$

## Exercise 9.3

Find the indefinite integrals.

1. $\displaystyle\int \frac{3x^2-4x+1}{(x^2+1)(x-2)} \, dx$

4. $\displaystyle\int \frac{x}{(1-2x)^4} \, dx$

2. $\displaystyle\int \frac{1}{\sqrt{9-16x^2}} \, dx$

5. $\displaystyle\int \frac{1}{3+\cos x} \, dx$, using $t = \tan \frac{1}{2}x$

3. 1 $\displaystyle\int \frac{x}{1+x^2} \, dx$

   2 $\displaystyle\int \tan^{-1} x \, dx$

Find the value of:

6. $\displaystyle\int_{\pi/6}^{\pi/4} \frac{\cos x}{\sin^3 x} \, dx$

9. $\displaystyle\int_0^\alpha \frac{\cos x}{4-\sin^2 x} \, dx$, where $\sin \alpha = \frac{2}{3}$

7. $\displaystyle\int_0^1 (3x^2+5)(2x^3+10x+4)^{\frac{1}{2}} \, dx$

10. $\displaystyle\int_0^{\frac{1}{2}} \frac{\sin^{-1} x}{\sqrt{1-x^2}} \, dx$

8. $\displaystyle\int_2^3 \frac{1}{x(x^2+1)} \, dx$

11. $\displaystyle\int_0^{\sqrt{3}/2} \frac{x^3}{\sqrt{1-x^2}} \, dx$

12. By putting $\tan x = \dfrac{\sin x}{\cos x}$, show that $\displaystyle\int \tan x \, dx = \ln|\sec x| + c$.

13. Show that $\displaystyle\int \frac{1}{a^2-x^2} \, dx = \frac{1}{2a} \ln \frac{a+x}{a-x} + c$, where $0 < x < a$, by using partial fractions.

14. Find $\int \tan^2 x\, dx$ by a suitable trigonometric substitution.

15. Use the substitution $t = \tan \frac{1}{2}x$ to show that $\int \csc x\, dx = \ln|\tan \frac{1}{2}x| + c$, and find $\int_{\pi/3}^{\pi/2} \csc x\, dx$ in terms of $\ln 3$.

16. Find $\int_{\alpha}^{\beta} \dfrac{1}{1 + \cos x - \sin x}\, dx$, where $\alpha = 2\tan^{-1}\frac{1}{3}$ and $\beta = 2\tan^{-1}\frac{1}{2}$, using the substitution $t = \tan \frac{1}{2}x$.

17. Use the substitution $x = a \sin \theta$ to show that $\int \dfrac{1}{\sqrt{a^2 - x^2}}\, dx = \sin^{-1}\dfrac{x}{a} + c.$

18. Use the substitution $x = a \tan \theta$ to show that $\int \dfrac{1}{a^2 + x^2}\, dx = \dfrac{1}{a}\tan^{-1}\dfrac{x}{a} + c.$

19. Use the formula $\dfrac{d(uv)}{dx} = v\dfrac{du}{dx} + u\dfrac{dv}{dx}$ and integrate with respect to $x$ to verify the formula for integration by parts.

# C  Revision

## Exercise C1

1. In the function $f(x) = 3x^2 + 8x + k$, show that the minimum value occurs when $x = -\frac{4}{3}$. If this minimum value is 0, find the value of $k$.

2. Use the factor thorem to factorise $x^4 + x^3 - 7x^2 - x + 6$. Sketch the graph of $y = x^4 + x^3 - 7x^2 - x + 6$.

3. Write down the arithmetic mean and the geometric mean of two unequal positive numbers $x$ and $y$. Show that the arithmetic mean is greater than the geometric mean.

4. Express in partial fractions $\dfrac{x^2 + 9x + 13}{(x+1)(x+2)^2}$.

5. Show that $\sin 2x + \sin 4x + \sin 6x + \sin 8x = 4 \cos x \cos 2x \sin 5x$.

6. Solve the equation $8 \tan \theta = 3 \cos \theta$ for $0° < \theta < 180°$.

7. Solve the equation $\tan 2\theta = -1$ giving the general solution (in radians).

8. If $y = \ln(1 - \cos x)$, where $\cos x \ne 1$, show that $\dfrac{d^2y}{dx^2}$ is always negative.

9. Find the equation of the tangent at the point $(2, 1)$ on the curve $2x^2 + xy - 2y^2 = 8$.

10. Find the stationary point on the curve $y = e^{3x} - 3e^{2x} - 9e^x$ and show that it is a minimum point.

11. Find the area $A$ of an equilateral triangle in terms of side $a$. If $a$ is increased by a small amount $\delta a$, show that the approximate increase in $A$ is $\dfrac{\sqrt{3}a}{2} \delta a$.

12. Find $\displaystyle\int 2 \cos 5x \cos 3x \, dx$.

13. Find $\displaystyle\int_0^1 \dfrac{1}{\sqrt{2 - x^2}} \, dx$.

14. Use the substitution $x = \sec \theta$ to find $\displaystyle\int_{\sqrt{2}}^2 \dfrac{1}{x\sqrt{x^2 - 1}} \, dx$.

15. Find $\displaystyle\int_0^2 (x - 2) e^x \, dx$.

## Exercise C2

Select the correct answer to each question.

1.  $a^3 - b^3 =$

    A  $(a+b)(a^2-b^2)$              B  $(a-b)(a^2+b^2)$

    C  $(a-b)(a^2+ab+b^2)$           D  $(a-b)(a^2-ab+b^2)$

    E  $(a+b)(a^2-ab+b^2)$

2.  The equation of the normal to the curve $y = x^4 - 3x^2$ at the point where $x = 1$ is

    A  $x-2y-1=0$          B  $x-2y+3=0$          C  $x-2y-5=0$

    D  $2x+y=0$            E  $2x+y-4=0$

3.  If $\sin P = \frac{4}{5}$ and $\sin Q = \frac{12}{13}$ and $P$ and $Q$ are obtuse angles then $\sin(Q-P) =$

    A  $\frac{8}{65}$       B  $\frac{16}{65}$       C  $\frac{33}{65}$       D  $\frac{63}{65}$       E  $-\frac{16}{65}$

4.  The gradient of the parabola with parametric equations $x = at^2$, $y = 2at$ at the point $t = -2$ is

    A  $-\frac{1}{2}$       B  $\frac{1}{2}$       C  $2$       D  $-2$       E  $2a$

5.  The coefficient of $x^2$ in the expansion of $\dfrac{1+2x}{1-x}$ is

    A  $1$          B  $-1$          C  $-2$          D  $3$          E  $-3$

6.  If $x > 0$, $\displaystyle\int \frac{1}{x(x+2)}\,dx =$

    A  $\frac{1}{2}\ln x(x+2)+c$     B  $\frac{1}{2}\ln\dfrac{x}{x+2}+c$     C  $\frac{1}{2}\ln\dfrac{x+2}{x}+c$

    D  $\ln\dfrac{x}{x+2}+c$         E  $\ln\dfrac{x+2}{x}+c$

7.  If the roots of the equation $5x^2 - 4x - 2 = 0$ are $\alpha$, $\beta$ then $\dfrac{1}{\alpha}+\dfrac{1}{\beta}=$

    A  $-2\frac{1}{2}$       B  $-2$       C  $\frac{4}{5}$       D  $1\frac{1}{4}$       E  $2$

8.  The curve $y = x^4(x-10)$ has point(s) of inflexion when

    A  $x=0$       B  $x=6$       C  $x=10$       D  $x=0$ or $6$       E  $x=0$ or $8$

9.  $\displaystyle\int_1^2 x\ln x\,dx =$

    A  $2\ln 2-3$              B  $2\ln 2-2$              C  $2\ln 2-1$

    D  $4\ln 2-8\frac{1}{2}$       E  $2\ln 2-\frac{3}{4}$

10. The arc $AB$ of a circle has length 4 units and the angle subtended by $AB$ at the centre of the circle is $120°$. The length of the chord $AB$ is

   **A** 4          **B** $\dfrac{6}{\pi}$          **C** $\dfrac{3\sqrt{3}}{\pi}$          **D** $\dfrac{6\sqrt{3}}{\pi}$          **E** $\dfrac{12\sqrt{3}}{\pi}$

11. If $y = (5x^2+3)^4$ then $\dfrac{dy}{dx} =$

   **A** $4(5x^2+3)^3$          **B** $10x(5x^2+3)^3$          **C** $15x(5x^2+3)^3$

   **D** $40x(5x^2+3)^3$          **E** $\dfrac{(5x^2+3)^5}{25}$

12. The solution of the equation $\log_3 x \log_4 x = \log_3 4$ is

   **A** $x = 3$          **B** $x = 4$          **C** $x = 3$ or $-3$

   **D** $x = 4$ or $-4$          **E** $x = 4$ or $\frac{1}{4}$

13. If the base of a triangle increases steadily at the rate of $p$ units/s and the height of the triangle decreases steadily at the rate of $q$ units/s, find an expression for the rate of increase of area (per second) at the instant when the base is $b$ units and the height is $h$ units.

   **A** $\frac{1}{2}pq$          **B** $-\frac{1}{2}pq$          **C** $\frac{1}{2}(p-q)$          **D** $\frac{1}{2}(hp-bq)$          **E** $\frac{1}{2}(hp+bq)$

14. Which of the following curves is not symmetrical about the origin?

   **A** $\cos x$          **B** $x+\dfrac{1}{x}$          **C** $x^3$          **D** $\tan^{-1} x$          **E** $\sin 2x$

15. $\displaystyle\int_{\pi/6}^{\pi/4} \sec^2 x \, dx =$

   **A** $\dfrac{3-\sqrt{3}}{3}$          **B** $\dfrac{3+\sqrt{3}}{3}$          **C** $1-\sqrt{3}$          **D** $-4$          **E** $4-\dfrac{8\sqrt{3}}{9}$

## Exercise C3

1. Find $\displaystyle\int_0^4 \dfrac{2x}{\sqrt{x^2+9}}\, dx$.

2. Simplify $\dfrac{1+\cos 2x}{1-\cos 2x}$ and if $y = \dfrac{1+\cos 2x}{1-\cos 2x}$ find $\dfrac{dy}{dx}$.

3. If the roots of the equation $2x^2 - 5x - 8 = 0$ are $\alpha$, $\beta$, find the values of   1   $\alpha^3+\beta^3$
   2  $(\alpha^2+\beta)(\alpha+\beta^2)$.

4. If $f(x) = x^2+1$ and $g(x) = x+2$, find the value of $x$ for which $fg(x) = gf(x)$.

5. Sketch the graph of $y = \dfrac{8-4x}{5+2x}$, and state the equations of its asymptotes. For what range of values of $x$ is $y < -1$?

6. Simplify $\sqrt[4]{\cos^2\theta + \sin^4\theta - \sin^2\theta}$.

7. If the numbers $x-5$, $x-14$, $x-50$ are the first 3 terms of a geometric progression, find the value of $x$, and find an expression for the sum of $n$ terms.

8. The volume $v$ of a particular-shaped container is given by the formula $v = kr^3$, where $r$ is the base-radius and $k$ is a positive constant. Find the approximate percentage increase in the volume if $r$ is increased from 5 to 5.01 units and the other measurements are increased in proportion.

9. Find the possible values of $k$ if the curve $y = 3kx^2 - 12x + k + 1$ touches the $x$-axis, and for each value of $k$ state whether the curve has a maximum or minimum point.

10. Find $\displaystyle\int_1^3 \frac{7}{(2x-1)(x+3)}\,dx$.

11. If the sum of $n$ terms of the arithmetic series $32 + 45 + 58 + \ldots$ is equal to the sum of $2n$ terms of the arithmetic series $5 + 9 + 13 + \ldots$, find the value of $n$.

12. Express $5\cos\theta - 12\sin\theta$ in the form $R\cos(\theta + \alpha)$. Show that $5\cos\theta - 12\sin\theta \leqslant 13$. Solve the equation $5\cos\theta - 12\sin\theta = 13$ in the range $0° \leqslant \theta \leqslant 360°$.

13. A regular $n$-sided polygon is inscribed in a circle of radius $r$. Find the total area of the segments lying between the circle and the polygon, in terms of $r$ and $n$.
In the case when $n = 12$, show that this area is approximately $4\tfrac{1}{2}\%$ of the area of the circle.

14. By using a suitable substitution, find $\displaystyle\int \frac{x}{\sqrt{1-x^2}}\,dx$. Using this result, find $\displaystyle\int \sin^{-1}x\,dx$.

15. If the coefficients of $x^2$ and $x^3$ in the expansion of $(1 + ax + bx^2)\ln(1+x)$ are zero, find the values of $a$ and $b$ and the term in $x^4$.

**To the Student:**

# 4    Practice Exams

Do you have a 'mock' or trial exam? This has several advantages:

1    It will give you some idea of your standard and show you that you can do things well if you have learnt the work.
2    It will give you practice in working in time and working under pressure, and planning how to tackle the paper and make a wise choice of questions.
3    If you tend to panic when things won't come right, it is better that this should happen in a 'mock' exam where there is not too much at stake, and you can use your commonsense to overcome it and so learn to cope better in the real exam.
4    It will give your teacher some idea of your standard, and he/she can then decide how best to use the remaining available time.
5    If you have done some last-minute revision, you can see how effective this has been. As a general rule, steady work is much more satisfactory. Last minute revision, by concentrating on a few topics, may actually reduce your chances, especially if you have tired yourself.

Read the suggestions given on page 141 and page 183 for the actual exam, as most of these can be put into practice for the 'mock' exam.

After the exam, you will be told your marks and given back your paper. Either your teacher will go through all the questions with the class, or you may be told to correct them for yourself. <u>Ask</u> about anything you do not understand. Do not get discouraged by a low mark if you know that with sensible study you can improve it before the proper exam. But <u>decide</u> what to do about it.

In an exam it is the marks which count. Could you have got more marks if you had spent more time on some questions and less on others, of if you had answered the paper in a different order? Should you have learnt formulae more thoroughly, and revised some topics better so that you could have attempted other questions?

<u>Here are some ways in which you may have lost marks</u>:
Not reading a question carefully enough.
Not showing enough necessary working, or doing it on scrap paper instead of with the rest of the answer.
Writing illegibly, especially by altering numbers or plus signs so that they were ambiguous, perhaps not being able to read your own writing so that you miscopied 6 instead of $b$, 5 instead of $s$, and so on.
Not using brackets in an algebraic expression where they were needed, so that the rest of the working-out went wrong, or generally not taking enough care with algebraic manipulation.

Not drawing a diagram where this would have been helpful in understanding the question, or, where a sketch diagram was asked for, drawing a poor one which did not show the important details of the curve.

Giving an approximate answer, because you had used your calculator at an early stage, instead of keeping exact numbers such as $\pi$, $\sqrt{3}$, $\ln 3$ in your working, or when an approximate answer was required, giving it to 2 decimal places when you were told to give it to 2 significant figures.

Giving an answer which a simple check would have shown was obviously wrong, probably because of pressing a wrong key on your calculator.

Since this was a practice exam, having made some of these mistakes, you will be careful to avoid them in future.

Make a list of topics you still need to revise, and plan how you will spend your remaining time before the proper exam.

Your teacher may give you further timed tests. If not, you may like to give yourself some. You can use past exam papers, or the revision papers in this book. Find a quiet room at a time when you will not be interrupted for 3 hours. Try to work as in an actual exam, doing the questions in a sensible order and trying to work to time.

# 10  Vectors

**Vectors** have magnitude and direction, e.g. displacement, velocity, force.

**Notation.** In printed books they are written in heavy type. **a**
In writing, they are underlined. $\underline{a}$
If represented by a straight line $PQ$, written $\overline{PQ}$, $\overrightarrow{PQ}$ or **PQ**.

**Position vectors**

When a vector $\overrightarrow{OP}$ is used to specify the position of a point $P$ relative to a point $O$ it is called the position vector of $P$ for the origin $O$. This vector uniquely determines the position of $P$ relative to $O$.

**Scalars** are numbers which have magnitude but no direction. e.g. mass, volume.

**The modulus** of a vector is its magnitude. It is written as $|\mathbf{a}|$, or as $a$ (without being underlined). The modulus of $\overrightarrow{PQ}$ is $PQ$.

**Unit vectors** are vectors with unit magnitude.
The unit vector in the direction of **a** is represented by **â**. So $\mathbf{a} = a\mathbf{\hat{a}}$.

**Zero vector** is **0**. It has no direction.

**Negative vector** $-\mathbf{a}$. It has the same modulus as **a** but the opposite direction.

**Equal vectors** have the same modulus and the same direction.
e.g. $\overrightarrow{AB} = \overrightarrow{CD}$

**Addition of vectors**

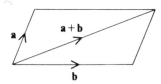

**Subtraction**

$\mathbf{a} - \mathbf{b}$ is the same as $\mathbf{a} + (-\mathbf{b})$

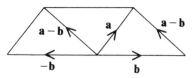

**Multiplication by a scalar**

If $m$ is a positive real number, then $m\mathbf{a}$ is a vector in the same direction as $\mathbf{a}$ with a modulus $ma$.

**Scalar product**

The scalar product of two vectors $\mathbf{a}$, $\mathbf{b}$ whose directions are inclined at an angle $\theta$ to each other is the scalar quantity $ab \cos \theta$ and is denoted by $\mathbf{a}\,.\,\mathbf{b}$

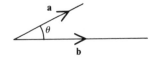

$\mathbf{a}\,.\,\mathbf{b} = ab \cos \theta$

The scalar product has these laws:

$\mathbf{a}\,.\,\mathbf{b} = \mathbf{b}\,.\,\mathbf{a}$

$\mathbf{a}\,.\,(\mathbf{b}+\mathbf{c}) = \mathbf{a}\,.\,\mathbf{b}+\mathbf{a}\,.\,\mathbf{c}$

$\mathbf{a}\,.\,\mathbf{a} = \mathbf{a}^2 = a^2$

**The angle between two vectors**

$$\cos \theta = \frac{\mathbf{a}\,.\,\mathbf{b}}{ab}$$

If two vectors $\mathbf{a}$, $\mathbf{b}$ are perpendicular then $\mathbf{a}\,.\,\mathbf{b} = 0$

If two vectors are parallel and in the same direction then $\mathbf{a}\,.\,\mathbf{b} = ab$, if in the opposite direction then $\mathbf{a}\,.\,\mathbf{b} = -ab$

**The resolved part** of a vector $\mathbf{a}$ in the direction of vector $\mathbf{b}$ is $a \cos \theta$

This equals $\dfrac{\mathbf{a}\,.\,\mathbf{b}}{b}$

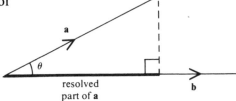

resolved part of **a**

**Position vectors**

If the position vectors of points $A$, $B$ with respect to origin $O$ are $\mathbf{a}$, $\mathbf{b}$ then $\overrightarrow{AB} = \mathbf{b}-\mathbf{a}$ and $\overrightarrow{BA} = \mathbf{a}-\mathbf{b}$

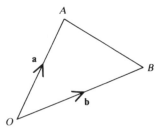

The position vector of the mid-point $M$ of $AB$ is $\frac{1}{2}(\mathbf{a}+\mathbf{b})$

The position vector of the point $P$ dividing $AB$ in the ratio $m:n$ is $\dfrac{n\mathbf{a}+m\mathbf{b}}{m+n}$

If the position vectors of $C$, $D$ are $\mathbf{c}$, $\mathbf{d}$ then:

$AB$ is parallel to $CD$ if $\mathbf{d}-\mathbf{c} = k(\mathbf{b}-\mathbf{a})$, where $k$ is a scalar

$A$, $B$ and $C$ lie on a straight line if $\mathbf{c} - \mathbf{b} = k(\mathbf{b} - \mathbf{a})$

$AB$ is perpendicular to $CD$ if $(\mathbf{b} - \mathbf{a}) \cdot (\mathbf{d} - \mathbf{c}) = 0$

$AB$ and $CD$ are equal in length if $|\mathbf{b} - \mathbf{a}| = |\mathbf{d} - \mathbf{c}|$

## Components of a Vector

$\mathbf{i}$, $\mathbf{j}$, $\mathbf{k}$ are unit vectors in the directions of the axes $OX$, $OY$, $OZ$.

$\mathbf{r} = x\mathbf{i} + y\mathbf{j} + z\mathbf{k}$

(In two dimensions, $\mathbf{r} = x\mathbf{i} + y\mathbf{j}$)

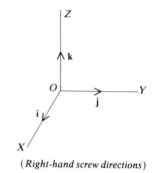

(*Right-hand screw directions*)

**The modulus of r** $\quad r = \sqrt{x^2 + y^2 + z^2}$

Vectors may be written as row or column vectors.

e.g. $\mathbf{i} + 2\mathbf{j} + 3\mathbf{k} = \begin{pmatrix} 1 \\ 2 \\ 3 \end{pmatrix} = (1, 2, 3)$

## Components of a position vector

If $P$ has coordinates $(x, y, z)$ with respect to axes $OX$, $OY$, $OZ$ and $\mathbf{r}$ is the position vector of $P$ with respect to the origin $O$, then $\mathbf{r} = x\mathbf{i} + y\mathbf{j} + z\mathbf{k}$

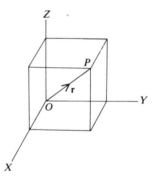

**Sums and differences** and multiplication by a scalar may be expressed in terms of components.

If $A$ is $(x_1, y_1, z_1)$ and $B$ is $(x_2, y_2, z_2)$ then

$\overrightarrow{OA} = x_1\mathbf{i} + y_1\mathbf{j} + z_1\mathbf{k}$, $\quad \overrightarrow{OB} = x_2\mathbf{i} + y_2\mathbf{j} + z_2\mathbf{k}$

$\overrightarrow{AB} = \overrightarrow{OB} - \overrightarrow{OA} = (x_2 - x_1)\mathbf{i} + (y_2 - y_1)\mathbf{j} + (z_2 - z_1)\mathbf{k}$

Modulus of $\overrightarrow{AB} = AB = \sqrt{(x_2 - x_1)^2 + (y_2 - y_1)^2 + (z_2 - z_1)^2}$

## Scalar product

$\mathbf{i} \cdot \mathbf{i} = \mathbf{j} \cdot \mathbf{j} = \mathbf{k} \cdot \mathbf{k} = 1$, $\quad \mathbf{i} \cdot \mathbf{j} = \mathbf{i} \cdot \mathbf{k} = \mathbf{j} \cdot \mathbf{k} = 0$

If $\mathbf{a} = x_1\mathbf{i} + y_1\mathbf{j} + z_1\mathbf{k}$ and $\mathbf{b} = x_2\mathbf{i} + y_2\mathbf{j} + z_2\mathbf{k}$, then

$\mathbf{a} \cdot \mathbf{b} = (x_1\mathbf{i} + y_1\mathbf{j} + z_1\mathbf{k}) \cdot (x_2\mathbf{i} + y_2\mathbf{j} + z_2\mathbf{k})$

$\quad = x_1 x_2 + y_1 y_2 + z_1 z_2$

**The angle between two vectors.**

$$\cos \theta = \frac{x_1 x_2 + y_1 y_2 + z_1 z_2}{\sqrt{(x_1^2 + y_1^2 + z_1^2)(x_2^2 + y_2^2 + z_2^2)}}$$

If two vectors are perpendicular, then $x_1 x_2 + y_1 y_2 + z_1 z_2 = 0$

If two vectors are parallel, then $\dfrac{x_1}{x_2} = \dfrac{y_1}{y_2} = \dfrac{z_1}{z_2}$

The resolved part of a vector **a** in the direction **b** is $\dfrac{x_1 x_2 + y_1 y_2 + z_1 z_2}{\sqrt{x_2^2 + y_2^2 + z_2^2}}$

**Equal vectors**
**a** = **b** if $x_1 = x_2$, $y_1 = y_2$, $z_1 = z_2$.

# Lines

**Vector equation of a straight line** passing through a given point and parallel to a given vector.

If point $A$ has position vector **a** and the given vector is **b** then the equation
**r** = **a** + $t$**b**, where $t$ is a scalar,
is an equation for the line through $A$ in direction **b**.

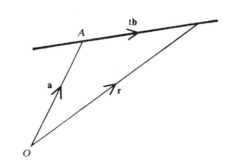

**Vector equation of a straight line** passing through two given points with position vectors **a**, **b**.

$\overrightarrow{AB}$ is **b** − **a**
An equation for the line is
**r** = **a** + $t$(**b** − **a**)
i.e. **r** = $(1 - t)$**a** + $t$**b**

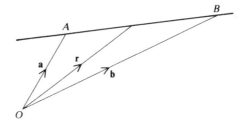

**Angle between two lines**
If the vector equations of the two lines are **r** = **a**$_1$ + $s$**b**$_1$ and **r** = **a**$_2$ + $t$**b**$_2$, the angle between

the lines is the angle $\theta$ between the vectors **b**$_1$ and **b**$_2$, so $\cos \theta = \dfrac{\mathbf{b}_1 . \mathbf{b}_2}{b_1 b_2}$

If **b**$_1$ . **b**$_2$ = 0, the lines are perpendicular.
If **b**$_1$ is a scalar multiple of **b**$_2$, the lines are parallel.

**Condition for two lines to intersect**
Two lines **r** = **a**$_1$ + $s$**b**$_1$, **r** = **a**$_2$ + $t$**b**$_2$ (where **b**$_1$ ≠ $k$**b**$_2$) intersect where **a**$_1$ + $s$**b**$_1$ = **a**$_2$ + $t$**b**$_2$

If values of $s$ and $t$ can be found to satisfy this, then the lines intersect, and putting in the value of $s$ or $t$ will give the point of intersection.
If values of $s$ and $t$ cannot be found, the lines will be skew.
(If **b**$_1$ = $k$**b**$_2$, where $k$ is a scalar, then the lines are parallel.)

## * The equation of a plane

This can be written in the form $\mathbf{r} \cdot \mathbf{n} = d$, where $d$ is a positive scalar. ($\mathbf{n}$ is a vector perpendicular to the plane.)

**The angle between two planes** $\mathbf{r} \cdot \mathbf{n}_1 = d_1$ and $\mathbf{r} \cdot \mathbf{n}_2 = d_2$ is equal to the angle between $\mathbf{n}_1$ and $\mathbf{n}_2$ and is $\theta$, where $\cos \theta = \dfrac{\mathbf{n}_1 \cdot \mathbf{n}_2}{n_1 n_2}$

## A line and a plane

A line $\mathbf{r} = \mathbf{a} + t\mathbf{b}$ and a plane $\mathbf{r} \cdot \mathbf{n} = d$ will be perpendicular if the directions of $\mathbf{b}$ and $\mathbf{n}$ are parallel, i.e. if $\mathbf{b}$ is a scalar multiple of $\mathbf{n}$.

The line and plane will be parallel if the directions of $\mathbf{b}$ and $\mathbf{n}$ are perpendicular, i.e. if $\mathbf{b} \cdot \mathbf{n} = 0$.

To find the point of intersection of a line with a plane, substitute for $\mathbf{r}$ from $\mathbf{r} = \mathbf{a} + t\mathbf{b}$ into $\mathbf{r} \cdot \mathbf{n} = d$, and hence find $t$. Putting this value of $t$ into $\mathbf{r} = \mathbf{a} + t\mathbf{b}$ gives the point of intersection.

If $\mathbf{r} = x\mathbf{i} + y\mathbf{j} + z\mathbf{k}$ and $\mathbf{n} = a\mathbf{i} + b\mathbf{j} + c\mathbf{k}$ then the equation of the plane $\mathbf{r} \cdot \mathbf{n} = d$ can be written as $ax + by + cz = d$.

## Examples

**10.1**  In the diagram, $BD : DC = 3 : 2$ and $AE : EB = 1 : 4$. If $\overrightarrow{AC} = \mathbf{a}$ and $\overrightarrow{BC} = \mathbf{b}$, express $\overrightarrow{AD} + \overrightarrow{CE}$ in terms of $\mathbf{a}$ and $\mathbf{b}$.

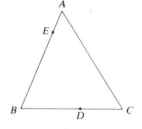

$$\overrightarrow{CD} = \tfrac{2}{5}\overrightarrow{CB} = -\tfrac{2}{5}\mathbf{b}$$
$$\overrightarrow{AD} = \overrightarrow{AC} + \overrightarrow{CD} = \mathbf{a} - \tfrac{2}{5}\mathbf{b}$$
$$\overrightarrow{AB} = \overrightarrow{AC} + \overrightarrow{CB} = \mathbf{a} - \mathbf{b}$$
$$\overrightarrow{AE} = \tfrac{1}{5}\overrightarrow{AB} = \tfrac{1}{5}(\mathbf{a} - \mathbf{b})$$
$$\overrightarrow{CE} = \overrightarrow{CA} + \overrightarrow{AE} = -\mathbf{a} + \tfrac{1}{5}(\mathbf{a} - \mathbf{b}) = -\tfrac{4}{5}\mathbf{a} - \tfrac{1}{5}\mathbf{b}$$
$$\therefore \quad \overrightarrow{AD} + \overrightarrow{CE} = \mathbf{a} - \tfrac{2}{5}\mathbf{b} - \tfrac{4}{5}\mathbf{a} - \tfrac{1}{5}\mathbf{b} = \tfrac{1}{5}\mathbf{a} - \tfrac{3}{5}\mathbf{b}$$

**10.2**  If $\mathbf{a} = \mathbf{i} + 2\mathbf{j} - 2\mathbf{k}$ and $\mathbf{b} = 6\mathbf{i} - 9\mathbf{j} + 2\mathbf{k}$ find $a$, $b$, $|\mathbf{b} - \mathbf{a}|$, $\mathbf{a} \cdot \mathbf{b}$, the angle between $\mathbf{a}$ and $\mathbf{b}$, the resolved part of $\mathbf{a}$ in the direction $\mathbf{b}$.

$$a = \sqrt{x_1^2 + y_1^2 + z_1^2} = \sqrt{1^2 + 2^2 + (-2)^2} = 3$$
$$b = \sqrt{6^2 + (-9)^2 + 2^2} = 11$$
$$\mathbf{b} - \mathbf{a} = (6-1)\mathbf{i} + (-9-2)\mathbf{j} + (2+2)\mathbf{k} = 5\mathbf{i} - 11\mathbf{j} + 4\mathbf{k}$$
$$|\mathbf{b} - \mathbf{a}| = \sqrt{5^2 + (-11)^2 + 4^2} = 9\sqrt{2}$$
$$\mathbf{a} \cdot \mathbf{b} = x_1 x_2 + y_1 y_2 + z_1 z_2 = 1 \times 6 + 2 \times (-9) + (-2) \times 2 = -16$$

The angle between $\mathbf{a}$ and $\mathbf{b}$ is $\theta$ where $\cos \theta = \dfrac{\mathbf{a} \cdot \mathbf{b}}{ab} = \dfrac{-16}{3 \times 11}$

The angle is $\cos^{-1}(-\tfrac{16}{33})$

The resolved part of $\mathbf{a}$ in the direction $\mathbf{b}$ is $a \cos \theta$ or $\dfrac{\mathbf{a} \cdot \mathbf{b}}{b} = -\tfrac{16}{11}$.

Topics marked * are not included in the national common core and may not be needed for your syllabus.

**10.3**   If $A$, $B$, $C$, $D$ have position vectors $2\mathbf{i}-3\mathbf{k}$, $5\mathbf{i}+7\mathbf{j}+6\mathbf{k}$, $-\mathbf{i}-4\mathbf{j}$, $5\mathbf{i}+8\mathbf{j}+10\mathbf{k}$ respectively, show that the lines $AB$ and $CD$ intersect and find the point of intersection.

$\overrightarrow{AB} = 5\mathbf{i}+7\mathbf{j}+6\mathbf{k}-(2\mathbf{i}-3\mathbf{k}) = 3\mathbf{i}+7\mathbf{j}+9\mathbf{k}$

Equation of $\overrightarrow{AB}$ is $\mathbf{r}=\mathbf{a}+t(\mathbf{b}-\mathbf{a})$, $\mathbf{r}=2\mathbf{i}-3\mathbf{k}+t(3\mathbf{i}+7\mathbf{j}+9\mathbf{k})$

$\overrightarrow{CD} = 6\mathbf{i}+12\mathbf{j}+10\mathbf{k}$

Equation of $\overrightarrow{CD}$ is $\mathbf{r}=-\mathbf{i}-4\mathbf{j}+s(6\mathbf{i}+12\mathbf{j}+10\mathbf{k})$

If the lines intersect then at the point of intersection

$2\mathbf{i}-3\mathbf{k}+t(3\mathbf{i}+7\mathbf{j}+9\mathbf{k}) = -\mathbf{i}-4\mathbf{j}+s(6\mathbf{i}+12\mathbf{j}+10\mathbf{k})$

i.e. $2+3t = -1+6s$

$\qquad 7t = -4+12s$

$\qquad -3+9t = 10s$

From the first two equations, $s=1\frac{1}{2}$, $t=2$.
This solution also satisfies the third equation.
The lines $AB$ and $CD$ intersect.
Putting $t=2$ (or $s=1\frac{1}{2}$) gives the point of intersection.
This point is $2\mathbf{i}-3\mathbf{k}+2(3\mathbf{i}+7\mathbf{j}+9\mathbf{k})$, i.e. $8\mathbf{i}+14\mathbf{j}+15\mathbf{k}$.

**10.4\***   Find the distance of the point $\mathbf{i}-4\mathbf{j}+2\mathbf{k}$ from the plane $\mathbf{r}.(2\mathbf{i}+3\mathbf{j}-\mathbf{k})=9$.

A line through $\mathbf{i}-4\mathbf{j}+2\mathbf{k}$ perpendicular to the plane has equation
$\mathbf{r}=\mathbf{i}-4\mathbf{j}+2\mathbf{k}+t(2\mathbf{i}+3\mathbf{j}-\mathbf{k})$

This meets the plane where $(\mathbf{i}-4\mathbf{j}+2\mathbf{k}+t(2\mathbf{i}+3\mathbf{j}-\mathbf{k})).(2\mathbf{i}+3\mathbf{j}-\mathbf{k})=9$

$\therefore \quad 2-12-2+t(4+9+1)=9$

$\therefore \quad t=1\frac{1}{2}$

The point of intersection is $\mathbf{i}-4\mathbf{j}+2\mathbf{k}+1\frac{1}{2}(2\mathbf{i}+3\mathbf{j}-\mathbf{k})$, i.e. $4\mathbf{i}+\frac{1}{2}\mathbf{j}+\frac{1}{2}\mathbf{k}$. The distance between the points $\mathbf{i}-4\mathbf{j}+2\mathbf{k}$ and $4\mathbf{i}+\frac{1}{2}\mathbf{j}+\frac{1}{2}\mathbf{k}$ is $\sqrt{3^2+4\frac{1}{2}^2+1\frac{1}{2}^2}=\dfrac{3\sqrt{14}}{2}$. This is the distance of the point from the plane.


## Exercise 10.1

### Vectors in two dimensions

1. Points $A$, $B$, $C$ have position vectors $\mathbf{i}+3\mathbf{j}$, $9\mathbf{i}+15\mathbf{j}$, $5\mathbf{i}+7\mathbf{j}$ respectively. Find the length of the line joining $A$ to the mid-point of $BC$.

2. Find the position vectors of the two points of trisection of the line joining the points with position vectors $-\mathbf{i}+3\mathbf{j}$, $8\mathbf{i}-9\mathbf{j}$.

3. Show that the points with position vectors $3\mathbf{i}+2\mathbf{j}$, $5\mathbf{i}+6\mathbf{j}$, $4\mathbf{i}-4\mathbf{j}$, $2\mathbf{i}-8\mathbf{j}$ are the vertices of a parallelogram.

4. If $\mathbf{a}=12\mathbf{i}-5\mathbf{j}$ and $\mathbf{b}=3\mathbf{i}+4\mathbf{j}$ find the cosine of the angle between $\mathbf{a}$ and $\mathbf{b}$.

5.  If $A$, $B$, $C$ have position vectors $-\mathbf{i}+2\mathbf{j}$, $\mathbf{i}+3\mathbf{j}$, $3\mathbf{i}-\mathbf{j}$ respectively, show that $AB$ is perpendicular to $BC$.

6.  Show that the three points with position vectors $13\mathbf{i}-2\mathbf{j}$, $22\mathbf{i}+\mathbf{j}$, $10\mathbf{i}-3\mathbf{j}$ are collinear.

7.  Find an equation of the line joining the points with position vectors $4\mathbf{i}-\mathbf{j}$, $\mathbf{i}+3\mathbf{j}$.

8.  Find the point of intersection of the lines $\mathbf{r}=-2\mathbf{i}+\mathbf{j}+s(\mathbf{i}+2\mathbf{j})$ and $\mathbf{r}=3\mathbf{i}+4\mathbf{j}+t(2\mathbf{i}-3\mathbf{j})$.

9.  A line is drawn through the point with position vector $3\mathbf{i}+\mathbf{j}$ parallel to the vector $\mathbf{i}-\mathbf{j}$. Find the position vector of the point in which this line meets the line with equation $\mathbf{r}=-2\mathbf{i}+3\mathbf{j}+t(5\mathbf{i}+\mathbf{j})$.

10. The square of the distance of the point $P$ with position vector $x\mathbf{i}+y\mathbf{j}$ from the point with position vector $2\mathbf{i}+\mathbf{j}$ is twice the square of its distance from the point with position vector $6\mathbf{i}-2\mathbf{j}$. Show that the locus of $P$ is a circle whose centre is the point with position vector $10\mathbf{i}-5\mathbf{j}$ and find the radius of this circle.

## Exercise 10.2

1.  The vectors $\mathbf{a}$, $\mathbf{b}$, $\mathbf{c}$ have components $(2,-1,0)$, $(-3,1,-1)$, $(0,-1,3)$ respectively. Find the components of  1  $3\mathbf{a}+2\mathbf{b}-\mathbf{c}$  2  $4\mathbf{a}+\mathbf{b}$.

2.  Show that the three points represented by vectors with components $(1,-5,9)$, $(3,-9,7)$, $(-3,3,13)$ are collinear.

3.  The vertices $A$, $B$, $C$ of a triangle $ABC$ have position vectors $(7,-7,3)$, $(7,-23,-2)$, $(4,-2,10)$ respectively. $H$ is the point dividing $BC$ internally so that $BH=2HC$. Show that $AH$ is perpendicular to $BC$.

4.  $O$ is the origin and $A$, $B$, $C$ have position vectors $\mathbf{j}+2\mathbf{k}$, $3\mathbf{i}-2\mathbf{j}+\mathbf{k}$, $4\mathbf{i}+3\mathbf{j}+3\mathbf{k}$ respectively. Find the magnitude of the vectors $\overrightarrow{OA}$, $\overrightarrow{OB}$, $\overrightarrow{OC}$, $\overrightarrow{AB}$, $\overrightarrow{BC}$.

5.  Show that the points with position vectors $\mathbf{i}+2\mathbf{j}+2\mathbf{k}$, $3\mathbf{i}+6\mathbf{j}+5\mathbf{k}$, $\mathbf{i}+2\mathbf{j}$ and $-\mathbf{i}-2\mathbf{j}-3\mathbf{k}$ are the vertices of a parallelogram.

6.  If $\mathbf{a}=2\mathbf{i}+2\mathbf{j}-\mathbf{k}$, $\mathbf{b}=2\mathbf{i}+9\mathbf{j}+6\mathbf{k}$ and $\mathbf{c}=3\mathbf{i}-2\mathbf{j}+2\mathbf{k}$, show that $\mathbf{c}$ is perpendicular to both $\mathbf{a}$ and $\mathbf{b}$, and find the cosine of the angle between $\mathbf{a}$ and $\mathbf{b}$.

7.  Show that $\frac{2}{3}\mathbf{i}+\frac{1}{3}\mathbf{j}-\frac{2}{3}\mathbf{k}$ is a unit vector perpendicular to $\mathbf{i}+6\mathbf{j}+4\mathbf{k}$ and $2\mathbf{i}+2\mathbf{j}+3\mathbf{k}$.

8.  Find an equation of the line through the points with position vectors $2\mathbf{i}-3\mathbf{j}+\mathbf{k}$ and $\mathbf{j}+2\mathbf{k}$.

9.  Find whether the straight line through the points with position vectors $\mathbf{j}-3\mathbf{k}$ and $3\mathbf{i}+2\mathbf{j}-\mathbf{k}$ meets the straight line through the points with position vectors $2\mathbf{i}-3\mathbf{j}-5\mathbf{k}$ and $-5\mathbf{i}+4\mathbf{j}-3\mathbf{k}$.

10. Find the point of intersection of the lines $\mathbf{r}=(0,1,-2)+s(2,0,1)$ and $\mathbf{r}=(2,2,2)+t(-2,1,2)$. Find also the cosine of the acute angle between the lines.

11. Show that the sphere on points with position vectors $3\mathbf{i}-\mathbf{j}+3\mathbf{k}$ and $2\mathbf{i}+3\mathbf{j}-\mathbf{k}$ as diameter passes through the origin.

12. Find the resolved part of the vector $(2, -3, 4)$ in the direction of the vector $(2, 2, 1)$.

13. Find the unit vector in the direction $\overrightarrow{AB}$ where $A$ has position vector $2\mathbf{i} + 3\mathbf{j} - 2\mathbf{k}$ and $B$ has the position vector $4\mathbf{i} - 3\mathbf{j} + 7\mathbf{k}$.

## Exercise 10.3

1. In triangle $ABC$ the position vectors of $A$, $B$, $C$ are $\mathbf{a}$, $\mathbf{b}$, $\mathbf{c}$ respectively. $P$ is a point on $BC$ such that $BP = \frac{1}{3}PC$ and $Q$ is a point on $AC$ such that $AQ = \frac{5}{3}QC$. $AB$ produced and $QP$ produced meet at $R$. Show that $QP = \frac{3}{2}PR$ and $AR = 5BR$.

2. $\mathbf{a}$, $\mathbf{b}$, $\mathbf{c}$ are the position vectors of $A$, $B$, $C$ respectively. What is the position vector of $D$ where $ABCD$ is a parallelogram?

3. Show that the lines $\mathbf{r} = 2\mathbf{i} + s(-8\mathbf{i} - 6\mathbf{j} + 6\mathbf{k})$ and $\mathbf{r} = -2\mathbf{i} + 3\mathbf{j} + 9\mathbf{k} + t(4\mathbf{i} + 9\mathbf{j} + 3\mathbf{k})$ intersect, and find the point of intersection.

4. If $\overrightarrow{OA} = 2\mathbf{i} + 3\mathbf{j} + 4\mathbf{k}$, $\overrightarrow{OB} = 4\mathbf{i} + 9\mathbf{j} + \mathbf{k}$, $\overrightarrow{OC} = 10\mathbf{i} + 6\mathbf{j} - \mathbf{k}$, show that triangle $ABC$ is isosceles and right-angled.

5. Find the position vector of the point of intersection of the lines with equations $\mathbf{r} = \mathbf{a} + t(2\mathbf{a} + \mathbf{b})$, $\mathbf{r} = 2\mathbf{b} + s(\mathbf{a} - \mathbf{b})$.

6. In triangle $ABC$ the position vectors of $A$, $B$, $C$ are $\mathbf{a}$, $\mathbf{b}$, $\mathbf{c}$ respectively. If $D$ lies on $BC$ such that $BD:DC = 1:2$ and $E$ lies on $CA$ such that $CE:EA = 3:2$, find the position vectors of $D$ and $E$. $F$ is the point on $AD$ such that $AF:FD = 2:1$. Show that $F$ lies on $BE$ and find the ratio $BF:FE$.

7. $A$, $B$, $C$, $D$ have position vectors $(-2, -7, 1)$, $(-4, -7, 3)$, $(-3, -3, 4)$, $(-5, -2, 2)$ respectively. Show that $AB$ and $CD$ are skew lines. Show also that $DC$ is perpendicular to $CA$ and $CB$. If $BCDE$ is a rectangle, find the position vector of $E$.

8. Find the cosine of angle $ABC$ where the position vectors of $A$, $B$, $C$ are $(-3, 7, 7)$, $(-1, 0, 2)$, $(-3, 1, 1)$ respectively.

9. If the vectors $a\mathbf{i} - 7\mathbf{j} + 5\mathbf{k}$ and $2\mathbf{i} + \mathbf{j} + a\mathbf{k}$ are perpendicular, find the value of $a$, and with this value of $a$, show that the vector $-4\mathbf{i} + 3\mathbf{j} + 5\mathbf{k}$ is perpendicular to both these vectors.

10. Show that the lines $\mathbf{r} = (4, -8, -3) + t(4, 2, 1)$ and $\mathbf{r} = (14, 4, -4) + s(1, -3, 2)$ intersect at right angles and find the position vector of the point of intersection.

## *Exercise 10.4

### Planes

1. Show that the line $\mathbf{r} = (1, 4, -2) + t(2, 1, 2)$ is parallel to the plane $\mathbf{r} \cdot (2, 2, -3) = 4$.

2. Show that the line $\mathbf{r} = (1, -2, 5) + t(2, -2, 4)$ is at right-angles to the plane $\mathbf{r} \cdot (1, -1, 2) = 7$ and find the perpendicular distance from the point $(1, -2, 5)$ to the plane.

3. Show that the planes $\mathbf{r} \cdot (2\mathbf{i} + \mathbf{j} - 3\mathbf{k}) = 1$, $\mathbf{r} \cdot (2\mathbf{i} - \mathbf{j} + \mathbf{k}) = 1$ are perpendicular.

4. Show that the planes $\mathbf{r} . (2\mathbf{i} - 3\mathbf{j} + \mathbf{k}) = 6$, $\mathbf{r} . (4\mathbf{i} - 6\mathbf{j} + 2\mathbf{k}) = 1$ are parallel.

5. Find an equation for the line joining points with position vectors $(2, -1, 1)$ and $(-3, 1, 0)$. Find the position vector of the point where this line meets the plane $\mathbf{r} . (1, 2, 1) = 3$.

6. Write down an equation for the line through the point $(1, 6, 8)$ which is perpendicular to the plane $\mathbf{r} . (-1, 2, -1) = 5$, and find where this line meets the plane. Hence find the perpendicular distance from the point $(1, 6, 8)$ to this plane.

7. $A$ and $B$ have position vectors $(1, -2, 5)$ and $(3, 5, 0)$ respectively. Find the point $C$ where the line $AB$ meets the plane $\mathbf{r} . (-3, 4, -2) = 3$.

8. Show that the line $AB$, where $A$ has position vector $(1, -10, -2)$ and $B$ has position vector $(3, -3, 4)$, is parallel to the plane $\mathbf{r} . (2, 2, -3) = 5$. If $C$ is the point $(a, -1, 1)$ and $C$ lies on this plane, find the value of $a$. Show that $CB$ is perpendicular to the plane, and hence find the distance between the line $AB$ and the plane.

118

# 11 Integration (Applications)

**The definite integral as the limit of a sum**

$$\underset{\delta x \to 0}{\text{limit}} \sum_{x=a}^{x=b} y\delta x = \int_a^b y\,dx$$

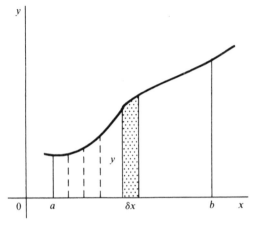

**To find the equation of a curve** from its gradient function.

**To Find the Area 'under a curve'** i.e. the area between the curve and the $x$-axis.

$$\text{Area} = \int_a^b y\,dx$$

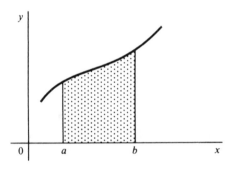

(If the area is below the $x$-axis, the answer will be negative. If the area is partly above and partly below the $x$-axis, consider each part separately.)

To find the area between the curve and the $y$-axis,

$$\text{area} = \int_{y=p}^{y=q} x\,dy$$

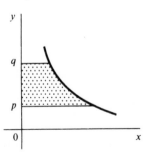

**To find the volume of revolution** when a curve is rotated about the $x$-axis.

$$\text{Volume} = \pi \int_a^b y^2 \, dx$$

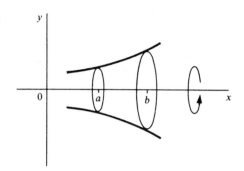

The volume of revolution when a curve is rotated about the $y$-axis is

$$\pi \int_{y=p}^{y=q} x^2 \, dy$$

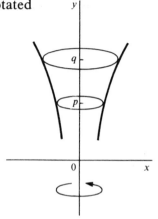

**\* To find the mean value of $y$**

$$\text{Mean value of } y = \frac{1}{b-a} \int_a^b y \, dx$$

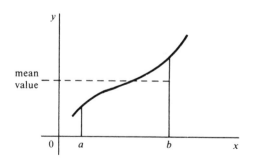

Other mean values can be found, e.g. the mean value of $xy$ (with respect to $x$) is

$$\frac{1}{b-a} \int_a^b xy \, dx$$

Topics marked \* are not included in the national common core and may not be needed for your syllabus.

**Examples**

**11.1** If $\dfrac{dy}{dx} = x^3 - \sin 2x$ and if $y = 1$ when $x = 0$, find the value of $y$ when $x = \dfrac{\pi}{2}$.

$$y = \frac{x^4}{4} + \frac{\cos 2x}{2} + c$$

When $x = 0$, $y = 1$, so $1 = \tfrac{1}{2} + c$, $c = \tfrac{1}{2}$

$$y = \frac{x^4}{4} + \frac{\cos 2x}{2} + \tfrac{1}{2}$$

When $x = \dfrac{\pi}{2}$, $y = \dfrac{\pi^4}{64} - \tfrac{1}{2} + \tfrac{1}{2} = \dfrac{\pi^4}{64}$.

**11.2** Find the area of the region enclosed by the curve $y = e^{-x}$, the axes and the line $x = 2$.

If this region is rotated through 1 revolution about the $x$-axis find the volume of the solid of revolution generated.

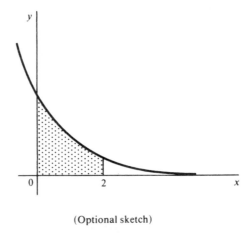

$$\text{Area} = \int_0^2 y \, dx$$

$$= \int_0^2 e^{-x} \, dx$$

$$= [-e^{-x}]_0^2$$

$$= -e^{-2} - (-1)$$

$$= 1 - e^{-2}$$

$$\text{Volume} = \pi \int_0^2 y^2 \, dx = \pi \int_0^2 e^{-2x} \, dx$$

$$= \pi \left[ -\frac{e^{-2x}}{2} \right]_0^2 = \pi \left\{ -\frac{e^{-4}}{2} - (-\tfrac{1}{2}) \right\}$$

$$= \frac{\pi}{2}(1 - e^{-4})$$

(Optional sketch)

**11.3** The area enclosed by the curve defined by the parametric equations $x = 2t^2$, $y = t^3$, the $y$-axis and the line $y = 8$ is completely rotated about the $y$-axis. Find the volume of the solid generated.

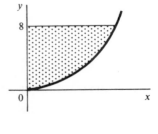

$$\text{Volume} = \pi \int_0^8 x^2 \, dy$$

$$= \pi \int_0^2 4t^4 \cdot 3t^2 \, dt$$

$$= \pi \left[ 12 \cdot \frac{t^7}{7} \right]_0^2$$

$$= \frac{1536\pi}{7}$$

$y = t^3$

$\dfrac{dy}{dt} = 3t^2$

$\int dy = \int 3t^2 \, dt$

when $y = 0$, $t = 0$
when $y = 8$, $t = 2$

**11.4*** If $y = \sqrt{10-x}$, find the mean value of $1 \quad y \quad 2 \quad y^2$ for $x = 1$ to 6.

Mean value of $y = \dfrac{1}{b-a} \displaystyle\int_a^b y \, dx$

$= \dfrac{1}{6-1} \displaystyle\int_1^6 \sqrt{10-x} \, dx$

$= \left[ -\tfrac{1}{5} \cdot \dfrac{2(10-x)^{\frac{3}{2}}}{3} \right]_1^6$

$= -\tfrac{16}{15} - (-\tfrac{54}{15}) = 2\tfrac{8}{15}$

Mean value of $y^2 = \dfrac{1}{b-a} \displaystyle\int_a^b y^2 \, dx$

$= \dfrac{1}{6-1} \displaystyle\int_1^6 (10-x) \, dx$

$= \left[ \dfrac{1}{5} \left( 10x - \dfrac{x^2}{2} \right) \right]_1^6$

$= \tfrac{42}{5} - \tfrac{19}{10} = 6\tfrac{1}{2}$

## Exercise 11.1

1.  If the gradient of a curve is given by $\dfrac{dy}{dx} = \dfrac{1}{\sqrt{x+3}}$ and if the curve passes through the point $(6, 3)$, find its equation.

2.  If $\dfrac{dy}{dx} = 1 + \sec^2 x$ and if $y = 2$ when $x = 0$, find the value of $y$ when $x = \pi/4$.

3.  If the gradient of a curve at any point $(x, y)$ is $\ln x$, and the point $(1, 4)$ lies on the curve, find the $y$-coordinate at the point on the curve where $x = 2$.

4.  Find the area enclosed between the curve $y = \dfrac{4}{x^2 - 4}$, the $x$-axis and the lines $x = 4$ and $x = 7$.

5.  Find the area between the curve $y = \dfrac{1}{\sqrt{1 - x^2}}$, the axes and the line $x = \tfrac{1}{2}$.

6.  Sketch the curve $y = \dfrac{x}{4 - x}$. Find the area enclosed by the curve, the $x$-axis and the line $x = 1$.

7.  Find the area in the first quadrant bounded by the $x$-axis, the line $x = 9a$ and the arc of the parabola defined by parametric equations $x = at^2$, $y = 2at$.
    This area is completely rotated about the line $y = -a$. Show that the volume of the solid of resolution generated is $\pi \displaystyle\int_0^{9a} (y+a)^2 \, dx - 9\pi a^3$ and find this volume.

8.   The area between the curve $y = x + \dfrac{3}{x}$, the $x$-axis and the lines $x = 1$ and $x = 3$ is rotated through a complete revolution about the $x$-axis. Find the volume generated.

9.   A hollow vase 20 cm high is such that any horizontal cross-section is circular. The radius at a height of $x$ cm above the base is $2e^{x/20}$ cm. Find the volume of water the vase will hold.

10.*  Find the mean value of $\cos^2 x + \sin 2x$ from $x = 0$ to $x = \pi/2$.

## Exercise 11.2

1.   Find the area of the region enclosed between the curves $y = x^2$ and $y = 3x - x^2$.

2.   Find the area enclosed between the curve $y = \sin^3 x$, the $x$-axis and the lines $x = \pi/3$ and $x = \pi/2$.

3.   Find the area of the region enclosed between the curve $y = (x - 2)(6 - x)$ and the $x$-axis. Show that the line $y = x - 2$ divides this area in the ratio $27 : 37$.

4.   The region in the first quadrant between the curve $y^2 = x$ and the circle $x^2 + y^2 = 2x$ is rotated through 1 revolution about the $x$-axis. Find the volume generated.

5.   If the gradient of a curve is given by $\dfrac{dy}{dx} = \dfrac{1}{9 + x^2}$, and $y = \pi/2$ when $x = \sqrt{3}$, find the value of $y$ when $x = 3\sqrt{3}$.

6.   The tangents to the curve $y = \sin x$ at the origin $O$ and at $A$, where $x = \pi/2$, meet at $B$. Find the coordinates of $B$ and show that the arc $OA$ cuts the area of triangle $OAB$ in the ratio $2(\pi - 3) : 4 - \pi$.

7.   The region of the ellipse defined by the parametric equations $x = 3 \cos t$, $y = 2 \sin t$, which lies in the first quadrant is rotated completely about the $x$-axis. Find the volume of the solid generated. Find also the volume of the solid generated if the same region is rotated completely about the $y$-axis.

8.   Find the area of the region between the curve $y = x\,e^x$, the $x$-axis and the line $x = 2$. Also find the volume of revolution if this area is rotated completely about the $x$-axis.

9.*  If $y = \sqrt{4 - x}$, find the mean value of $xy$ for $x = 0$ to 3.

10.*  If $y = \dfrac{x}{1 + x}$, find the mean value of $y^2$ between $x = 1$ and $x = 3$.

## *  Approximate Integration

### Trapezium rule

$$\int_{x_0}^{x_n} f(x)\,dx \approx \tfrac{1}{2}h[f_0 + 2(f_1 + f_2 + \ldots + f_{n-1}) + f_n]$$

There can be any number of strips.

**Simpson's rule**

$$\int_{x_0}^{x_n} f(x)\, dx \approx \tfrac{1}{3}h[f_0 + f_n + 4(f_1 + f_3 + \ldots + f_{n-1}) + 2(f_2 + f_4 + \ldots + f_{n-2})]$$

$n$ must be even, giving an even number of strips, i.e. an odd number of ordinates.

**For both rules:**

$f_r = f(x_r)$

$x_r = x_0 + rh$

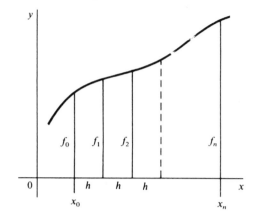

**Example 11.5**

Find the approximate value of $\int_0^{\pi/2} \sqrt{\cos x}\, dx$, by using **1** the trapezium rule,
**2** Simpson's rule, and using 6 strips.

It is sensible to set down the calculations in a table.

With 6 strips, i.e. 7 ordinates, $h = \tfrac{1}{6}$ of $\left(\dfrac{\pi}{2} - 0\right) = \dfrac{\pi}{12}$

| $x$ | $\cos x$ | $\sqrt{\cos x}$ | For $T.R$ | For $S.R$ |
|---|---|---|---|---|
| $0$ | $1.0$ | $1.0$ | $f_0 = 1.0$ | $f_0 = 1.0$ |
| $\dfrac{\pi}{12}$ | $0.9659$ | $0.9828$ | $2f_1 = 1.9656$ | $4f_1 = 3.9312$ |
| $\dfrac{\pi}{6}$ | $0.8660$ | $0.9306$ | $2f_2 = 1.8612$ | $2f_2 = 1.8612$ |
| $\dfrac{\pi}{4}$ | $0.7071$ | $0.8409$ | $2f_3 = 1.6818$ | $4f_3 = 3.3636$ |
| $\dfrac{\pi}{3}$ | $0.5$ | $0.7071$ | $2f_4 = 1.4142$ | $2f_4 = 1.4142$ |
| $\dfrac{5\pi}{12}$ | $0.2588$ | $0.5087$ | $2f_5 = 1.0174$ | $4f_5 = 2.0348$ |
| $\dfrac{\pi}{2}$ | $0$ | $0$ | $f_6 = 0$ | $f_6 = 0$ |
| | | | $\overline{8.9402}$ | $\overline{13.6050}$ |

For the trapezium rule:

$$\int_0^{\pi/2} \sqrt{\cos x}\; dx$$

$$\approx \tfrac{1}{2}h[f_0 + 2(f_1 + f_2 + f_3 + f_4 + f_5) + f_6]$$

$$= \frac{\pi}{24} \times 8.9402$$

$$= 1.17 \text{ (to 3 significant figures)}$$

For Simpson's rule:

$$\int_0^{\pi/2} \sqrt{\cos x}\; dx$$

$$\approx \tfrac{1}{3}h[f_0 + f_6 + 4(f_1 + f_3 + f_5) + 2(f_2 + f_4)]$$

$$= \frac{\pi}{36} \times 13.6050$$

$$= 1.19 \text{ (to 3 significant figures)}$$

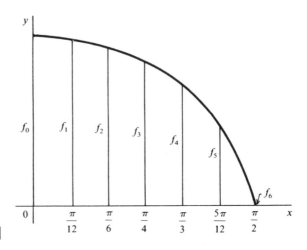

## * Exercise 11.3

(*Where appropriate, work in decimals and give final answers correct to 3 significant figures.*)

Find approximate values for these integrals using the trapezium rule.

1. $\displaystyle\int_{\pi/6}^{\pi/2} \operatorname{cosec} x\; dx$            Use 5 ordinates, 4 strips

2. $\displaystyle\int_0^3 3^x\; dx$            Use 7 ordinates, 6 strips

3. $\displaystyle\int_4^7 \frac{1}{x-1}\; dx$            Use 4 ordinates, 3 strips

4. $\displaystyle\int_5^{10} \log_{10} x\; dx$            Use 6 ordinates, 5 strips

5. $\displaystyle\int_{\frac{1}{3}}^{\frac{2}{3}} \sqrt{1-x}\; dx$            Use 3 ordinates, 2 strips

Find approximate values for these integrals using Simpson's rule.

6. $\displaystyle\int_1^9 \ln x\; dx$            Use 9 ordinates, 8 strips

7. $\displaystyle\int_0^{\pi/3} \sqrt{\tan x}\; dx$            Use 5 ordinates, 4 strips

8. $\displaystyle\int_1^3 x^{x-1}\; dx$            Use 3 ordinates, 2 strips

9. $\displaystyle\int_{\pi/6}^{\pi/2} \sin^2 x \, dx$        Use 5 ordinates, 4 strips

10. $\displaystyle\int_{0}^{6} \frac{1}{\sqrt{40-x^2}} \, dx$        Use 7 ordinates, 6 strips

11. Find the approximate value of $\displaystyle\int_{0}^{4} \frac{1}{1+x^2} \, dx$ using

    1  the trapezium rule with 5 ordinates,
    2  Simpson's rule with 5 ordinates.
    Find the exact value by integration and hence find the % error using each of the two rules.

12. Find the approximate value of $\displaystyle\int_{\frac{1}{2}}^{4} \frac{1}{x} \, dx$ using the trapezium rule with 8 ordinates.

    Find the exact value by integration and hence find an approximation for ln 2.

13. Find the approximate value of $\displaystyle\int_{0}^{\pi/3} \sec^2 x \, dx$ using Simpson's rule with 5 ordinates.

    Find the exact value by integration, and hence find the % error using Simpson's rule.

14. In the diagram, find an expression for the total area of trapeziums *ABED* and *BCFE*.
By extending the diagram, verify the formula for the trapezium rule.

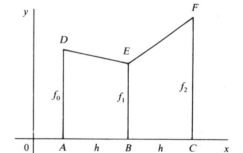

15. Find by integration an expression for the area between the arc of the parabola $f(x) = ax^2 + bx + c$, the $x$-axis and the lines $x = -h$, $x = h$.
Show that this can be written as $\frac{1}{3}h(f_0 + 4f_1 + f_2)$ where $f_0 = f(-h)$, $f_1 = f(0)$, $f_2 = f(h)$.

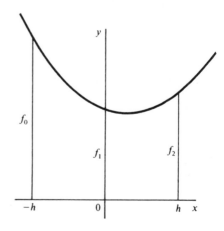

16. Assuming that the arc $DEF$ is approximately that of a parabola, so that the area between the arc $DEF$, the $x$-axis and the ordinates $AD$ and $CF$ is approximately $\frac{1}{3}h(f_0+4f_1+f_2)$, and extending the diagram, verify the formula for Simpson's rule.

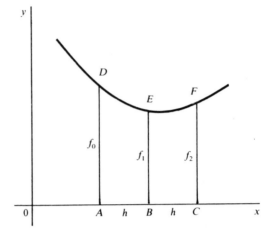

# 12* Complex Numbers

† A complex number has the form $x+iy$, where $x$ and $y$ are real and $i = \sqrt{-1}$.

The complex number $x+iy$ is zero if and only if $x = y = 0$.

**Complex conjugate numbers**
The complex numbers $x+iy$ and $x-iy$ are called conjugate numbers.
If $z = x+iy$ then $x-iy$ can be written as $z^*$.

$$zz^* = x^2 + y^2$$

**Sum, product, quotient**
If $z_1 = x_1 + iy_1$ and $z_2 = x_2 + iy_2$ then

$$z_1 + z_2 = x_1 + x_2 + i(y_1 + y_2)$$

$$z_1 z_2 = (x_1 + iy_1)(x_2 + iy_2) = x_1 x_2 - y_1 y_2 + i(y_1 x_2 + x_1 y_2)$$

$$\frac{z_1}{z_2} = \frac{x_1 + iy_1}{x_2 + iy_2}\left(\times\frac{x_2 - iy_2}{x_2 - iy_2}\right) = \frac{x_1 x_2 + y_1 y_2 + i(y_1 x_2 - x_1 y_2)}{x_2^2 + y_2^2}$$

**Equality**
$z_1 = z_2$ if and only if $x_1 = x_2$ and $y_1 = y_2$.

**Argand diagram**
The point $P$ (or the vector $\overrightarrow{OP}$) represents the complex number $z = x+iy$.

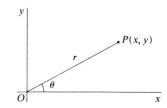

**The trigonometric form** of the complex number $z$ is $r(\cos\theta + i\sin\theta)$ where $x = r\cos\theta$, $y = r\sin\theta$.

**The modulus** of $z$, written $|z|$, is length $OP$

$$|z| = r = \sqrt{x^2 + y^2} \quad (|z| \text{ is always positive})$$

**The argument** (or amplitude) of $z$, written $\arg z$, is angle $\theta$

$\arg z = \theta$, where $\tan\theta = \dfrac{y}{x}$ and $-\pi < \theta \leqslant \pi$

Note the signs of $x$ and $y$ when determining $\theta$, to determine its quadrant.

Topics marked * are not included in the national common core and may not be needed for your syllabus.
† j can be used for $\sqrt{-1}$ instead of i.

## Product and quotient

If $z_1 = r_1(\cos\theta_1 + i\sin\theta_1)$ and $z_2 = r_2(\cos\theta_2 + i\sin\theta_2)$

$z_1 z_2 = r_1 r_2[\cos(\theta_1 + \theta_2) + i\sin(\theta_1 + \theta_2)]$

Modulus of $z_1 z_2 = r_1 r_2$

i.e. the modulus of the product $z_1 z_2 =$ the product of the moduli of $z_1$ and $z_2$

$|z_1 z_2| = |z_1||z_2|$

Argument of $z_1 z_2 = \theta_1 + \theta_2$

i.e. the argument of the product $z_1 z_2 =$ the **sum** of the arguments of $z_1$ and $z_2$

$\arg(z_1 z_2) = \arg z_1 + \arg z_2$

$$\frac{z_1}{z_2} = \frac{r_1}{r_2}[\cos(\theta_1 - \theta_2) + i\sin(\theta_1 - \theta_2)]$$

Modulus of $\dfrac{z_1}{z_2} = \dfrac{r_1}{r_2}$

i.e. the modulus of the quotient $\dfrac{z_1}{z_2} =$ the quotient of the moduli of $z_1$ and $z_2$

$$\left|\frac{z_1}{z_2}\right| = \frac{|z_1|}{|z_2|}$$

Argument of $\dfrac{z_1}{z_2} = \theta_1 - \theta_2$

i.e. the argument of the quotient $\dfrac{z_1}{z_2} =$ the **difference** of the arguments of $z_1$ and $z_2$

$$\arg\!\left(\frac{z_1}{z_2}\right) = \arg z_1 - \arg z_2$$

(Keep the arguments of products and quotients in the range $-\pi < \theta \leqslant \pi$ by adding or subtracting $2\pi$ if necessary.)

## Geometrical representation of addition and subtraction

**Addition** $z_1 + z_2$                                **Subtraction** $z_1 - z_2$

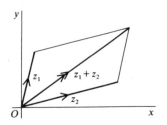                                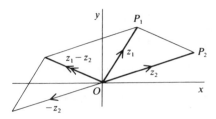

Note that $|z_1 - z_2| =$ length $P_2 P_1$

$\arg(z_1 - z_2) =$ the angle between $\overrightarrow{Ox}$ and $\overrightarrow{P_2 P_1}$

## Loci

If the variable number $z$ is such that $|z - z_1| = k$, where $k$ is a real positive constant, then the locus of $z$ is a circle, centre $z_1$, radius $k$. (If $|z - z_1| \leqslant k$ then the locus includes the region inside the circle.)

If the variable number $z$ is such that $|z - z_1| = |z - z_2|$, then the locus of $z$ is the perpendicular bisector of the line joining $z_1$ and $z_2$.

If the variable number $z$ is such that $\arg z = \alpha$, then the locus of $z$ is a line from the origin (but not including the origin) making an angle $\alpha$ with $\overrightarrow{Ox}$.

If the variable number $z$ is such that $\arg(z - z_1) = \alpha$, then the locus of $z$ is a line from $z_1$ (but not including $z_1$) making an angle $\alpha$ with $\overrightarrow{Ox}$.

## Examples

**12.1**  If $z_1 = 2 - 3i$ and $z_2 = 3 + 4i$ then:

$z_1 + z_2 = 2 - 3i + 3 + 4i = 5 + i$

$z_1 - z_2 = 2 - 3i - (3 + 4i) = -1 - 7i$

$$z_1 z_2 = (2 - 3i)(3 + 4i) = 6 - 9i + 8i - 12i^2$$
$$= 6 - i + 12 \quad (\text{since } i^2 = -1)$$
$$= 18 - i$$

$$\frac{z_1}{z_2} = \frac{2 - 3i}{3 + 4i}$$

$$= \frac{2 - 3i}{3 + 4i} \times \frac{3 - 4i}{3 - 4i}$$

$$= \frac{6 - 9i - 8i + 12i^2}{9 - 16i^2} = \frac{-6 - 17i}{25}$$

**12.2**  If $z = x + iy$ and $z^2 = 15 + 8i$, and $x$ and $y$ are real and positive, find the values of $x$ and $y$.

$(x + iy)^2 = 15 + 8i$

$x^2 - y^2 + 2xyi = 15 + 8i$

$\therefore \quad x^2 - y^2 = 15$ and $2xy = 8$

$x^2 - \dfrac{16}{x^2} = 15$

$x^4 - 15x^2 - 16 = 0$

$(x^2 + 1)(x^2 - 16) = 0$

$\therefore \quad x = 4$ (since $x$ is real and positive)

$y = 1$

$\therefore \quad z = 4 + i$

**12.3**    Solve the equation $z^2 - z + 1 = 0$

Using the formula $z = \dfrac{-b \pm \sqrt{b^2 - 4ac}}{2a}$

$$z = \frac{1 \pm \sqrt{1-4}}{2} = \frac{1 \pm \sqrt{3}i}{2}$$

**12.4**    Solve the equation $z^2 + 10z + 29 = 0$

$(z+5)^2 = -4$

$\qquad z + 5 = \pm 2i$

$\qquad\quad z = -5 \pm 2i$

**12.5**    If $z_1 = 2 - i$, $z_2 = 3 + 2i$, mark on Argand diagrams the points representing $z_1$, $z_2$, $z_1 + z_2$, $z_1 - z_2$.

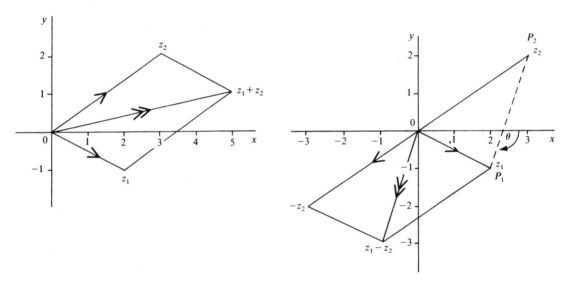

Note also that length $P_2P_1$ represents $|z_1 - z_2|$ and $\theta$ represents $\arg(z_1 - z_2)$

**12.6**    If $z_1 = 3 + 4i$ and $z_2 = 2 - i$ find $|z_1|$, $|z_2|$, $|z_1 z_2|$, $\left|\dfrac{z_1}{z_2}\right|$.

$|z_1| = \sqrt{3^2 + 4^2} = 5$

$|z_2| = \sqrt{2^2 + (-1)^2} = \sqrt{5}$

$|z_1 z_2| = |z_1| \cdot |z_2| = 5\sqrt{5}$

$\left|\dfrac{z_1}{z_2}\right| = \dfrac{|z_1|}{|z_2|} = \dfrac{5}{\sqrt{5}} = \sqrt{5}$

**12.7**    If $z_1 = 3\sqrt{2} + 3\sqrt{2}i$ and $z_2 = 2\sqrt{3} - 2i$, find arg $z_1$, arg $z_2$, arg $z_1 z_2$, arg $\dfrac{z_1}{z_2}$.

$\tan \theta_1 = \dfrac{3\sqrt{2}}{3\sqrt{2}} = 1$, $\theta_1$ is in the first quadrant, arg $z_1 = \dfrac{\pi}{4}$

$\tan \theta_2 = \dfrac{-2}{2\sqrt{3}} = -\dfrac{1}{\sqrt{3}}$, $\theta_2$ is in the fourth quadrant, arg $z_2 = -\dfrac{\pi}{6}$

$\arg(z_1 z_2) = \theta_1 + \theta_2 = \dfrac{\pi}{4} + \left(-\dfrac{\pi}{6}\right) = \dfrac{\pi}{12}$

$\arg \dfrac{z_1}{z_2} = \theta_1 - \theta_2 = \dfrac{\pi}{4} - \left(-\dfrac{\pi}{6}\right) = \dfrac{5\pi}{12}$

**12.8**    Show on sketches the locus of $P$, representing a number $z$ on the Argand diagram if

**1**   $|z - (2 + i)| = 1$,                    **2**   arg $z = -\dfrac{2\pi}{3}$,

**3**   $|z - 1| = |z - 2i|$,                  **4**   $\arg[z - (1 + i)] = \dfrac{\pi}{4}$

**1**   This locus is a circle, centre $(2 + i)$, radius 1.
(The region inside the circle represents $z$ where $|z - (2 + i)| < 1$)

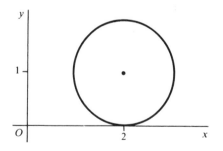

**2**   This locus is a straight line from the origin, making an angle of $-2\pi/3$ with the $x$-axis. (The locus does not include the origin.)

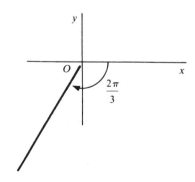

**3** This locus is the perpendicular bisector of the line joining the points 1, 2i.

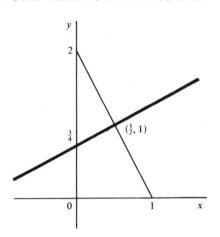

**4** This locus is the straight line from the point $1+i$ making an angle of $\pi/4$ with the $x$-axis. (The locus does not include the point $1+i$.)

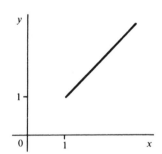

## Exercise 12.1

1. Simplify, expressing in the form $p+iq$,

   **1** $(7+2i)-(5-i)$

   **2** $(2-3i)(4+i)$

   **3** $\dfrac{4-3i}{i}$

   **4** $(1+i)^3$

   **5** $\dfrac{5+i}{1-i}$

2. If $z_1=4+3i$ and $z_2=-1-4i$, find expressions in the form $p+iq$ for:

   **1** $z_1+z_2$

   **2** $z_1-z_2$

   **3** $z_1z_1^*$

   **4** $z_1z_2$

   **5** $\dfrac{z_1}{z_2}$

3. Simplify $(\cos\alpha+i\sin\alpha)^2+(\cos\alpha-i\sin\alpha)^2$. Show that

   $$\frac{\cos\alpha+i\sin\alpha}{\cos\alpha-i\sin\alpha}=\cos2\alpha+i\sin2\alpha.$$

4. Show that $(\cos\alpha+i\sin\alpha)(1+\cos\alpha-i\sin\alpha)=1+\cos\alpha+i\sin\alpha$.

5. If $a = \frac{1}{2} - \frac{\sqrt{3}}{2}i$, show that **1** $a^2 - a + 1 = 0$ **2** $a^3 = -1$.

6. Solve for $z$, $\dfrac{z - 2i}{z + i} = \frac{4}{3}$.

7. Solve these equations, giving the roots in the form $p + iq$, where $p$ and $q$ are real.

 **1** $z^2 + 12z + 40 = 0$      **4** $z^2 + 9 = 0$

 **2** $4z^2 + 4z + 37 = 0$      **5** $z^2 + z + 1 = 0$

 **3** $9z^2 - 12z + 29 = 0$

8. Factorise **1** $x^2 + y^2$ **2** $x^4 - y^4$.

9. If $5 + \sqrt{2}i$ is a root of the equation $z^2 + bz + c = 0$, where $b$ and $c$ are real, what is the other root? Find the values of $b$ and $c$.

10. If $z = x + iy$ and $z^2 = 3 - 4i$, where $x$ and $y$ are real, find the possible values for $z$.

11. If $z = x + iy$, express $\dfrac{1}{2 + z}$ in the form $p + iq$.

12. Find the real numbers $x$ and $y$ if:

 **1** $x + iy = (3 + 5i)^2$

 **2** $x + iy = \dfrac{2 + i}{6 - 8i}$

 **3** $x + iy = \dfrac{1}{3 + 2i}$

13. Show that $z - 1$ is a factor of $z^3 - 7z^2 + 16z - 10$ and hence solve the equation $z^3 - 7z^2 + 16z - 10 = 0$.

Use the factor theorem to find a real root in each of the following equations and hence solve completely.

14. $z^3 + 2z - 12 = 0$

15. $z^3 - 3z^2 + 4z - 12 = 0$

16. $z^3 + z + 2 = 0$

17. $z^3 - 7z^2 + 31z - 25 = 0$

18. Find the values of the real numbers $p$ and $q$ if $z^3 - 3z^2 + pz + q$ is divisible by $z - i$.

19. If $1 + 3i$ is a root of the equation $z^3 + pz + q = 0$, where $p$ and $q$ are real, find the values of $p$ and $q$.

20. Find the values of the real numbers $p$ and $q$ if

$$\frac{p}{3 - i} + \frac{q}{1 + i} = 8i.$$

## Exercise 12.2

1.  Illustrate on an Argand diagram the points representing the numbers $z_1 = 3 + 5i$, $z_2 = 4 - 2i$, $z_1 + z_2$, $z_1 - z_2$, $z_1 - 5$, $z_2 + 3i$.

2.  Illustrate the points representing the numbers $-1$, $\frac{1}{2} + \frac{\sqrt{3}}{2}i$, $\frac{1}{2} - \frac{\sqrt{3}}{2}i$ on an Argand diagram. Show that they lie on the circle $|z| = 1$, and show also that they form the vertices of an equilateral triangle.

3.  Show that the points representing the numbers $-2 + i$, $-1 + 3i$, $1 + 7i$ on the Argand diagram are collinear.

4.  Find the modulus and argument of $z = 1 + i \tan \theta$, where $-\pi/2 < \theta < \pi/2$.

5.  Illustrate the points representing the numbers $z_1 = 2 - i$, $z_2 = 3 + 4i$, $z_1 + z_2$, $z_1 - z_2$, $z_1^*$ on an Argand diagram.

6.  Show that the points representing the numbers $5 + i$, $1 + 7i$, $-2 + 5i$, $2 - i$ on an Argand diagram are the vertices of a rectangle, and find its area.

7.  Express $z_1 = 1 + i$ and $z_2 = \sqrt{3} + i$ in the form $r(\cos \theta + i \sin \theta)$. Hence find the modulus and argument of:

    **1** $\quad z_1 z_2$        **2** $\quad \dfrac{z_2}{z_1}$        **3** $\quad z_1^2$        **4** $\quad \dfrac{z_1^2}{z_2}$.

8.  Find the modulus of

    **1** $\quad (1 + \sqrt{3}i)(3 - 4i)$        **2** $\quad \dfrac{7 - 4i}{1 + 8i}$.

9.  If $z_1 = 1 - i$, $z_2 = 1 + \sqrt{3}i$, find the argument of:

    **1** $\quad z_1 z_2$        **2** $\quad \dfrac{z_1}{z_2}$        **3** $\quad z_2^3$.

10. The points $P$, $Q$ on the Argand diagram represent the numbers $9 + 8i$, $12 - i$. If $O$ is the origin, show that $OP = OQ$.

11. Show on an Argand diagram the points representing the numbers $z_1 = 4 + 3i$, $z_2 = 2 - i$. Adding to your diagram as necessary, mark lines which represent $|z_1|$, $|z_2|$, $|z_1 + z_2|$, $|z_1 - z_2|$ and angles which represent $\arg z_1$, $\arg z_2$, $\arg(z_1 - z_2)$.

12. Find the modulus of $\dfrac{(3 + i)^2}{2 - i}$.

13. Find in its simplest form the argument of $\{\sin \theta + i(1 - \cos \theta)\}^2$, where $\theta$ is an acute angle.

14. If $z_1 = 2\left(\cos \dfrac{2\pi}{3} - i \sin \dfrac{2\pi}{3}\right)$ and $z_2 = 3\left(\cos \dfrac{5\pi}{6} + i \sin \dfrac{5\pi}{6}\right)$, find the modulus and argument of:

    **1** $\quad z_1$    **2** $\quad z_2$    **3** $\quad z_1 z_2$    **4** $\quad \dfrac{z_1}{z_2}$    **5** $\quad z_1^2$.

15. Sketch the locus of points representing the complex number $z$ if:

   **1** $|z| = 3$  **3** $|z - 2i| = 2$

   **2** $|z - 1| = 4$  **4** $|z - 1 - 2i| = \sqrt{5}$.

16. Sketch the locus of points representing the complex number $z$ if:

   **1** $\arg z = \dfrac{\pi}{6}$  **3** $\arg(z - 2) = \dfrac{\pi}{3}$

   **2** $\arg z = -\dfrac{\pi}{4}$  **4** $\arg(z + 3i) = \dfrac{\pi}{4}$.

17. Sketch the locus of points representing the complex number $z$ if:

   **1** $|z + 2| = |z + 2i|$

   **2** $|z - 3| = |z - 1 - 2i|$.

18. Mark the point representing the number $z$ on the Argand diagram such that $|z - 2| = 3$ and $\arg z = \pi/4$.

19. Shade the region on the Argand diagram representing numbers $z$ such that $1 < |z| < 2$ and $\pi/6 < \arg z < \pi/3$.

20. Shade the region on the Argand diagram representing numbers $z$ such that $|z - 1 - i| < 1$ and $0 < \arg z < \theta$ where $\theta$ is acute and $\tan \theta = \frac{1}{2}$.

# D Revision

## Exercise D1

1. Find the term independent of $x$ in the expansion of $\left(2x - \dfrac{1}{4x^2}\right)^9$.

2. The interior angles of an $n$-sided polygon are in arithmetical sequence with the smallest angle $86°$ and the common difference $8°$. Find the number of sides of the polygon. (The sum of the interior angles of an $n$-sided polygon is $180(n-2)°$.)

3. Show that the equation $x^2 - 2(k+1)x - (k-1)^2 = 0$ cannot have equal roots for any real value of $k$.

4. Sketch the graphs of $\mathbf{1}$ $y = x^3$ $\mathbf{2}$ $y^2 = x^3$.

5. Express $5\sin\theta - 12\cos\theta$ in the form $R\sin(\theta - \alpha)$. Solve the equation $5\sin\theta - 12\cos\theta = 7$ for $0° < \theta < 360°$.

6. Solve the equation $2\cos 2\theta = 7\cos\theta$ for $0° < \theta < 360°$.

7. If the real part of $\dfrac{z+i}{z-1}$ is zero, find the locus of the point representing $z$ on the Argand diagram.

8. Show that the 4 points on the Argand diagram representing the numbers $5 + 8i$, $2 + 6i$, $4 + 3i$, $7 + 5i$ form a square. What number is represented by the point at the centre of the square?

9. If $z = \cos\dfrac{2\pi}{5} + i\sin\dfrac{2\pi}{5}$, state the values of $|z|$ and arg $z$. Find $|z^5|$ and $\arg(z^5)$ and hence show that $z^5 = 1$.

10. $\mathbf{1}$ Show that $\displaystyle\int_0^{\pi/6} \sin^2\theta\,d\theta = \dfrac{\pi}{12} - \dfrac{\sqrt{3}}{8}$.

    $\mathbf{2}$ Find $\displaystyle\int_0^{\frac{1}{2}} \dfrac{x^2}{\sqrt{1-x^2}}\,dx$ using the substitution $x = \sin\theta$.

    $\mathbf{3}$ Find $\displaystyle\int_0^{\frac{1}{2}} 2x\sin^{-1}x\,dx$.

11. Find the coordinates of the points where the line $y = 4x$ meets the curve $y = x(x^2 - 2x + 4)$. Find the area enclosed between the line $y = 4x$ and the curve.

12. The area between the curve $y = 2x^{\frac{3}{2}}$, the $x$-axis and the line $x = 4$ is completely rotated about the $x$-axis. Find the volume of revolution.

13. Find the resolved part of the vector **a** in the direction **b** if $a = -2i + 6j - k$ and $b = 2i + 9j + 6k$.

14. $A$ and $B$ have position vectors **a** and **b** with respect to an origin $O$, and $C$ is a point on $AB$ such that $AC : CB = 2 : 3$. Show that the position vector of $C$ is $\frac{1}{5}(3a + 2b)$.

15. Show that the point $A$ $(-4, -14, 13)$ does not lie on the line $L$ with equation $r = (2, 4, 7) + t(1, -1, 2)$. Find a point $B$ on this line $L$ such that $AB$ is perpendicular to $L$, and find the distance $AB$.

## Exercise D2

Select the correct answer to each question.

1. If $a + b\sqrt{x} = c$ then $x =$

   **A** $\dfrac{c - a}{b}$    **B** $\left(\dfrac{c - a}{b}\right)^2$    **C** $\dfrac{c^2 - a^2}{b^2}$    **D** $\sqrt{\dfrac{c - a}{b}}$    **E** $\dfrac{c^2 + a^2}{b^2}$

2. The area bounded by the curve $y = x^3 - 2x + 4$, the $x$-axis and the ordinates $x = 1$ and $x = 4$ is

   **A** 45    **B** 46    **C** $48\frac{3}{4}$    **D** $60\frac{3}{4}$    **E** 64

3. $\dfrac{2 - 3i}{3 + 4i} =$

   **A** $\dfrac{-6 - 17i}{25}$    **B** $\dfrac{6 + 17i}{7}$    **C** $\dfrac{-18 + i}{7}$    **D** $\dfrac{18 - 17i}{25}$    **E** $\dfrac{-18 + 17i}{7}$

4. If $a = (4, -4, -7)$ and $b = (2, 1, -2)$, the acute angle between the vectors **a** and **b** is

   **A** $0°$    **B** $90°$    **C** $\cos^{-1}\frac{2}{81}$    **D** $\cos^{-1}\frac{2}{3}$    **E** $\cos^{-1}\frac{10}{27}$

5. The equation of the normal at $(2\sqrt{2}, \sqrt{2})$ on the ellipse $\dfrac{x^2}{16} + \dfrac{y^2}{4} = 1$ is

   **A** $x + 2y = 3\sqrt{2}$    **B** $x + 2y = 4\sqrt{2}$    **C** $2x + y = 5\sqrt{2}$
   **D** $2x - y = 3\sqrt{2}$    **E** $x - 2y = 0$

6. The sum of 20 terms of the arithmetic progression 15, 11, 7, ... is

   **A** $-61$    **B** $-460$    **C** $-610$    **D** 1060    **E** $-1060$

7. If $z_1 = 5\left(\cos\dfrac{\pi}{3} + i\sin\dfrac{\pi}{3}\right)$ and $z_2 = 3\left(\cos\dfrac{\pi}{4} - i\sin\dfrac{\pi}{4}\right)$ then $z_1 z_2 =$

   **A** $8\left(\cos\dfrac{\pi}{12} + i\sin\dfrac{\pi}{12}\right)$      **B** $8\left(\cos\dfrac{7\pi}{12} + i\sin\dfrac{7\pi}{12}\right)$

   **C** $15\left(\cos\dfrac{\pi}{12} + i\sin\dfrac{\pi}{12}\right)$      **D** $15\left(\cos\dfrac{7\pi}{12} - i\sin\dfrac{7\pi}{12}\right)$

   **E** $15\left(\cos\dfrac{7\pi}{12} + i\sin\dfrac{7\pi}{12}\right)$

8. If $y = \dfrac{x+1}{\sqrt{x}}$, $\dfrac{dy}{dx} =$

   A $2\sqrt{x}$    B $\dfrac{3x+1}{2x\sqrt{x}}$    C $\dfrac{x+1}{2x\sqrt{x}}$    D $\dfrac{1-x}{2x\sqrt{x}}$    E $\dfrac{x-1}{2x\sqrt{x}}$

9. If $z = 4\ln y$ and $y = e^x$ then $z =$

   A $4x$    B $4 + e^x$    C $4e^x$    D $4 + \ln x$    E $4 + x$

10. $x$ and $y$ are connected by the equation $y = 3\cot x$. When $x$ is increased from $\dfrac{\pi}{3}$ to

    $\left(\dfrac{\pi}{3} + 0.01\right)$ radians then the approximate change in $y$ is

    A   an increase of 0.03          B   an increase of 0.04
    C   an increase of $0.01\sqrt{3}$     D   a decrease of 0.03
    E   a decrease of 0.04

11. If the gradient of a curve at the point $(x, y)$ is given by the expression $\cos 2x - \sin x$,

    and the curve passes through $\left(\dfrac{\pi}{6}, \dfrac{\sqrt{3}}{2}\right)$, then the $y$-value where the curve meets the

    line $x = \pi$ is

    A $1 + \dfrac{3\sqrt{3}}{4}$    B $\dfrac{3\sqrt{3}}{4} - 1$    C $-1 - \dfrac{\sqrt{3}}{4}$    D $1 - \dfrac{\sqrt{3}}{4}$    E $-1 - \dfrac{\sqrt{3}}{2}$

12. If $\mathbf{a} = 7\mathbf{i} + 4\mathbf{j} - \mathbf{k}$ and $\mathbf{b} = \mathbf{i} + 2\mathbf{j} + 2\mathbf{k}$, which one of these vectors is not perpendicular
    to both $\mathbf{a}$ and $\mathbf{b}$?

    A  $2\mathbf{i} - 3\mathbf{j} + 2\mathbf{k}$        B  $-\mathbf{i} + 1\tfrac{1}{2}\mathbf{j} - \mathbf{k}$        C  $-10\mathbf{i} + 15\mathbf{j} - 10\mathbf{k}$

    D  $-3\mathbf{i} + 6\mathbf{j} + 3\mathbf{k}$        E  $4\mathbf{i} - 6\mathbf{j} + 4\mathbf{k}$

13. If $|z - 2 + \mathrm{i}| = |z - 1|$, then the locus of $z$ in the Argand diagram is

    A   the perpendicular bisector of the line joining points $2 - \mathrm{i}$ and $1$

    B   the perpendicular bisector of the line joining points $-2 + \mathrm{i}$ and $-1$

    C   the line joining points $2 - \mathrm{i}$ and $1$

    D   the circle centre $2 - \mathrm{i}$, radius $1$

    E   the circle centre $-2 + \mathrm{i}$, radius $1$

14. If $\sin x = -\tfrac{8}{17}$ and $\pi < x < \dfrac{3\pi}{2}$, then $\tan x =$

    A $\tfrac{8}{15}$    B $-\tfrac{15}{17}$    C $-\tfrac{8}{15}$    D $\tfrac{15}{8}$    E $\tfrac{15}{17}$

15. The area between the curve $y = \ln x$, the axes and the line $y = 1$ is rotated about the
    $y$-axis. The volume generated is

    A $\dfrac{\pi e^2}{2}$    B $\dfrac{\pi(e^2 - 1)}{2}$    C $\pi e^2$    D $\pi(e^2 - 1)$    E $\pi(e - 2)$

## Exercise D3

1. Show that $\dfrac{\cot\theta - \tan\theta}{\cot\theta + \tan\theta} - \cos 2\theta = 0.$

2. Find the possible values of $k$ if the equation $3x^2 - (k+3)x + 2k - 3 = 0$ has equal roots.

3. Sketch on an Argand diagram the locus of points satisfying $|z + 4 - 3i| = 15$. Find the value of $z$ at the point on this locus nearest to the origin.

4. If $e^y - e^{-y} = 4$, show that $y = \ln(2 + \sqrt{5})$.

5. Find $\arg z$ if $z = \dfrac{\cos 2\theta + i\sin 2\theta}{\cos\theta - i\sin\theta}$ and $0 < \theta < \dfrac{\pi}{4}$.

6. Find the points of intersection of the curves $y = x^2$ and $y = 18 - x^2$, and find the area of the region enclosed between the two curves.

7. If $f(x) = x^3 - 4x^2 + x$, for what range of values of $x$ is $f(x) > -6$?

8. If $f(x) = \ln x$, $g(x) = \dfrac{1 - x}{1 + x}$ and $h(x) = \dfrac{2x}{1 + x^2}$, where $0 < x < 1$, show that
   1 $g^{-1}(x) = g(x)$   2 $gh(x) = [g(x)]^2$   3 $fgh(x) = 2 \cdot fg(x)$

9. A particle moves along a line so that its velocity $v$ at time $t$ is given by $v = 3\cos t - \sin t$. Find the mean value of the velocity with respect to time in the interval $t = 0$ to $\dfrac{\pi}{2}$. Find the mean value of the acceleration with respect to time in the same interval.

10. If $\overrightarrow{OA} = 6\mathbf{i} + 4\mathbf{j} + 3\mathbf{k}$, $\overrightarrow{OB} = 2\mathbf{i} + \mathbf{j} + 3\mathbf{k}$ and $\overrightarrow{OC} = 6\mathbf{i} + 4\mathbf{j} + 15\mathbf{k}$, find the magnitudes of $\overrightarrow{AB}$ and $\overrightarrow{BC}$, and find the cosine of angle $ABC$. Write down the vector $\overrightarrow{OM}$, where $M$ is the mid-point of $BC$, and show that a sphere on $BC$ as diameter passes through $A$.

11. The area bounded by the curve $y = \cos x$, the line $x = \pi/6$ and the $x$-axis from $x = \pi/6$ to $x = \pi/2$ is rotated completely about the $x$-axis. Find the volume of revolution.

12. Solve the equation $\cos\theta + \sqrt{3}\sin\theta = \sqrt{2}$, for $0° < \theta < 360°$.

13. Express $\dfrac{4}{(1+x)(1-3x)}$ in partial fractions. Hence expand this expression in ascending powers of $x$ as far as the term in $x^3$, and also give the general term $x^n$. For what range of values of $x$ is this expansion valid?

14. If $A$, $B$, $C$, $D$ have position vectors $(4, 0, 1)$, $(-3, -8, 3)$, $(1, 0, 9)$ and $(10, 12, 10)$ respectively, show that the line through $A$ and $B$, and the line through $C$ and $D$ intersect, and find the position vector of the point of intersection $E$. Show also that $A$ and $B$ lie on the plane $\mathbf{r} \cdot (2, -3, -5) = 3$, but $C$ and $D$ do not.

15. Show that the curve $y = (x^2 + 1)\,e^{-x}$ has no maximum or minimum points. Find the $x$-coordinates of the points of inflexion on the curve and find the gradients of the curve at these points.

16. If $\ln(1 + ax) + e^{bx} = 1 + \frac{9}{2}x^3$, where $x$ is small and $x^4$ and higher powers of $x$ can be neglected, find the values of $a$ and $b$.

**To the student:**

# 5   Before the Exam

1    Get your equipment ready:
**Pen** (and spare cartridges)
**Pencil** and sharpener
**Rubber**
**Ruler**
**Compasses**
**Calculator.** Buy new batteries and make sure they work. Spend a few minutes playing with your calculator. Recall what functions you can get with each key. How can you get $\sqrt[3]{3375}$, $\tan^{-1}\frac{4}{3}$ (in radians), $10^{4.2}$, $\pi^2$. Remove the instruction booklet which you must not take into the exam room.
**Watch.** Does it also need new batteries? If you have not got a watch then buy or borrow one. Do not rely on being able to see a clock in the room.

2    Depending on the weather decide what to wear, so as to be comfortable, with warm clothing if the weather is cold, or a jacket which can be taken off if you get too hot. (If it gets very stuffy during the exam, ask the invigilator if a window can be opened. If you are in a chilly draught, ask him if it can be closed.)

3    Read the instructions on last year's paper or the specimen paper, and plan ahead how you are going to start the paper, and how much time you are planning to allocate to the various questions. Ask to see a copy of the formulae booklet if you have not already been given one. Find out which formulae are in it and make sure you know the rest. Use the checklist on page 175.

4    Check your exam timetable for all your exams. Make sure that if you think an exam is in the afternoon it <u>is</u> in the afternoon. Check it with someone else in your class. See how the Maths exam fits in with other subjects. Decide how much time you have for last-minute revision. (If you have two 3-hour exams the day before you will need to plan differently than if you have no exams in the previous 2 or 3 days.) Decide what last-minute revision you are going to do. It is probably best if most of the real work is completed at least a week before, with just a memory check needed. A full day's hard work on the day before your exam is probably not wise. Get out into the fresh air, then go to bed at a reasonable time. Eat a sensible breakfast, then get to the exam room in good time.

# 13*   Coordinate Geometry. Lines, Circles

## Distances, Angles, Lines

If there are two points $A(x_1, y_1)$ and $B(x_2, y_2)$, then

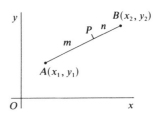

the gradient of $AB$ is $\dfrac{y_2 - y_1}{x_2 - x_1}$,

the distance $AB$ is $\sqrt{(y_2 - y_1)^2 + (x_2 - x_1)^2}$,

the mid-point of $AB$ has coordinates $\left(\dfrac{x_1 + x_2}{2}, \dfrac{y_1 + y_2}{2}\right)$,

the point $P$ which divides $AB$ in the ratio $m:n$ has coordinates $\left(\dfrac{nx_1 + mx_2}{m + n}, \dfrac{ny_1 + my_2}{m + n}\right)$.

A line through the origin with gradient $m$ has equation $y = mx$.

A line with gradient $m$ and intercept $c$ has equation $y = mx + c$.

A line with gradient $m$ and passing through $(x_1, y_1)$ has equation $y - y_1 = m(x - x_1)$.

To find the equation of a line through 2 points $(x_1, y_1)$, $(x_2, y_2)$, first find the gradient $m$ of the line, simplify this if possible, then use $y - y_1 = m(x - x_1)$.

The general form of the equation of a straight line is $ax + by + c = 0$. ($c$ in this equation is not the intercept.)
To find its gradient, re-arrange in the form $y = mx + c$.

If a point $(x_1, y_1)$ lies on a line $ax + by + c = 0$, then $x_1$ and $y_1$ satisfy the equation $ax_1 + by_1 + c = 0$.

The length of the perpendicular from the point $(h, k)$ to the line $ax + by + c = 0$ is

$$\frac{|ah + bk + c|}{\sqrt{a^2 + b^2}}.$$

The angle between 2 lines, gradients $m_1$ and $m_2$ is $\theta$, where $\tan \theta = \dfrac{m_1 - m_2}{1 + m_1 m_2}$.

The lines are parallel if $m_1 = m_2$.
The lines are perpendicular if $m_1 m_2 = -1$.

Topics marked * are not included in the national common core and may not be needed for your syllabus.

**Examples**

**13.1**    If $A$ is $(-1, 5)$ and $B$ is $(8, 2)$, then

the gradient of $AB$ is $\dfrac{y_2 - y_1}{x_2 - x_1} = \dfrac{2-5}{8-(-1)} = -\frac{1}{3}$,

the distance $AB$ is $\sqrt{(y_2 - y_1)^2 + (x_2 - x_1)^2}$

$$= \sqrt{(2-5)^2 + (8+1)^2}$$
$$= \sqrt{90} = 3\sqrt{10},$$

the mid-point of $AB$ has coordinates $\left(\dfrac{x_1 + x_2}{2}, \dfrac{y_1 + y_2}{2}\right)$,

i.e. $\left(\dfrac{-1+8}{2}, \dfrac{5+2}{2}\right)$, i.e. $(3\frac{1}{2}, 3\frac{1}{2})$,

the point which divides $AB$ in the ratio $2:1$ has coordinates

$\left(\dfrac{x_1 + 2x_2}{3}, \dfrac{y_1 + 2y_2}{3}\right)$, i.e. $\left(\dfrac{-1+2\times8}{3}, \dfrac{5+2\times2}{3}\right)$, i.e. $(5, 3)$.

Lines parallel to $AB$ have gradient $-\frac{1}{3}$.
Lines perpendicular to $AB$ have gradient $3$, (since $-\frac{1}{3} \times 3 = -1$).

**13.2**    To find the equation of a line through $A$ $(-1, 5)$ with gradient $3$.

$y - y_1 = m(x - x_1)$
$y - 5 = 3(x + 1)$
The equation is $y = 3x + 8$.

**13.3**    To find the distance of the point $(3, 2)$ from the line $8x + 15y - 20 = 0$.

The distance is $\dfrac{|ah + bk + c|}{\sqrt{a^2 + b^2}}$ where $a = 8$, $b = 15$, $c = -20$, $h = 3$, $k = 2$

$$= \dfrac{8 \times 3 + 15 \times 2 - 20}{\sqrt{8^2 + 15^2}}$$

$$= \tfrac{34}{17} = 2$$

**13.4**    To find the angle between the lines $3x - 2y = 7$ and $x + 3y = 6$.

The gradients are $m_1 = \frac{3}{2}$ and $m_2 = -\frac{1}{3}$

$\tan \theta = \dfrac{m_1 - m_2}{1 + m_1 m_2} = \dfrac{\frac{3}{2} + \frac{1}{3}}{1 - \frac{3}{2} \cdot \frac{1}{3}} = \dfrac{11}{3}$

(A negative result would refer to the obtuse angle between the lines.)
The (acute) angle is $\tan^{-1} \frac{11}{3}$.

**13.5**    If $A$ is $(4, 1)$, $B$ is $(1, 8)$, $C$ is $(6, 5)$, find the area of triangle $ABC$.

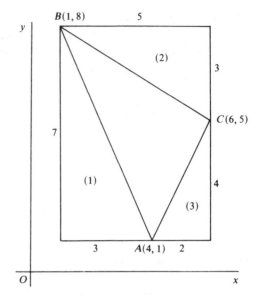

One way to find an area of a triangle is to enclose it in a rectangle, as in the diagram, and find the area by subtraction.

Area of triangle $ABC$
= area of rectangle
   − area of triangles (1), (2), (3)
$= 7 \times 5 - \frac{1}{2} \times 3 \times 7 - \frac{1}{2} \times 2 \times 4 - \frac{1}{2} \times 5 \times 3$
$= 13$

## Exercise 13.1

1.  If $A$ is $(3, 0)$, $B$ is $(4, 1)$, $C$ is $(1, 3)$ and $D$ is $(0, 2)$, show that $ABCD$ is a parallelogram. Find the gradients of the diagonals $AC$ and $BD$ and find the tangent of the acute angle between these diagonals.

2.  In triangle $ABC$, $A$ is $(-3, 1)$, $B$ is $(5, -3)$, $C$ is $(1, 7)$. Find the equations of
    1   the line $BC$,
    2   the line through $A$ perpendicular to $BC$.
    3   the median $AM$,
    4   the perpendicular bisector of $BC$.

3.  Find the area of the triangle whose sides have equations $y = x - 3$, $y + 2x = 9$, $y = 4x - 9$.

4.  Show that the point $(-12, 2)$ is equidistant from the lines $3x + 4y = 12$ and $5x - 12y = 20$.

5.  $ABCD$ is a rhombus. $A$ is $(3, -1)$, $B$ is $(8, 4)$ and the equation of $AC$ is $y = 3x - 10$. Find the coordinates of the point of intersection of the diagonals and hence find the coordinates of $C$ and $D$. Find also the area of the rhombus.

6.  Find the tangent of the acute angle between the lines $2x - 7y = 4$ and $2x + y = 5$.

7.  In triangle $ABC$, $A$ is $(4, 7)$, $B$ is $(-5, -3)$, $C$ is $(7, -1)$. Find the coordinates of $D$, the mid-point of $BC$. The centroid $G$ of triangle $ABC$ divides $AD$ internally in the ratio $2:1$. Find the coordinates of $G$.
    Find the equation of $BG$ and verify that $BG$ produced meets $AC$ at its mid-point $E$, and also that $BG : GE = 2:1$.

8.  Show that the triangle $ABC$ with $A$ $(7, 17)$, $B$ $(17, -7)$ and $C$ $(-9, -7)$ is isosceles. The perpendiculars from $A$, and $B$, to the opposite sides of the triangle intersect at point $H$. Find the coordinates of $H$.

9. The equations of two sides of a parallelogram are $3x - 4y - 13 = 0$ and $8x - 15y + 26 = 0$. One of the vertices of the parallelogram is the origin. Find the coordinates of the other vertices, and the lengths of the sides of the parallelogram.

10. In triangle $ABC$, $A$ is $(7, 3)$, $B$ is $(2, 13)$, $C$ is $(14, 10)$. $D$ divides $AB$ internally in the ratio $2:3$ and $E$ divides $AC$ internally in the ratio $4:3$. Find the coordinates of $D$ and $E$. If the lines $DE$ and $BC$ when produced meet at $F$, show that $BC = CF$.

## Circles

The general equation of a circle is $x^2 + y^2 + 2gx + 2fy + c = 0$.

(Note that 1   the coefficients of $x^2$ and $y^2$ are equal, 2   there is no term in $xy$.)

The equation of a circle radius $r$, centre at the origin, is $x^2 + y^2 = r^2$

The equation of a circle radius $r$, centre $(a, b)$ is $(x - a)^2 + (y - b)^2 = r^2$

The parametric equations are $x = a + r \cos t$, $y = b + r \sin t$.

**To find the equation of the tangent** at the point $P(x_1, y_1)$ of the circle:
*1st method.*
The radius $CP$ is perpendicular to the tangent, so:
Find the coordinates of the centre, $C$.
Find the gradient of $CP$.
Find the gradient of $PT$, perpendicular to $CP$.
Hence find the equation of $PT$, using $y - y_1 = m(x - x_1)$.

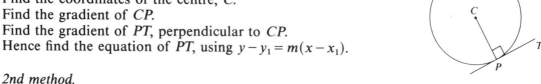

*2nd method.*
This is the general method for all curves.

Find the gradient of the tangent by differentiation, and then substitute the values of $x_1$, $y_1$.

Hence find the equation, using $y - y_1 = m(x - x_1)$.

**To find the points of intersection** of two circles.
Solve their equations simultaneously, first eliminating $x^2$ and $y^2$.
This leaves a linear equation which represents the common chord.
Substitute this linear equation into the equation of either circle to find the points of intersection.

**To find the equation of a circle passing through 3 given points $P$, $Q$, $R$.**
*1st method.*
Find the equations of the perpendicular bisectors of $PQ$ and $QR$. Solve these equations simultaneously to find the centre $C(a, b)$. Find the distance $CP$ for the radius $r$.
Use $(x - a)^2 + (y - b)^2 = r^2$.

*2nd method.*
Substitute the coordinates of $P$, $Q$, $R$ in turn into $x^2 + y^2 + 2gx + 2fy + c = 0$. This gives 3 equations which can be solved simultaneously to find the values of $g$, $f$ and $c$.

**Examples**

**13.6**   Find the values of $a$ and $b$ if the equation $2x^2 + ay^2 + bxy + 4x - 5y - 10 = 0$ represents a circle and find its centre and radius.

The coefficients of $x^2$ and $y^2$ are equal, so $a = 2$.
There is no term in $xy$ so $b = 0$.
The circle has equation $2x^2 + 2y^2 + 4x - 5y - 10 = 0$.
This can be written as $(x + 1)^2 + (y - 1\frac{1}{4})^2 = \frac{121}{16}$.
The centre is $(-1, 1\frac{1}{4})$, and the radius is $2\frac{3}{4}$.

**13.7**   Find the equation of the tangent at the point $P$ $(-7, 5)$ on the circle $x^2 + y^2 + 6x - 4y - 12 = 0$.

*1st method.*
The equation of the circle can be written as $(x + 3)^2 + (y - 2)^2 = 25$.
The centre $C$ is $(-3, 2)$,

The gradient of $CP$ is $\dfrac{y_2 - y_1}{x_2 - x_1} = \dfrac{2 - 5}{-3 + 7} = -\frac{3}{4}$.

The gradient of the tangent at $P$ is $\frac{4}{3}$.
The equation of the tangent at $P$ is $y - y_1 = m(x - x_1)$
$$\text{i.e. } y - 5 = \tfrac{4}{3}(x + 7)$$
$$\text{i.e. } 3y = 4x + 43.$$

*2nd method.*
Differentiate $x^2 + y^2 + 6x - 4y - 12 = 0$ with respect to $x$.

$$2x + 2y\frac{dy}{dx} + 6 - 4\frac{dy}{dx} = 0.$$

At $(-7, 5)$, $-14 + 10\dfrac{dy}{dx} + 6 - 4\dfrac{dy}{dx} = 0$, $\dfrac{dy}{dx} = \frac{4}{3}$.

∴   The gradient of the tangent is $\frac{4}{3}$.
Find its equation as shown above.

**13.8**   Find the points of intersection of the circles $x^2 + y^2 + 2x - 4y - 20 = 0$ and $x^2 + y^2 + 6x - 16y + 28 = 0$.

Subtract to eliminate $x^2$ and $y^2$, giving $-4x + 12y - 48 = 0$, i.e. $-x + 3y - 12 = 0$.
This is the equation of the common chord.
Substitute $x = 3y - 12$ in the first equation.
$(3y - 12)^2 + y^2 + 2(3y - 12) - 4y - 20 = 0$.
This simplifies to $y^2 - 7y + 10 = 0$
∴   $y = 2$ or $5$.
When $y = 2$, $x = 3y - 12 = -6$.
When $y = 5$, $x = 3$.
The points of intersection are $(-6, 2)$ and $(3, 5)$.

**13.9** Find the equation of the circle passing through the points $A$ $(9, -4)$, $B$ $(5, 4)$ and $C$ $(-2, 7)$.

*1st method.*

Gradient of $AB$ is $\dfrac{y_2 - y_1}{x_2 - x_1} = \dfrac{4+4}{5-9} = -2$

Mid-point of $AB$ is $\left(\dfrac{x_1 + x_2}{2}, \dfrac{y_1 + y_2}{2}\right)$, i.e. $(7, 0)$

The perpendicular bisector of $AB$ has gradient $\frac{1}{2}$.
Its equation is $y - y_1 = m(x - x_1)$
    i.e. $y - 0 = \frac{1}{2}(x - 7)$
Similarly, the equation of the perpendicular bisector of $BC$ is found to be $y = \frac{7}{3}x + 2$.
These bisectors meet where $\frac{1}{2}x - 3\frac{1}{2} = \frac{7}{3}x + 2$
$\therefore$    $x = -3$, and $y = -5$.
The centre of the circle is $(-3, -5)$.
The distance from the centre to $A$ is $\sqrt{(y_2 - y_1)^2 + (x_2 - x_1)^2}$

$$= \sqrt{(-4+5)^2 + (9+3)^2}$$

$$= \sqrt{145}.$$

The radius is $\sqrt{145}$.
The equation of the circle is $(x+3)^2 + (y+5)^2 = 145$
i.e. $x^2 + y^2 + 6x + 10y - 111 = 0$.

*2nd method.*
The equation is $x^2 + y^2 + 2gx + 2fy + c = 0$
$(9, -4)$ satisfies this so $81 + 16 + 18g - 8f + c = 0$    (i)
$(5, 4)$ satisfies this so $25 + 16 + 10g + 8f + c = 0$    (ii)
$(-2, 7)$ satisfies this so $4 + 49 - 4g + 14f + c = 0$    (iii)
Subtracting (iii) from (ii) and (ii) from (i) to eliminate $c$ gives
$-12 + 14g - 6f = 0$
$56 + 8g - 16f = 0$
Solving these equations gives $f = 5$ and $g = 3$.
Substituting in (i) gives $c = -111$.
$\therefore$    The equation is $x^2 + y^2 + 6x + 10y - 111 = 0$.

## Exercise 13.2

1. Find the equation of the circle which has a diameter $AC$ where $A$ is $(2, -1)$ and $C$ is $(12, 5)$.
   Find the coordinates of $B$ and $D$ where $ABCD$ is a square, with $A$, $B$, $C$, $D$ in anticlockwise order.

2. Show that the circle $x^2 + y^2 - 10x - 14y + 49 = 0$ passes through the centre of the circle $x^2 + y^2 - 4x - 6y + 9 = 0$.

3. A circle with centre $(2\frac{1}{2}, 1)$ touches the line $6x - 8y + 3 = 0$. Find the equation of the circle and show that the circle touches the $x$-axis.

4. Show that the point $(9, -2)$ lies on the circle $x^2 + y^2 - 4x + 6y - 37 = 0$ and find the coordinates of the other end of the diameter through this point.

5. Find the coordinates of the points where the line $y = 3x + 10$ meets the circle $x^2 + y^2 + 2x - 4y - 60 = 0$.

6. Find the equation of the chord of the circle $x^2 + y^2 - 8x - 6y + 4 = 0$ whose mid-point is $(3, 1)$.

7. Find the equation of the tangent to the circle $x^2 + y^2 - 2x - 4y + 4 = 0$ at the point $(\frac{2}{5}, 2\frac{4}{5})$.

8. Find the equation of the circle passing through $(0, 0)$, $(1, -1)$ and $(4, 8)$ and show that it also passes through $(-1, 3)$.

9. Find the equations of the tangents to the circle $x^2 + y^2 - 2x = 49$ at the points where it is met by the line $3x + y - 23 = 0$. Find also the coordinates of the point of intersection of the tangents.

10. Find the equation of the common chord, and hence find the points of intersection of the two circles
$$x^2 + y^2 - 4x - 2y - 140 = 0, \quad x^2 + y^2 - 48x - 24y + 520 = 0.$$

## Exercise 13.3

1. Find the area of the triangle whose vertices are $(1, 2)$, $(4, 4)$ and $(9, -6)$.

2. If the lines $4x - 5y = 26$ and $2x + 7y = 32$ intersect at the point $T$, find the distance of $T$ from the line $3x + 4y = 5$.

3. In triangle $ABC$, $A$ is $(-3, 2)$, $B$ is $(1, -1)$ and $C$ is $(7, 7)$. $D$ is the mid-point of $BC$ and $E$ is the point on $AC$ such that $AE : EC = 3 : 2$. Find the coordinates of $F$, the point of intersection of $AD$ and $BE$.

4. Triangle $ABC$ has vertices $A(-9, 17)$, $B(-6, -7)$, $C(26, -3)$. Show that the triangle is right-angled. Find the equations of the three sides of the triangle and show that $P(1, 2)$ is equidistant from these three sides.

5. $ABCD$ is a parallelogram where $A$ is $(0, 8)$, $B$ is $(12, 5)$ and $C$ is $(5, -7)$. Find the coordinates of $D$, and the area of the parallelogram.

6. Show that the acute angle between the lines $4y = 3x + 5$ and $3y = 4x + 2$ is exactly double the acute angle between the lines $4y = 3x + 5$ and $31y = 17x + 45$.

7. $A$ and $B$ are points $(x_1, y_1)$ and $(x_2, y_2)$ and $O$ is the origin. If the distance $OA = a$ and the distance $OB = b$, show that
$$\cos \angle AOB = \frac{x_1 x_2 + y_1 y_2}{ab}.$$

8. Find the radii of the two circles which have their centres at the origin and which touch the circle $x^2 + y^2 - 8x - 6y + 21 = 0$.

9. Find the equation of the circle passing through the points $(-1, 2)$, $(2, 6)$ and $(6, 3)$, and show that it passes through the origin.

10. Find the distance from the point $P$ $(4, 5)$ to the centre of the circle with equation $x^2 + y^2 + 40x + 4y + 179 = 0$. Hence find the lengths of the tangents from $P$ to the circle.

11. Find the centres and radii of the circles
$x^2 + y^2 - 4x + 4y + 4 = 0$ and $x^2 + y^2 + 4x - 2y - 4 = 0$
and show that the circles touch each other. Find the coordinates of $T$, the point of contact, and find also the equation of the common tangent at $T$.

## Linear Relationships

A straight line has an equation of the form $y = mx + c$, where $m$ is the gradient and $c$ the intercept on the $y$-axis.
If a set of points lie on a straight line, then using two of the points, $(x_1, y_1)$ and $(x_2, y_2)$, the gradient $m$ is $\dfrac{y_2 - y_1}{x_2 - x_1}$, and the equation of the line is $y - y_1 = m(x - x_1)$, from which $c$ can be calculated if it cannot be read directly from the graph.

### $y = ax^n$

If a set of points are thought to satisfy a relation $y = ax^n$ then $\log y = \log a + n \log x$. Plotting $Y = \log y$ against $X = \log x$, the points should lie on a straight line $Y = nX + A$, where $A = \log a$. The gradient gives the value of $n$, the intercept gives the value of $A$, from which $a$ can be found. (Logs can be in base e, base 10, or any convenient base.)

### $\dfrac{1}{x} + \dfrac{1}{y} = \dfrac{1}{a}$

If a set of points are thought to satisfy a relation $\dfrac{1}{x} + \dfrac{1}{y} = \dfrac{1}{a}$, then plotting $Y = \dfrac{1}{y}$ against $X = \dfrac{1}{x}$, the points should lie on a straight line $X + Y = A$, where $A = \dfrac{1}{a}$. The gradient should be $-1$, and the intercept gives the value of $A$, from which $a$ can be found.

### Other relations
Other relations can be reduced to linear form, e.g. for $y = ax^3 + b$, plot $y$ against $X = x^3$.

### Example 13.10

The table gives values of $x$ and $y$, which are believed to be related by the equation $y = ax^3 + bx^2$. By plotting $\dfrac{y}{x^2}$ against $x$, show that this may be so, and by drawing an appropriate straight line find approximate values for $a$ and $b$.

| $x$ | 2 | 3 | 4 | 5 | 6 | 7 |
|-----|-----|-----|-----|-----|-----|-----|
| $y$ | 100 | 270 | 540 | 960 | 1550 | 2300 |

The equation may be written $\dfrac{y}{x^2} = ax + b$

If the values of $\dfrac{y}{x^2}$ are plotted against $x$, this should give the straight line

$Y = ax + b$, where $Y = \dfrac{y}{x^2}$, with gradient $a$ and intercept $b$.

| $x$ | 2 | 3 | 4 | 5 | 6 | 7 |
|-----|-----|-----|------|------|------|------|
| $\dfrac{y}{x^2}$ | 25 | 30 | 33.8 | 38.4 | 43.1 | 46.9 |

Plot the graph and verify that the six points lie approximately on a straight line, and find the gradient and intercept.
The gradient $a = 4.5$, the intercept $b = 16$.
$x$ and $y$ are related approximately by the relation $y = 4.5x^3 + 16x^2$.

## Exercise 13.4

1.  The table gives corresponding values of variables $x$ and $y$ (rounded to 1 decimal place).

    | $x$ | 1.1 | 1.4 | 1.6 | 2.2 | 2.8 | 3.5 |
    |-----|-----|-----|-----|------|------|------|
    | $y$ | 2.6 | 5.4 | 8.1 | 20.9 | 43.7 | 85.1 |

    By plotting $\log_{10} y$ against $\log_{10} x$, verify that these values of $x$ and $y$ satisfy approximately a relationship of the form $y = ax^b$, where $a$ and $b$ are constants. From your graph find approximate values for $a$ and $b$, to 1 decimal place.

2.  The following corresponding values of $x$ and $y$ are believed to be related by the equation $y = ax^b$, where $a$ and $b$ are constants.

    | $x$ | 1.2 | 1.6 | 2.0 | 2.8 | 3.2 | 4.8 |
    |-----|-----|-----|-----|-----|-----|-----|
    | $y$ | 1.3 | 1.5 | 1.6 | 1.8 | 2.0 | 2.3 |

    By plotting $\ln y$ against $\ln x$, show that this may be so and use your graph to find approximate values for $a$ and $b$, to 1 decimal place.

3.  The values of $x$ and $y$ given in the table were obtained in an experiment. It is believed that $x$ and $y$ are connected by an equation of the form $\dfrac{1}{x} + \dfrac{1}{y} = \dfrac{1}{a}$, where $a$ is a constant.

    Show, by drawing a suitable straight line graph, that this is so. Use your graph to find the value of $a$, to 2 decimal places.

    | $x$ | 0.13 | 0.15 | 0.17 | 0.20 | 0.40 | 1.20 |
    |-----|------|------|------|------|------|------|
    | $y$ | 3.23 | 0.75 | 0.47 | 0.33 | 0.18 | 0.14 |

4. The table gives corresponding values of variables $x$ and $y$. By plotting ln $y$ against $x$, verify that these values of $x$ and $y$ satisfy approximately a relationship of the form $y = ab^x$, and find the values of $a$ and $b$, to 1 decimal place.

| $x$ | 0.2 | 0.4 | 0.6 | 0.8 | 1.0 |
|---|---|---|---|---|---|
| $y$ | 1.88 | 2.34 | 2.89 | 3.63 | 4.48 |

5. The variables $x$ and $y$ are thought to satisfy an equation of the form $y^2 = ax^3 + b$, where $a$ and $b$ are constants. Corresponding values of $x$ and $y$ are shown in the table. By drawing an appropriate linear graph show that this equation may be correct, and find the values of $a$ and $b$. (Give $a$ to the nearest integer and $b$ to the nearest 10.)

| $x$ | 2 | 3 | 4 | 5 | 6 | 7 |
|---|---|---|---|---|---|---|
| $y$ | 8.4 | 12.8 | 18.7 | 25.6 | 33.3 | 41.8 |

# 14* Differential Equations

## First Order Differential Equations with Separable Variables

An equation of the form $g(y)\dfrac{dy}{dx} = f(x)$ can be written

$\displaystyle\int g(y)\,dy = \int f(x)\,dx$, and solved by integration.

A general solution will contain an arbitrary constant.
A particular solution is one which fits certain conditions.

### Examples

**14.1**    Find the general solution of $\dfrac{dy}{dx} = 2x(1 + y^2)$, and the particular solution if $y = 1$ when $x = 0$.

$$\int \frac{1}{1 + y^2}\,dy = \int 2x\,dx$$
$$\tan^{-1} y = x^2 + c$$
i.e. the general solution is $y = \tan(x^2 + c)$.

If $y = 1$ when $x = 0$ then $c = \dfrac{\pi}{4}$

The particular solution is $y = \tan\!\left(x^2 + \dfrac{\pi}{4}\right)$.

**14.2**    Find the general solution of $x\dfrac{dy}{dx} = 3y$, and the particular solution if $y = 16$ when $x = 2$.

$$\int \frac{1}{y}\,dy = \int \frac{3}{x}\,dx$$
$\ln y = 3 \ln x + c$
$\ln y = 3 \ln x + \ln a$        (putting $\ln a$ instead of $c$)
$\ln y = \ln ax^3$
$y = ax^3$. This is the general solution.
For the particular solution, $c = \ln 2$ or $a = 2$,
$y = 2x^3$.

Topics marked * are not included in the national common core and may not be needed for your syllabus.

**14.3** A curve is such that the gradient of the curve at any point $P(x, y)$ is equal to half the gradient of the line $AP$, where $A$ is the point $(1, 0)$. Find the equation of the curve given also that it passes through the point $(9, 4)$.

$$\frac{dy}{dx} = \frac{1}{2} \cdot \frac{y - 0}{x - 1}$$

$$\int \frac{2}{y} \, dy = \int \frac{1}{x - 1} \, dx$$

$$2 \ln y = \ln(x - 1) + \ln a$$

$$y^2 = a(x - 1)$$

When $x = 9$, $y = 4$ so $a = 2$

The curve has the equation $y^2 = 2(x - 1)$.

## Applications to the Exponential Laws of Growth or Decay

If the rate of growth of $x$ is proportional to $x$, then $\dfrac{dx}{dt} = kx$ $(k > 0)$ so $\displaystyle\int \frac{1}{x} \, dx = \int k \, dt$

$\ln x = kt + c$

If $x = x_0$ when $t = 0$ then $c = \ln x_0$

Then $x = x_0 \, e^{kt}$

(Further information is needed to find the value of $k$.)

If the rate of decay of $x$ is proportional to $x$, then $\dfrac{dx}{dt} = -kx$ $(k > 0)$ so $x = x_0 \, e^{-kt}$

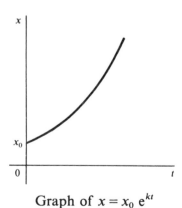

Graph of $x = x_0 \, e^{kt}$

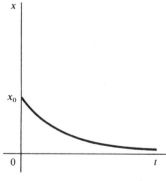

Graph of $x = x_0 \, e^{-kt}$

*Examples of these laws:*

The rate at which a stable population grows is proportional to the number in the population.

### Newton's Law of Cooling

The rate of cooling of a body is proportional to the temperature of the body above that of the surrounding air.

For certain chemical reactions, the rate of decrease of the mass of the reacting substance at any time is proportional to the mass of the substance remaining.

For radioactive substances, the rate of decrease of the mass of the substance is proportional to the mass present at that time.

## Example 14.4

Newton's Law of Cooling states that the rate of cooling of a body is proportional to the temperature of the body above that of the surrounding air. If the temperature of a body is $\theta°$ above that of the surrounding air, and initially $\theta = \theta_0$, express this law as a differential equation and solve it.

A body at a temperature of 90°C is placed in a room where the air-temperature is 18°C. 10 minutes later its temperature is 50°C. How much longer will it take under these conditions to cool to 45°C?

$$\frac{d\theta}{dt} = -k\theta$$

$$\int \frac{1}{\theta} d\theta = \int -k \, dt$$

$\ln \theta = -kt + c$

If $\theta = \theta_0$ when $t = 0$, $c = \ln \theta_0$

$$\ln \frac{\theta}{\theta_0} = -kt$$

$$\theta = \theta_0 \, e^{-kt}$$

When $t = 0$, $\theta = \theta_0 = 90 - 18 = 72$

When $t = 10$, $\theta = 50 - 18 = 32$

$32 = 72 \, e^{-10k}$, $e^{-10k} = \frac{4}{9}$

When $\theta = 45 - 18 = 27$,

$27 = 72 \, e^{-kt}$

$\frac{3}{8} = (e^{-10k})^{t/10}$, $\frac{3}{8} = (\frac{4}{9})^{t/10}$

$$\ln \tfrac{3}{8} = \frac{t}{10} \ln \tfrac{4}{9}$$

$$t = \frac{10 \ln \tfrac{3}{8}}{\ln \tfrac{4}{9}} \approx 12.1$$

It will take 2.1 minutes longer (to the nearest 0.1 minute).

## Exercise 14.1

Find the general solution of these differential equations, and also the particular solution with the additional information given.

1. $\dfrac{dy}{dx} = \sqrt{y}$, also when $x = 4$, $y = 0$

2. $x^2 \dfrac{dy}{dx} = y$, also when $x = 1$, $y = e^2$

3. $e^x \dfrac{dy}{dx} = 1 + y^2$, also when $x = 0$, $y = 0$

4. $\operatorname{cosec} x \dfrac{dy}{dx} + y = 1$, also when $x = \dfrac{\pi}{2}$, $y = 0$

5. $\dfrac{dy}{dx} = \sin x \sec y$, also when $x = \dfrac{\pi}{3}$, $y = \dfrac{\pi}{6}$

Find the particular solutions of the following differential equations with the information given.

6. $\cot x \dfrac{dy}{dx} = y$, and when $x = 0$, $y = 2$

7. $3 \dfrac{dy}{dx} = -4y^{\frac{3}{2}}$, and when $x = 5$, $y = \frac{1}{9}$

8. $3x \dfrac{dy}{dx} = y^2 - 5y + 4$, and when $x = 1$, $y = 7$

9. $\dfrac{dy}{dx} = \dfrac{x-3}{y}$, and when $x = 5$, $y = 6$

10. $(1 - x^2) \dfrac{dy}{dx} - y = 1$, and when $x = 0$, $y = 3$

## Exercise 14.2

1. If $y \dfrac{dy}{dx} = e^y$ and $y = 0$ when $x = 1$, find the value of $y$ when $x = 2$.

2. If $x \dfrac{dy}{dx} = y(1 - x)$ and $x = 1$ when $y = 1$, find the value of $y$ when $x = e$.

3. If $6y \dfrac{dy}{dx} + x = 0$ and $x = 3$ when $y = 4$. find the possible values of $y$ when $x = 9$.

4. Find the equation of the curve passing through $(0, 3)$ which has its gradient at every point equal to twice the $y$-coordinate at that point.

5. The velocity $v$ of an object under certain conditions is given by the differential equation $\dfrac{dv}{dt} = v^2 + 4$. When $t = 0$, $v = 2$. Find the equation connecting $v$ and $t$.

6.  The tangent to a curve at a general point $P(x, y)$ meets the $x$-axis at $Q$ and the $y$-axis at $R$. If $P$ is the mid-point of $QR$, write down the coordinates of $Q$ and $R$ and hence the gradient of the line $QR$. Write down a differential equation and solve it to find the equation of the curve given the additional information that it passes through the point $(4, 9)$.

7.  The number $y$ of bacteria in a colony at time $t$ follows the law $\dfrac{dy}{dt} = ky$, where $k$ is a positive constant. When $t = 0$, $y = Y$, and when $t = 20$, $y = 2Y$. Find the value of $k$, and find the time when $y = 3Y$. (Give the time as an exact value, and also correct to 1 decimal place.)

8.  The rate of decay of a radioactive substance is proportional to the amount $y$ remaining. Write down a differential equation to express this and give the general solution.
    If $y_0$ is the amount when $t = 0$, and at the end of time $t_1$ only $\frac{1}{3}y_0$ remains, how much remains after time $3t_1$?

9.  The rate at which a substance cools in air is proportional to the difference between the temperature of the substance and the temperature of the surrounding air. If this temperature difference is $\theta$ write down a differential equation to express this and give the general solution.
    A particular substance cools from 100°C to 55°C in 30 minutes when the surrounding air is at 19°C. What will be the temperature of the substance after a further 15 minutes?

10. The rate at which a certain population increases is proportional to the number $p$ in the population. If the population at an initial time $t = 0$ is $p_0$, write down a differential equation and solve it.
    If when $t = 10$, $p = \frac{11}{10}p_0$, find the time at which the population will be twice its initial number, giving the answer to the nearest integer.

# 15* Coordinate Geometry. Curves

## The Parabola $y^2 = 4ax$

Parametric equations $x = at^2$, $y = 2at$

The equation of the tangent at $(at^2, 2at)$ is $ty = x + at^2$

The equation of the normal at $(at^2, 2at)$ is $y + tx = 2at + at^3$

The focus is the point $(a, 0)$

The directrix is the line $x = -a$.

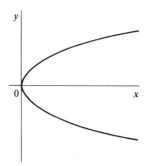

## The Rectangular Hyperbola $xy = c^2$

Parametric equations $x = ct$, $y = \dfrac{c}{t}$

The equation of the tangent at $\left( ct, \dfrac{c}{t} \right)$ is $t^2 y + x = 2ct$

The equation of the normal at $\left( ct, \dfrac{c}{t} \right)$ is $ty = t^3 x + c - ct^4$

$x = 0$ and $y = 0$ are asymptotes.

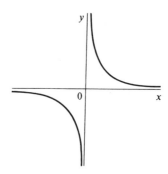

## The Ellipse $\dfrac{x^2}{a^2} + \dfrac{y^2}{b^2} = 1$

Parametric equations $x = a \cos t$, $y = b \sin t$

The equation of the tangent at $(x_1, y_1)$ is $\dfrac{xx_1}{a^2} + \dfrac{yy_1}{b^2} = 1$

The equation of the tangent at $(a \cos t, b \sin t)$

is $\dfrac{x \cos t}{a} + \dfrac{y \sin t}{b} = 1$

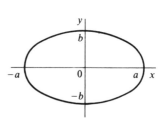

The equation of the normal at $(a \cos t, b \sin t)$ is $ax \sin t - by \cos t = (a^2 - b^2) \sin t \cos t$

---

Topics marked * are not included in the national common core and may not be needed for your syllabus.

The foci are the points $(\pm ae, 0)$, where $e < 1$

The directrices are the lines $x = \pm\dfrac{a}{e}$

$a$, $b$ and $e$ are connected by the equation $b^2 = a^2(1 - e^2)$

$e$ is called the eccentricity of the ellipse.

## The Curve $y^2 = x^3$

Parametric equations $x = t^2$, $y = t^3$

The equation of the tangent at $(t^2, t^3)$ is $2y = 3tx - t^3$

The equation of the normal at $(t^2, t^3)$ is $2x + 3ty = 2t^2 + 3t^4$

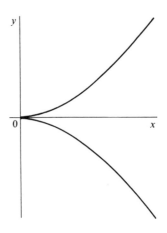

## Locus

A locus is a curve (or line) traced out by a point which moves so as to satisfy certain given conditions.

To find the cartesian equation of the locus of a point:

Let the point have coordinates $(\alpha, \beta)$.

Use the given conditions to write down equations involving $\alpha$ and/or $\beta$.

From these equations, obtain **one** equation which involves $\alpha$ and/or $\beta$ and no variables (such as $t$, $\theta$, or $p$ and $q$).

Since $(\alpha, \beta)$ lies on the locus, replacing $\alpha$ by $x$ and $\beta$ by $y$ will give the cartesian equation of the locus.

## Examples

**15.1**   $P\left(cp, \dfrac{c}{p}\right)$ lies on the rectangular hyperbola $xy = c^2$ and the normal at $P$ meets

the hyperbola again at $Q\left(cq, \dfrac{c}{q}\right)$. Show that $p^3 q = -1$.

$xy = c^2$

Differentiating, $x\dfrac{dy}{dx} + y = 0$

$\dfrac{dy}{dx} = -\dfrac{y}{x}$

The gradient of the tangent at $P$ is $-\dfrac{c}{p \cdot cp} = -\dfrac{1}{p^2}$

The gradient of the normal at $P$ is $p^2$

The gradient of the chord $PQ = \dfrac{y_2 - y_1}{x_2 - x_1}$

$$= \dfrac{\dfrac{c}{q} - \dfrac{c}{p}}{cq - cp} = -\dfrac{1}{pq}$$

The gradient of the normal = the gradient of the chord $PQ$

$$p^2 = -\dfrac{1}{pq}$$

$$p^3 q = -1.$$

**15.2**   $P(ap^2, 2ap)$ and $Q(aq^2, 2aq)$ are two points on the parabola $y^2 = 4ax$ such that angle $POQ = 90°$, where $O$ is the origin. Find the equation of the locus of the mid-point of $PQ$.

The gradient of $OP = \dfrac{2ap}{ap^2} = \dfrac{2}{p}$

The gradient of $OQ = \dfrac{2}{q}$

$OP$ is perpendicular to $OQ$, so $\dfrac{2}{p} \times \dfrac{2}{q} = -1$

$$\text{i.e. } pq = -4$$

Let the mid-point of $PQ$ be $(\alpha, \beta)$.

$$\alpha = \dfrac{ap^2 + aq^2}{2} = \dfrac{a}{2}[(p+q)^2 - 2pq]$$

$$\beta = \dfrac{2ap + 2aq}{2} = a(p+q)$$

Using $pq = -4$ and $p + q = \dfrac{\beta}{a}$ to eliminate $p$ and $q$,

$$\alpha = \dfrac{a}{2}\left[\left(\dfrac{\beta}{a}\right)^2 + 8\right]$$

$$2a\alpha = \beta^2 + 8a^2$$

The locus is the curve $y^2 = 2ax - 8a^2$.

**15.3**   Find the equation of the tangent at the point $T(t^2, t^3)$ on the curve $y^2 = x^3$. If this tangent meets the $x$-axis at $P$ and the $y$-axis at $Q$, show that $TP:PQ = 2:1$.

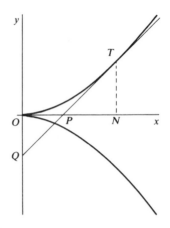

Differentiating, $2y\dfrac{dy}{dx} = 3x^2$

At $T$, $\dfrac{dy}{dx} = \dfrac{3t}{2}$

The equation of the tangent at $T$ is

$$y - t^3 = \frac{3t}{2}(x - t^2)$$

i.e. $2y = 3tx - t^3$

At $P$, $y = 0$, $x = \dfrac{t^2}{3}$

$TP:PQ = NP:PO$ (see the diagram, using similar triangles)

$$= t^2 - \frac{t^2}{3} : \frac{t^2}{3}$$

$$= 2:1$$

## Exercise 15.1

*Questions 1 to 3 refer to the parabola $y^2 = 4ax$, which has parametric equations $x = at^2$, $y = 2at$.*

1.  Find the gradient of the chord of the parabola joining points $P(ap^2, 2ap)$ and $Q(aq^2, 2aq)$.

2.  Find the coordinates of the point of intersection $R$, of the tangents at the points $P(ap^2, 2ap)$ and $Q(aq^2, 2aq)$ to the parabola. If $R$ lies on the line $x = -a$, show that
    1  angle $PRQ$ is a right-angle,
    2  the chord $PQ$ cuts the $x$-axis at $(a, 0)$.

3.  The tangent at $P(at^2, 2at)$ to the parabola cuts the $y$-axis at $T$. The normal at $P$ cuts the $x$-axis at $N$ and $M$ is the mid-point of $PN$. $S$ is the point $(a, 0)$. Show that $PTSM$ is a rectangle.

*Questions 4 to 7 refer to the rectangular hyperbola $xy = c^2$, which has parametric equations $x = ct$, $y = \dfrac{c}{t}$.*

4.  Find the gradient of the chord of the rectangular hyperbola joining points $P\left(cp, \dfrac{c}{p}\right)$ and $Q\left(cq, \dfrac{c}{q}\right)$.

5. The tangent at $P\left(ct, \dfrac{c}{t}\right)$ to the hyperbola meets the $x$-axis at $Q$. $O$ is the origin. Show that triangle $OPQ$ is isosceles.

6. The normal at $P\left(ct, \dfrac{c}{t}\right)$ to the hyperbola meets the line $y = x$ at $C$ and the line $y = -x$ at $D$. Show that $P$ is the mid-point of $CD$.

7. $P\left(cp, \dfrac{c}{p}\right)$, $Q\left(cq, \dfrac{c}{q}\right)$ and $R\left(cr, \dfrac{c}{r}\right)$ are three points on the hyperbola such that angle $QPR$ is a right angle. Show that the normal to the hyperbola at $P$ is parallel to the chord $QR$.

*Questions 8 to 11 refer to the ellipse* $\dfrac{x^2}{a^2} + \dfrac{y^2}{b^2} = 1$, *which has parametric equations* $x = a \cos t$, $y = b \sin t$.

8. Show that the gradient of the chord of the ellipse joining points $P(a \cos \theta, b \sin \theta)$ and $Q(a \cos \phi, b \sin \phi)$ is $-\dfrac{b}{a} \cot \dfrac{\theta + \phi}{2}$.

9. The ordinate through $(ca, 0)$, where $0 < c < 1$, meets the ellipse at a point $P$ in the first quadrant. Show that the tangent at $P$ cuts the $x$-axis at $(a/c, 0)$.

10. The points $P(a \cos \theta, b \sin \theta)$ and $Q(a \cos \phi, b \sin \phi)$ are such that the mid-point of $PQ$ lies on the line $ay = bx$. Show that the gradient of the chord $PQ$ is $-b/a$.

11. The line from $P(a \cos t, b \sin t)$ perpendicular to the $y$-axis meets it at $N$, the tangent at $P$ to the ellipse cuts the $y$-axis at $T$. $O$ is the origin. Show that $ON \times OT = b^2$.

*Other curves*

12. Find the equation of the tangent to the curve $8y^2 = x^3$ at the point $T(8t^2, 8t^3)$. Show that this tangent meets the curve again at $Q(2t^2, -t^3)$.

13. Find the equation of the tangent to the curve with parametric equations $x = a \cos^3 t$, $y = a \sin^3 t$ at the point $P(a \cos^3 t, a \sin^3 t)$. If this tangent meets the $x$-axis at $Q$ and the $y$-axis at $R$, find the length of $QR$, showing that it is independent of $t$.

14. $P(2p^2, 2p^3)$ and $Q(2q^2, 2q^3)$ are two points on the curve $2y^2 = x^3$. Find the coordinates of $T$, the point of intersection of the tangents to the curve at $P$ and $Q$. If $p + q = 2$, show that $T$ lies on the line $3x + y = 8$.

15. If the coordinates $\alpha, \beta$ of a point $P(\alpha, \beta)$ are given by the following equations, find the cartesian equation of the locus of $P$.

1 $\alpha = 2t - 1$, $\beta = 3t + 2$, where $t$ is a variable

2 $\alpha = 4t$, $\beta = 2t^2 + 1$, where $t$ is a variable

3 $\alpha = 3 - \cos \theta$, $\beta = 2 + \sin \theta$, where $\theta$ is a variable

4 $\alpha = p + q$, $\beta = p^2 + q^2$, where $p$ and $q$ are variables such that $pq = -1$

15.   **5**  $\alpha = \dfrac{p^2 + q^2}{2}$, $\beta = \dfrac{p + q}{2}$, where $p$ and $q$ are variables such that $p + q = 6$

      **6**  $\alpha = p^2 + q^2$, $\beta = p - q$, where $p$ and $q$ are variables such that $pq = 2$

      **7**  $\alpha = \dfrac{5}{t}$, $\beta = \dfrac{t^2}{2}$, where $t$ is a variable

      **8**  $\alpha = 4 \cos \theta$, $\beta = \sin \theta$, where $\theta$ is a variable

      **9**  $\alpha = \dfrac{1}{t} + 1$, $\beta = 2t - 1$, where $t$ is a variable

      **10**  $\alpha = \dfrac{1}{p} + \dfrac{1}{q}$, $\beta = 3pq$, where $p$ and $q$ are variables such that $p + q = 2$.

## Exercise 15.2

1.  $P$ is the point $(ap^2, 2ap)$ on the parabola $y^2 = 4ax$. The normal at $P$ meets the parabola again at $Q(aq^2, 2aq)$. Find an equation connecting $P$ and $Q$. Through $P$ and $Q$ lines are drawn parallel to the $y$-axis to meet the $x$-axis at $B$ and $C$ respectively. If $A$ is the point $(-a, 0)$, show that $AB : BC = p^2 : 4$.

2.  $P$ is the point $\left( ct, \dfrac{c}{t} \right)$ on the rectangular hyperbola $xy = c^2$. If the tangent to the hyperbola at $P$ meets the $x$-axis at $Q$ and the $y$-axis at $R$, show that $P$ is the mid-point of $QR$.

3.  $P$ is the point $(7 \cos t, 3 \sin t)$ on the ellipse $\dfrac{x^2}{49} + \dfrac{y^2}{9} = 1$. The line through $P$ parallel to the $y$-axis meets the $x$-axis at $N$, and $NP$ is produced to a point $Q$ such that $NP : PQ = 3 : 4$. Show that, as $t$ varies, the locus of $Q$ is a circle.
    Find the equations of the tangent to the circle at $Q$, and the tangent to the ellipse at $P$. Show that these tangents intersect on the $x$-axis.

4.  $A(t, 0)$ and $B(t - 1, t + 1)$ are variable points. $M$ is the point on $AB$, between $A$ and $B$, such that $AM : MB = 3 : 2$. Find the equation of the locus of $M$ as $t$ varies.

5.  Find the possible values of $k$ in terms of $a$ and $c$ if the line $y = k - a^2 x$ touches the rectangular hyperbola $xy = c^2$ for all values of $a$.

6.  Points $P(ap^2, 2ap)$ and $Q(aq^2, 2aq)$ lie on the parabola $y^2 = 4ax$. Show that if the chord $PQ$ passes through the point $(2a, 0)$ then $pq = -2$. When this condition is satisfied, show that the locus of the mid-point of $PQ$ is $y^2 = 2ax - 4a^2$.

7.  Two points $P(3p^2, 2p^3)$ and $Q(3q^2, 2q^3)$ on the curve $27y^2 = 4x^3$ are such that angle $POQ$ is a right angle, where $O$ is the origin. The tangents to the curve at $P$ and $Q$ intersect at $R$. Find the locus of $R$ as $p$ and $q$ vary.

8. $P\left(cp, \dfrac{c}{p}\right)$ and $Q\left(cq, \dfrac{c}{q}\right)$ are two points on the rectangular hyperbola $xy = c^2$, and the gradient of the chord $PQ$ is $m$, where $m$ is a constant. Show that the locus of the mid-point of $PQ$ is a line through the origin with gradient $-m$.

9. $P(ap^2, 2ap)$ and $Q(aq^2, 2aq)$ are two points on the parabola $y^2 = 4ax$. The tangents to the parabola at $P$ and $Q$ meet at $T$, and angle $PTQ$ is a right angle. The normals to the parabola at $P$ and $Q$ meet at $N$. Show that the line $TN$ is parallel to the $x$-axis.

10. Find the equation of the tangent at $P(5 \cos t, 4 \sin t)$ to the ellipse $\dfrac{x^2}{25} + \dfrac{y^2}{16} = 1$. Find the perpendicular distances to this tangent from the point $S(3, 0)$ and from the point $S'(-3, 0)$. Show that the product of these distances is independent of $t$.

11. $P\left(p, \dfrac{c}{p}\right)$ and $Q\left(cq, \dfrac{c}{q}\right)$ are two points on the rectangular hyperbola $xy = c^2$. The chord $PQ$ meets the $x$-axis at $A$ and the $y$-axis at $B$. Show that $PA = QB$.

12. $P$ is the point $(6 \cos t, 3 \sin t)$ on the ellipse $\dfrac{x^2}{36} + \dfrac{y^2}{9} = 1$. The tangent at $P$ meets the $y$-axis at $T$. $A$ is the point $(6, 0)$ and the line $AP$ meets the $y$-axis at $C$. $B$ is the point $(-6, 0)$ and the line $BP$ meets the $y$-axis at $D$. Show that $T$ is the mid-point of $CD$.

13. $P\left(ct, \dfrac{c}{t}\right)$ is a point on the rectangular hyperbola $xy = c^2$. The tangent to the hyperbola at $P$ meets the $y$-axis at $T$, and the normal at $P$ meets the $x$-axis at $N$. Find the coordinates of $T$ and $N$. Show that the equation of the locus of the mid-point of $NT$ as $t$ varies is $y^4 + 2xyc^2 = c^4$.

14. Find the point of intersection of the curves $8y^2 = x^3$ and $xy = 2$. If the acute angle between the tangents to these curves at this point is $\theta$, find $\tan \theta$.

15. Show that the line $y = mx + \dfrac{a}{m}$ is a tangent to the parabola $y^2 = 4ax$ for all values of $m \neq 0$.

16. $A$ is the fixed point $(1, 0)$ and $T$ is the variable point $(2t, t)$ on the line $y = \frac{1}{2}x$. The line through $T$ perpendicular to $AT$ cuts the $y$-axis at $R$. $M$ is the mid-point of $RT$. Find the locus of $M$ as $t$ varies.

17. **Definition of a parabola**
The parabola is the locus of a point which moves so that its distance from a fixed point, called the focus, is equal to its distance from a fixed line, called the directrix.

Find the locus of a point $P(\alpha, \beta)$ which moves so that its distance from $S(a, 0)$ is equal to its distance from the line $x = -a$, showing that the locus is the parabola $y^2 = 4ax$.

18. **Definition of an ellipse**

    The ellipse is the locus of a point which moves so that its distance from a fixed point, called a focus, is in a constant ratio $e < 1$ to its distance from a fixed line, called a directrix.

    Find the locus of a point $P(\alpha, \beta)$ which moves so that its distance from $S(ae, 0)$ is $e$ times its distance from the line $x = a/e$, where $e < 1$. Putting $1 - e^2 = b^2/a^2$, show that the locus is the ellipse $x^2/a^2 + y^2/b^2 = 1$.

19. **A property of the ellipse**

    The ellipse has two foci, $S(ae, 0)$ and $S'(-ae, 0)$ and

    two directrices $x = \dfrac{a}{e}$ and $x = -\dfrac{a}{e}$. Therefore, in the

    diagram, by the definition of question 18, $PS = ePZ$ and $PS' = ePZ'$. Show that $PS + PS' = 2a$.

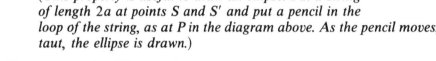

    (*This property is useful to draw an ellipse. Fix a string of length $2a$ at points $S$ and $S'$ and put a pencil in the loop of the string, as at $P$ in the diagram above. As the pencil moves, keeping the string taut, the ellipse is drawn.*)

20. **A property of the parabola**

    In the diagram, $P$ is the point $(at^2, 2at)$ on the parabola $y^2 = 4ax$. $S$ is the focus $(a, 0)$. The tangent to the parabola at $P$ meets the $x$-axis at $T$. Show that $ST = SP$. Hence show that the angles $QPK$ and $TPS$ are equal, where $PK$ is parallel to the $x$-axis.

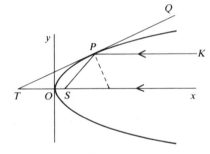

    (*This shows that $SP$ and $KP$ make equal angles with the normal at $P$. If the parabola has a reflective surface, all rays from $S$ will be reflected parallel to the axis of the parabola. This property is used, for example, in searchlights where a source at $S$ sends out a parallel beam of light. In radio telescopes, rays coming from a far distance, parallel to the axis of the parabolic mirror, are all reflected onto the focus.*)

# E   Revision

**Exercise E1**

1. Simplify the infinite product $x^{\frac{1}{3}} \cdot x^{\frac{2}{9}} \cdot x^{\frac{4}{27}} \cdot x^{\frac{8}{81}} \ldots$.

2. Sketch the graph of $y = \dfrac{6-x}{2-3x}$. For what range of values of $x$ is $y < 1$?

3. Find the first 3 terms in the expansion in ascending powers of $x$ of $(3+x)^{-3}$.

4. If $f(x) = \dfrac{x-2}{x+2}$, what is the domain and range of the function? Show that $f(x) \cdot f(-x) = 1$, and find the value of $f(2x) + f\left(\dfrac{2}{x}\right)$.

5. If $A$, $B$, $C$ are the angles of a triangle, write down the connection between $\tan A$ and $\tan(B+C)$. Hence show that $\tan A + \tan B + \tan C = \tan A \tan B \tan C$.

6. Show that $\dfrac{\sin\theta + \sin 3\theta}{\cos\theta + \cos 3\theta} = \tan 2\theta$.

7. Solve the equation $10 \tan\theta = 3 \sec^2\theta$ for $0° < \theta < 90°$.

8. Find the approximate value of $\dfrac{1 - \cos 2\theta}{\theta^2}$ if $\theta$ is small.

9. Find the cartesian equation of the curve whose parametric equations are $x = \cos t$, $y = \cos 2t$.

10. If $z_1 = 2(\cos\alpha + i\sin\alpha)$ and $z_2 = 4(\cos 2\alpha + i\sin 2\alpha)$, find $|z_1|$, $|z_2|$, $\arg z_1$ and $\arg z_2$. Find $z_1 z_2$, $\dfrac{z_2}{z_1}$, and show that $z_2 = z_1^2$.

11. Find the tangent of the acute angle between the lines $4x - 3y = 6$ and $x + 5y + 9 = 0$.

12. The line $x + 3y = 24$ intersects the circle $x^2 + y^2 + 4x + 6y - 112 = 0$ at points $A$ and $B$. Find the coordinates of the mid-point of $AB$.

13. The tangent to the curve $y = x^n$ at $T(a, a^n)$ cuts the $x$-axis at $P$ and the $y$-axis at $Q$. Find the ratio $TP : TQ$ in its simplest form.

14. If $y = e^x \sin 3x$, show that $\dfrac{d^2 y}{dx^2} - 2\dfrac{dy}{dx} + 10y = 0$.

15. If $y = \ln \tan 2x$, find $\dfrac{dy}{dx}$.

16. Find the equation of the normal to the curve $2x^3 - 4x^2y + y^3 + 10 = 0$ at the point $(3, 2)$.

17. Find $\displaystyle\int \dfrac{e^x + 2}{e^x + 2x}\, dx$.

18. If $y = \sqrt{4 - x}$, find the mean value of $y^2$ in the interval $x = 0$ to $x = 4$.

19. A line is drawn through $A$ and $B$ where $A$ has position vector $3\mathbf{p} + \mathbf{q}$ and $B$ has position vector $4\mathbf{p} - 2\mathbf{q}$. Find the position vector of the point in which this line meets the line with equation $\mathbf{r} = \mathbf{p} + t\mathbf{q}$.

20. If $\overrightarrow{OA} = 7\mathbf{i} - 3\mathbf{j} - 2\mathbf{k}$, $\overrightarrow{OB} = 3\mathbf{i} + 4\mathbf{j} + 2\mathbf{k}$ and $\overrightarrow{OC} = 2\mathbf{i} + 6\mathbf{j} + 4\mathbf{k}$, find the cosine of angle $ABC$.

## Exercise E2

Select the correct answer to each question.

1. The acute angle between the lines $5x - 4y = 8$ and $7x + 2y = 9$ is $\theta$ where $\tan \theta =$

   **A** $\frac{9}{4}$      **B** $\frac{19}{4}$      **C** $\frac{38}{27}$      **D** $\frac{18}{43}$      **E** $\frac{38}{43}$

2. The line $\mathbf{r} = 2\mathbf{i} - \mathbf{j} + \mathbf{k} + s(-\mathbf{i} + \mathbf{j} + 3\mathbf{k})$ and the plane $\mathbf{r} \cdot (2\mathbf{i} + 4\mathbf{j} - \mathbf{k}) = 3$ meet at the point with position vector

   **A** $-\mathbf{i} + \mathbf{j} + 3\mathbf{k}$      **B** $2\mathbf{i} - \mathbf{j} + \mathbf{k}$      **C** $4\mathbf{i} - 4\mathbf{j} - 12\mathbf{k}$

   **D** $5\mathbf{i} - 4\mathbf{j} - 8\mathbf{k}$      **E** $6\mathbf{i} - 5\mathbf{j} - 11\mathbf{k}$

3. If $y = -\cos 2x$, the area between the curve and the $x$-axis from $x = \pi/4$ to $x = 3\pi/4$ is

   **A** $\frac{1}{2}$      **B** $1$      **C** $\sqrt{2}/2$      **D** $\sqrt{2}$      **E** $2$

4. The complete solution of the equation $\sin 3x = \sin x$ for $0 \leqslant x \leqslant \pi$ is $x =$

   **A** $0$ or $\pi$      **B** $0, \dfrac{\pi}{4}$ or $\pi$      **C** $0, \dfrac{\pi}{4}, \dfrac{3\pi}{4}$ or $\pi$

   **D** $\dfrac{\pi}{4}$ or $\dfrac{3\pi}{4}$      **E** $0, \dfrac{\pi}{4}, \dfrac{\pi}{2}, \dfrac{3\pi}{4}$ or $\pi$

5. If $z = \dfrac{3 + i}{1 - 2i}$ then $z^*$ (the conjugate of $z$) =

   **A** $\dfrac{3 + i}{1 + 2i}$      **B** $\dfrac{3 - i}{1 - 2i}$      **C** $-\dfrac{1 - 7i}{3}$      **D** $\dfrac{1 + 7i}{5}$      **E** $\dfrac{1 - 7i}{5}$

6.  If $x = a(1 - \cos \theta)$ and $y = a\theta \sin \theta$ then $\dfrac{dy}{dx} =$

    **A**  $\theta \cot \theta$           **B**  $1 + \theta \cot \theta$           **C**  $1 - \theta \cot \theta$

    **D**  $\theta \operatorname{cosec} \theta + \cot \theta$           **E**  $\dfrac{\sin \theta}{\theta \cos \theta + \sin \theta}$

7.  If $\dfrac{dy}{dx} = y \sin x$ and $y = 3$ when $x = \pi/2$, then when $x = \pi$, $y =$

    **A**  $e$           **B**  $e + 3$           **C**  $3e$           **D**  $1/e$           **E**  $3/e$

8.  If $A$ is the point $(3, 2)$ and $B$ is the point $(-7, 6)$, then the equation of the perpendicular bisector of $AB$ is

    **A**  $2y = 5x - 11$           **B**  $2y = 5x + 18$           **C**  $2y = 5x + 47$

    **D**  $2x - 5y + 44 = 0$           **E**  $2x + 5y - 16 = 0$

9.  When $y = 4 \sin 3t$, $\dfrac{d^2 y}{dx^2}$ in terms of $y$ is

    **A**  $-36y$       **B**  $-9y$           **C**  $-y$           **D**  $9y$           **E**  $3\sqrt{16 - y^2}$

10. If $3 \ln x + \ln(y - 1) = 0$, then $y$ in terms of $x$ is

    **A**  $1 + \dfrac{1}{3x}$       **B**  $1 + \dfrac{1}{x^3}$           **C**  $1 + \dfrac{e}{3x}$           **D**  $1 + \dfrac{e}{x^3}$           **E**  $2 - x^3$

11. If $x^2 + 2x - 8 > 0$, then the complete range for $x$ is

    **A**  $x < -4$           **B**  $x < 2$           **C**  $x > 2$           **D**  $-4 < x < 2$

    **E**  $x < -4$ or $x > 2$

12. The area bounded by the $x$-axis, the lines $x = 1$ and $x = 4$, and the arc of the parabola $y^2 = 4x$ between $(1, 2)$ and $(4, 4)$ is rotated completely about the $x$-axis. The volume of revolution is

    **A**  $30\pi$           **B**  $32\pi$           **C**  $64\pi$           **D**  $28\pi/3$           **E**  $32\pi/3$

13. If $f(x) = \cos x$ and $g(x) = x^2 + 3$ then $gf(x)$ is

    **A**  $\cos^2 x + 3$           **B**  $\cos^2(x + 3)$           **C**  $\cos(x^2 + 3)$

    **D**  $(\cos x + 3)^2$           **E**  $\cos^{-1}(x^2 + 3)$

14. The maximum point on the curve $y = x - 2 \cos x$ for $x$ between $0$ and $2\pi$ occurs when $x =$

    **A**  $\dfrac{\pi}{6}$           **B**  $\dfrac{\pi}{2}$           **C**  $\dfrac{5\pi}{6}$           **D**  $\dfrac{7\pi}{6}$           **E**  $\dfrac{11\pi}{6}$

15. Which one of these expressions is not equal to the others?

    **A**  $x e^0$           **B**  $\ln e^x$           **C**  $x \ln e$           **D**  $x \ln 1$           **E**  $e^{\ln x}$

16. If $3\cos\theta + 2\sin\theta$ is expressed as $R\cos(\theta - \alpha)$, then $\sin\alpha =$

  A $\frac{2}{3}$        B $\frac{3}{2}$        C $\dfrac{2}{\sqrt{13}}$        D $-\dfrac{2}{\sqrt{13}}$        E $\dfrac{3}{\sqrt{13}}$

17. $\displaystyle\int_{-1}^{1}\frac{1}{5-3x}\,dx =$

  A $-\frac{2}{3}\ln 2$     B $-\frac{1}{3}\ln 2$     C $-2\ln 2$     D $\frac{2}{3}\ln 2$     E $2\ln 2$

18. If the roots of a quadratic equation are $\alpha$, $\beta$ and $\alpha + \beta = -8$ and $\alpha^2 + \beta^2 = 42$ then the equation is

  A $x^2 + 8x + 11 = 0$          B $x^2 - 8x + 11 = 0$          C $x^2 + 11x - 8 = 0$

  D $x^2 - 11x + 8 = 0$          E $x^2 + 8x + 42 = 0$

19. If $x$ and $y$ are connected by the differential equation $\dfrac{dy}{dx} = y^2 + 1$, and $y = 1$ when $x = 0$, then when $x = \pi/12$, $y =$

  A $1$          B $\sqrt{3}$          C $\sqrt{3}/3$          D $2 - \sqrt{3}$          E $2 + \sqrt{3}$

20. $\displaystyle\int\left(4x^3 - \frac{2}{x^2}\right)dx$ is

  A $12x^2 + \dfrac{4}{x^3} + c$          B $12x^2 + \dfrac{6}{x^3} + c$          C $x^4 - \dfrac{2}{x} + c$

  D $x^4 - \dfrac{1}{x} + c$          E $x^4 + \dfrac{2}{x} + c$

## Exercise E3

Select the correct answer to each question.

1. The gradient of the line joining the points $(\cos\theta, \sin\theta)$ and $(\cos\phi, \sin\phi)$ is

  A $\cot\dfrac{\theta + \phi}{2}$          B $-\cot\dfrac{\theta + \phi}{2}$          C $\tan\dfrac{\theta - \phi}{2}$

  D $-\tan\dfrac{\theta - \phi}{2}$          E $\tan(\phi - \theta)$

2. The resolved part of the vector $\mathbf{a} = -\mathbf{i} + 2\mathbf{j} + 2\mathbf{k}$ in the direction of $\mathbf{b} = 2\mathbf{i} - 6\mathbf{j} + 9\mathbf{k}$ is

  A $\frac{4}{3}$        B $\frac{4}{9}$        C $\frac{4}{11}$        D $\frac{4}{33}$        E $\frac{32}{11}$

3. If $y = \ln(x+2)^3$ then $\dfrac{dy}{dx} =$

  A $\dfrac{1}{3(x+2)}$          B $\dfrac{3}{x+2}$          C $\dfrac{1}{3(x+2)^2}$

  D $\dfrac{3}{(x+2)^2}$          E $\dfrac{1}{(x+2)^3}$

4. The coefficient of $x^3$ in the expansion of $(1-\frac{1}{2}x)^{\frac{1}{2}}$ is

   **A** $-\frac{1}{128}$    **B** $\frac{1}{128}$    **C** $-\frac{3}{128}$    **D** $\frac{3}{128}$    **E** $-\frac{1}{32}$

5. The circle with equation $x^2+y^2-6x-4y-23=0$ has radius

   **A** $5\sqrt{3}$    **B** 6    **C** $\sqrt{10}$    **D** $\sqrt{13}$    **E** $\sqrt{23}$

6. Which one of these expressions is not equal to the others?

   **A** $1+\tan^2 x$    **B** $\dfrac{1}{\cos^2 x}$    **C** $\dfrac{1}{1-\sin^2 x}$

   **D** $\dfrac{\tan^2 x}{\sin^2 x}$    **E** $\dfrac{\cos^2 x}{\cot^2 x}$

7. If $y=(3-2x^2)^5$ then $\dfrac{dy}{dx}=$

   **A** $-4x(3-2x^2)$    **B** $5(3-3x^2)^4$    **C** $20x(3-2x^2)^4$
   **D** $-20x(3-2x^2)^4$    **E** $-20(3-2x^2)^4$

8. The roots of the equation $\dfrac{x+2}{x}=\dfrac{2}{x+2}$ are

   **A** $\pm 2$    **B** $-1\pm\sqrt{5}$    **C** $1\pm\sqrt{5}$    **D** $1\pm\sqrt{3}i$    **E** $-1\pm\sqrt{3}i$

9. The area in the first quadrant enclosed by the curve $y^2=x^5$, the $x$-axis and the lines $x=1$ and $x=4$ is

   **A** $12\frac{2}{5}$    **B** $12\frac{4}{5}$    **C** $36\frac{2}{7}$    **D** $36\frac{4}{7}$    **E** $444\frac{1}{2}$

10. The line $2x+y-12=0$ meets the parabola $y^2=4x$ at $A$ and $B$. The mid-point of the chord $AB$ is the point

   **A** $(7,-2)$    **B** $(6\frac{1}{2},-1)$    **C** $(6,0)$    **D** $(5\frac{1}{2},1)$    **E** $(5,2)$

11. $\dfrac{24+x}{x^2-x-12}\equiv\dfrac{A}{x-4}+\dfrac{B}{x+3}$, then $2A+B=$

   **A** $-5$    **B** $-2$    **C** 1    **D** 2    **E** 5

12. If the points with position vectors $(22,22,1)$, $(4,13,a)$ and $(-2,b,-3)$ are collinear then $a+b=$

   **A** $-12$    **B** $-8$    **C** 4    **D** 8    **E** 12

13. The sum of the first 12 terms of the geometric progression $5$, $-1\frac{2}{3}$, $\frac{5}{9}$, ... is

   **A** $\frac{15}{8}[1-(\frac{5}{3})^{12}]$    **B** $\frac{15}{4}\left(1-\dfrac{1}{3^{12}}\right)$    **C** $\frac{15}{2}\left(1-\dfrac{1}{3^{12}}\right)$

   **D** $\frac{15}{2}\left(1+\dfrac{1}{3^{12}}\right)$    **E** $\frac{15}{4}\left(1+\dfrac{1}{3^{12}}\right)$

14. If $|z+1|=9$ then the locus of $z$ on the Argand diagram is
   A   the perpendicular bisector of the line joining $(1,0)$ and $(9,0)$
   B   a circle centre $(1,0)$, radius 9
   C   a circle centre $(-1,0)$, radius 9
   D   a circle centre $(1,0)$, radius 3
   E   a circle centre $(-1,0)$, radius 3

15. $P$ and $Q$ are points $(p^2, p^3)$, $(q^2, q^3)$ on the curve $y^2 = x^3$. The gradient of the chord $PQ$ is

   A   $p-q$
   B   $p+q$
   C   $\dfrac{p^2+pq+q^2}{p-q}$

   D   $\dfrac{p^2-pq+q^2}{p-q}$
   E   $\dfrac{p^2+pq+q^2}{p+q}$

16. The complete solution of $2\cos^2 x - 3\cos x + 1 = 0$ between $-\pi$ and $\pi$ inclusive is $x =$

   A   $\dfrac{\pi}{3}$
   B   $\dfrac{\pi}{3}, -\dfrac{\pi}{3}$
   C   $\dfrac{\pi}{3}, 0, -\dfrac{\pi}{3}$

   D   $\dfrac{\pi}{3}, -\dfrac{\pi}{3}, \pi, -\pi$
   E   $0, \dfrac{\pi}{3}, \dfrac{2\pi}{3}, \pi$

17. The rate of growth of a substance is proportional to the amount of the substance present at that time.
   The differential equation and its solution, where $k$ is a positive constant and $x_0$ is the value of $x$ when $t=0$, are

   A   $\dfrac{dx}{dt} = kx,\ x = x_0\, e^{kt}$
   B   $\dfrac{dx}{dt} = kx,\ x = x_0\, e^{-kt}$

   C   $\dfrac{dx}{dt} = k,\ x = kt + x_0$
   D   $\dfrac{dx}{dt} = -kx,\ x = x_0\, e^{-kt}$

   E   $\dfrac{dx}{dt} = -kx,\ x = x_0\, e^{kt}$

18. The argument of the complex number $\sqrt{3} - i$ is

   A   $-\dfrac{\pi}{6}$
   B   $\dfrac{\pi}{6}$
   C   $-\dfrac{\pi}{3}$
   D   $-\dfrac{5\pi}{6}$
   E   $\dfrac{5\pi}{6}$

19. $A$ is the point $(2,5)$, $B$ is $(-7,32)$. $P$ divides $AB$ internally in the ratio $1:2$, $Q$ divides $AB$ internally in the ratio $4:5$. The mid-point of $PQ$ is
   A   $(-1\frac{1}{2}, 15\frac{1}{2})$   B   $(-2, 17)$   C   $(-2\frac{1}{2}, 18\frac{1}{2})$   D   $(-3, 20)$   E   $(-3\frac{1}{2}, 21\frac{1}{2})$

20. If $f(x) = \frac{1}{2}(x+1)$, the inverse function $f^{-1}(x)$ is

   A   $\dfrac{2}{x+1}$   B   $2(x+1)$   C   $2x+1$   D   $2x-1$   E   $\dfrac{1}{2(x+1)}$

## Exercise E4

1. *ABCD* is a tetrahedron and the position vectors of *A, B, C, D* are **a, b, c, d** respectively. Find the position vectors of the mid-points of *AB* and *CD*, and the mid-point of the line joining these two points. Hence show that the lines joining the mid-points of opposite edges of a tetrahedron are concurrent and bisect each other.

2. If $f(x) = \ln x$, where $x \geqslant 1$, and $g(x) = x^2$, where $x \geqslant 0$, find $gf(x)$ and $(gf)^{-1}(x)$. Verify that $(gf)^{-1}(x) = f^{-1}g^{-1}(x)$.

3. In triangle *ABC*, the lengths of the sides are in arithmetical progression and the largest angle is 120°. If the largest side is 7 units find the lengths of the other two sides.

4. Use the factor theorem to find a real root of the equation $z^3 - 7z^2 + 12z + 20 = 0$ and hence find all roots, real and complex. On an Argand diagram show the points representing the 3 roots. Verify that the point $z = 1.9$ is equidistant from these 3 points.

5. Find the equation of the tangent to the curve given by $x = 2t^2 - 3$, $y = t^3 + 4t$ at the point on the curve where $t = 2$. Find also the coordinates of the point at which this tangent meets the curve again.

6. Find the perpendicular distance from the origin to the line $ax + by + c = 0$. If this line intersects the circle $x^2 + y^2 = r^2$ in 2 real points, show that $c^2 < r^2(a^2 + b^2)$.

7. Find the point of intersection of the plane $\mathbf{r} \cdot (1, -1, 3) = 20$ and the line perpendicular to the plane which passes through the point with position vector $(1, 1, 3)$.

8. Solve the equation $\cos 3\theta - \cos \theta = \sin \theta$, giving the general solution (in radians).

9. In a right circular cylinder the base-radius increases steadily at the rate of $u$ cm/s and the height increases steadily at the rate of $2u$ cm/s. Find the rate of increase of the volume of the cylinder at the time when the radius is $a$ cm and the height is $3a$ cm.

10. Find $\displaystyle\int_2^4 x \ln x \, dx$ and $\displaystyle\int_2^4 x(\ln x)^2 \, dx$, giving the results in terms of $\ln 2$.

11. From a point *A* the angle of elevation of the top of a flagpole, which is due north of *A* on level ground, is $\alpha$. From a point *B* which is $d$ units east of *A* on the same level, the angle of elevation of the top of the flagpole is $\beta$. Show that the height of the flagpole is $\dfrac{d}{\sqrt{\cot^2 \beta - \cot^2 \alpha}}$, and show that this expression is equivalent to $\dfrac{d \sin \alpha \sin \beta}{\sqrt{\sin(\alpha - \beta) \sin(\alpha + \beta)}}$.

12. On the rectangular hyperbola $xy = c^2$, *P* is the point $\left(cp, \dfrac{c}{p}\right)$ and *Q* is the point $\left(cq, \dfrac{c}{q}\right)$. The line through *P* parallel to the *x*-axis meets the *y*-axis at *A* and the line through *Q* parallel to the *y*-axis meets the *x*-axis at *B*. Show that *PQ* and *AB* are parallel.

13. The circle $x^2 + y^2 = 1$ is cut by the line $x = \sqrt{3}/2$ at points $B$ and $C$. If $D$ is the point $(1, 0)$, find by integration the area of the segment $BDC$. By using the standard formula for the area of sector $BOC$ and subtracting the area of triangle $BOC$, where $O$ is the origin, verify that your result is correct.

14. In a certain reaction the rate of growth of a substance is proportional to the amount $x$ of the substance present at that time. Originally there were 10 units of the substance and after 1 minute there were 30 units. How much longer would it take before there were 300 units of substance, to the nearest 0.1 minute?

15. If $y = \dfrac{x^2 - 2x - 1}{x^2 - 4x + 3}$, express $y$ in partial fractions. Hence find $\dfrac{dy}{dx}$ and $\dfrac{d^2y}{dx^2}$. Show that the gradient of the function is always negative, and that there is a point of inflexion when $x = 2$. Find the equation of the tangent to the curve at this point.

## Exercise E5

1. Find the remainder when $2x^3 - 3x^2 + 7x - 4$ is divided by $x - 2$.

2. Find $\displaystyle\int_0^{\pi/2} \sin^2 x \cos^3 x \, dx$.

3. Expand $(1 - 2x)^{\frac{1}{2}}$ in ascending powers of $x$ as far as the term in $x^3$. For what range of values of $x$ is the expansion valid? By putting $x = 0.01$ find an approximate value for $\sqrt{2}$, to 3 decimal places.

4. If $f(x) = \dfrac{x}{x - 3}$, what is the domain, and range of $f(x)$? Find the inverse function $f^{-1}(x)$ and verify that $ff^{-1}(x) = x$. What is the domain, and range of $f^{-1}(x)$? Sketch the graphs of $f(x)$ and $f^{-1}(x)$. For what values of $x$ is $f(x) = f^{-1}(x)$?

5. A triangle has two sides lengths 4 and 5 units with included angle $\theta$. If its area is $A$ square units find $\dfrac{dA}{d\theta}$ in terms of $\theta$. When $\theta$ is an acute angle and $\sin\theta = \frac{4}{5}$, $\theta$ is increased by 0.01 radians. What is the approximate increase in the area?

6. Solve the equation $2\ln(2x - 1) - \ln(x + 1) = 3\ln 3 - \ln 2$.

7. Show on an Argand diagram the locus of points representing the number $z$ where $|z - 1 - i| \leqslant \sqrt{2}$ and $0 \leqslant \arg z \leqslant \pi/4$. Mark the region satisfying both conditions and find the area of this region.

8. Express $f(\theta) = \cos\theta + 7\sin\theta$ in the form $R\cos(\theta - \alpha)$. State the maximum and minimum values of $f(\theta)$. Solve the equation $f(\theta) = 5$ in the range $0° \leqslant \theta \leqslant 360°$.

9. A triangle is formed by the intersection of the three lines $y = 2x - 4$, $y = 7x + 6$, $x + 7y = 92$. Find the equation of its circumcircle.

10. From the top of a cliff, height $h$, two ships are observed out at sea. One is due south at an angle of depression $\alpha$ and the other is due south-west at an angle of depression $\beta$. Show that the distance between the two ships is $h(\cot^2 \alpha + \cot^2 \beta - \sqrt{2} \cot \alpha \cot \beta)^{\frac{1}{2}}$.

11. Find the maximum and minimum points on the curve with equation
$y = 8 \sin x - 3\sqrt{3} \tan x$, for $-\pi/2 < x < \pi/2$.

12. The position vectors of $A$, $B$, $C$ are $3\mathbf{i} - 2\mathbf{j} + 4\mathbf{k}$, $-2\mathbf{i} + 8\mathbf{j} + 9\mathbf{k}$ and $12\mathbf{i} + 7\mathbf{j} + 13\mathbf{k}$ respectively. Find the position vector of the point $D$ on $AB$ such that $AD : DB = 3 : 2$, and show that $CD$ is perpendicular to $AB$.

13. The tangent at $T\left(\dfrac{3\sqrt{3}}{2}, \dfrac{1}{2}\right)$ on the ellipse $x^2 + 9y^2 = 9$ meets the $x$-axis at $P$ and the $y$-axis at $Q$. Find the length of $PQ$.

14. The gradients of two curves satisfy the differential equations $3x^2 y \dfrac{dy}{dx} = 2$ and $2x^2 \dfrac{dy}{dx} = y^2$. Both curves pass through the point $(2, 1)$. Find their equations and find the tangent of the acute angle at which the curves intersect at $(2, 1)$.

15. Express $\dfrac{2 + 3x + x^2}{(1 + x^2)(3 - x)}$ in partial fractions.

Hence show that $\displaystyle\int_1^2 \dfrac{2 + 3x + x^2}{(1 + x^2)(3 - x)}\,dx = \tfrac{1}{2} \ln 40$.

## Exercise E6

1. $f(x) = \dfrac{1}{1 + \sin x}$ for $-\dfrac{\pi}{2} < x \leqslant \dfrac{\pi}{2}$. Find $f^{-1}(x)$. What is the domain of $f^{-1}(x)$?

2. The position vectors of $A$, $B$, $C$, $D$ are $(1, 3, 3)$, $(3, -1, 1)$, $(-12, -1, -4)$ and $(-6, -7, 8)$ respectively. Find the cosine of the angle between the directions of $\overrightarrow{AB}$ and $\overrightarrow{CD}$.

3. Use the factor theorem to show that $x = \tfrac{1}{2}$ is a root of the equation $8x^3 - 4x^2 - 6x + 3 = 0$. Hence solve the equation.
Solve the equation $8 \sin^3 \theta - 4 \sin^2 \theta - 6 \sin \theta + 3 = 0$ for $-\pi/2 < \theta < \pi/2$.

4. The complex number $z = x + iy$ is such that $\dfrac{z + 5 + 5i}{z + 7 - i} = a$, where $a$ is real and $\neq 1$.
Show that if $z$ is represented in the Argand diagram by a point $P$, then the locus of $P$ as $a$ varies is a straight line, and find its equation. Find the particular point on this line representing $z$ when $a = -1$.

5. Triangle $ABC$, with angle $A = 90°$, lies in a horizontal plane. At $C$ there is a vertical pole $CD$. If $CD = CA = h$, and $BA = AD$, find the angle between $BD$ and the horizontal.

6. Using Simpson's rule with 7 ordinates (6 strips), find an approximate value for
$\displaystyle\int_0^6 \sqrt{36 - x^2}\,dx$.

By using the substitution $x = 6 \cos \theta$, find the exact value of the integral, and calculate the % error using Simpson's rule.

7. If $\tan \alpha$ and $\tan \beta$ are the roots of the equation $(k+4)\tan^2 x - 6\tan x + k - 4 = 0$, show that $\tan(\alpha + \beta) = \frac{3}{4}$.

8. The gradient of a curve at a general point $(x, y)$ varies as the product $xy$. Write down a differential equation expressing this. The curve passes through the point $(2, 5)$ and the tangent to the curve at this point makes an angle of $45°$ with the positive direction of the $x$-axis. Find the equation of the curve in the form $y = f(x)$.

9. Find the product $P$ of the first $n$ terms of the geometric sequence $a, ar, ar^2, \ldots,$ in terms of $a$, $r$ and $n$. If the $n$th term is $b$, show that $P^2 = (ab)^n$.

10. A circle passes through the origin and has its centre at the point $A(8, 6)$. Find its equation.
A second circle with centre $B$ has equation $x^2 + y^2 - 24x - 18y + 200 = 0$. Show that this circle passes through $A$ and also show that the circles touch each other. Find the equation of the common tangent.

11. Express $\dfrac{x}{(1-2x)(1-3x)}$ in partial fractions and hence expand this function in ascending powers of $x$, giving the first 3 terms and the general term $x^r$. For what range of values of $x$ is this expansion valid?

12. $P(ap^2, 2ap)$ and $Q(aq^2, 2aq)$ are points on the parabola $y^2 = 4x$ such that the gradient of the chord $PQ$ is $\frac{1}{4}$. The tangents at $P$ and $Q$ meet at $T$. Find the locus of $T$ as $p$ and $q$ vary.

13. The pairs of values of $x$ and $y$ in the table satisfy approximately the relationship $y = ax^b$.

| $x$ | 10 | 20 | 30 | 60 | 80 | 100 |
|---|---|---|---|---|---|---|
| $y$ | 7.0 | 11.1 | 14.5 | 23.0 | 27.9 | 32.3 |

By plotting $\log_{10} y$ against $\log_{10} x$ and drawing an appropriate straight line, find values for $a$ and $b$, giving them to 1 decimal place. Use your graph to estimate the value of $y$ when $x = 50$, to the nearest integer.

14. 1 Express $1 - \dfrac{1}{1+a}$ as a single fraction.     3 Find the value of $\displaystyle\int_0^1 2x \tan^{-1} x \, dx$.

    2 Find the value of $\displaystyle\int_0^1 \dfrac{x^2}{1+x^2} dx$.

15. Find the maximum point on the curve $y = \dfrac{(2-x)(x-8)}{x}$. Where does the curve cross the $x$-axis?
Find the area of the finite region in the first quadrant between the curve and the $x$-axis, giving the answer in terms of $\ln 2$.

16. Show that $\dfrac{1 - \cos 2\theta}{1 + \cos 2\theta} = \tan^2 \theta$.
Express $\ln \tan \theta$ as a series of powers of $\cos 2\theta$, giving the first 3 terms. For what values of $\theta$ in the range $0 \leqslant \theta \leqslant 2\pi$ is this expansion **not** valid?

# Formulae Checklist

## Algebra

*Chapter 1*

1. Factorise $x^3 + y^3$
2. Factorise $x^3 - y^3$

### Quadratic equations:

3. Solution of $ax^2 + bx + c = 0$
4. Condition for real, unequal roots:
5. Condition for equal roots:
6. Condition for no real roots:
7. If roots $\alpha, \beta$ then $\alpha + \beta = $ , $\alpha\beta = $
8. Equation in terms of the sum $S$, and product $P$, of its roots:
9. Condition for f$(x)$ to have a factor $(x - a)$:
10. The remainder when f$(x)$ is divided by $(x - a)$:

### Indices:

11. $a^m \times a^n = $
12. $a^m \div a^n = $
13. $(a^m)^n = $
14. $a^0 = $
15. $a^{-n} = $
16. $a^{1/n} = $
17. $a^{m/n} = $        (2 forms)

## Logarithms:

18. If $y = a^x$, then $x = $
19. $\log_a x + \log_a y = $
20. $\log_a x - \log_a y = $
21. $\log_a x^k = $
22. $a^{\log_a x} = $
23. $\log_a(a^x) = $
24. $\log_a \dfrac{1}{x} = $
25. $\log_a y = $        (in base $b$)
26. If $y = e^x$, then $x = $
27. $e^{\ln x} = $
28. $\ln(e^x) = $
29. $a^x = $        (as a power of e)

*Chapter 3*

### Arithmetic series:

30. $n$th term $= $
31. $s_n = $        (2 forms)
32. If $a, b, c$ are in A . P, then:

### Geometric series:

33. $n$th term $= $
34. $s_n = $
35. If $a, b, c$ are in G . P, then:
36. 1   $s_\infty = $
     2   Condition for this sum to exist:

**Binomial Expansion:**

37.  1  $(1+x)^n =$
        (first 3 terms and general term)

     2  Condition for this series if $n$ is not a
        positive integer:

38.  1  Definition of $\binom{n}{r}$

     2  Definition of 0!

39.  If $n$ is a positive integer,
     $(a+x)^n =$
     (first 3 terms, general term, last term)

40.  If $n$ is a positive integer, alternative form
     for $\binom{n}{r}$:

41.  1  $\ln(1+x) =$

     2  Condition for this series:

42.  1  $e^x =$

     2  Condition for this series:

*Chapter 5*

**Inverse functions:**

43.  $f^{-1}[f(x)] =$

44.  $f[f^{-1}(x)] =$

**Inverse functions of:**

45.  $e^x$

46.  $x^3$

47.  $\dfrac{1}{x}$

48.  $\sin x$     $\left(-\dfrac{\pi}{2} \leqslant x \leqslant \dfrac{\pi}{2}\right)$

**Inequalities:**

49.  Solution of $x^2 < a^2$

50.  Solution of $x^2 > a^2$

*Chapter 6*

**Effect of transformations:**

51.  $y = f(x)$ to $y = a\, f(x)$

52.  $y = f(x)$ to $y = f(ax)$

53.  $y = f(x)$ to $y = f(x) + a$

54.  $y = f(x)$ to $y = f(x - a)$

# Trigonometry

*Chapter 2*

55.  $\pi$ radians in degrees

56.  1° in radians

**Definitions of:**

57.  $\sin \theta$

58.  $\cos \theta$

59.  $\tan \theta$

60.  $\sec \theta$

61.  $\operatorname{cosec} \theta$

62.  $\cot \theta$                    (2 forms)

63.  Quadrant diagram giving signs of ratios:
     Value of  1  $x$ in radians,  2  $\sin x$  3  $\cos x$
     4  $\tan x$, when $x$ is:

64.  0°

65.  90°

66.  180°

67.  270°

68.  360°

69.  30°

70.  45°

71.  60°

In terms of angle $(90° - \theta)$:

72.  $\cos \theta =$

73.  $\operatorname{cosec} \theta =$

74.  $\cot \theta =$

In terms of $\theta$:

75. $\sin(-\theta) =$

76. $\cos(-\theta) =$

77. $\tan(-\theta) =$

**Pythagoras' theorem:**

78. Equation connecting $\cos A$, $\sin A$

79. Equation connecting $\sec A$, $\tan A$

80. Equation connecting $\operatorname{cosec} A$, $\cot A$

81. $\cos(A + B) =$

82. $\cos(A - B) =$

83. $\sin(A + B) =$

84. $\sin(A - B) =$

85. $\tan(A + B) =$

86. $\tan(A - B) =$

87. $\cos 2A =$          (3 forms)

88. $\sin 2A =$

89. $\tan 2A =$

In terms of $\cos 2A$:

90. $\cos^2 A =$

91. $\sin^2 A =$

92. $\sin A + \sin B =$

93. $\sin A - \sin B =$

94. $\cos A + \cos B =$

95. $\cos A - \cos B =$

96. $2 \sin A \cos B =$

97. $2 \cos A \cos B =$

98. $2 \sin A \sin B =$

**General solution** for $\theta$ if:

99. $\sin \theta = \sin \alpha$

100. $\cos \theta = \cos \alpha$

101. $\tan \theta = \tan \alpha$

**Transformations:** $R =$ , $\sin \alpha =$ , $\cos \alpha =$ , if:

102. $a \cos \theta + b \sin \theta = R \cos(\theta - \alpha)$

103. $a \cos \theta + b \sin \theta = R \sin(\theta + \alpha)$

104. $a \cos \theta - b \sin \theta = R \cos(\theta + \alpha)$

105. $a \sin \theta - b \cos \theta = R \sin(\theta - \alpha)$

**Inverse trig functions:**

106. Range for $\sin^{-1} x$

107. Range for $\cos^{-1} x$

108. Range for $\tan^{-1} x$

*Chapter 8*

**Triangle formulae:**

109. sine rule:

110. cosine rule: $a^2 =$

111. cosine rule: $\cos A =$

112. area of triangle $=$        (trig. form)

113. area of triangle $=$        ($s$ form)

**Circle formulae:**

114. length of arc $=$

115. area of sector $=$

**Approximations** if $\theta$ is small:

116. $\sin \theta \approx$

117. $\tan \theta \approx$

118. $\cos \theta \approx$

In terms of $t = \tan \frac{1}{2} x$:

119. $\sin x =$

120. $\cos x =$

121. $\tan x =$

122. $\dfrac{\mathrm{d}x}{\mathrm{d}t} =$

## Differentiation

*Chapter 4*

123.  Definition of $f'(x)$

Derived functions of:

124.  $x^n$

125.  $e^x$

126.  $a^x$

127.  $\ln x$

128.  $\sin x$

129.  $\cos x$

130.  $\tan x$

131.  $\operatorname{cosec} x$

132.  $\sec x$

133.  $\cot x$

134.  $\sin^{-1} x$

135.  $\cos^{-1} x$

136.  $\tan^{-1} x$

137.  $\dfrac{\mathrm{d}(uv)}{\mathrm{d}x} =$

138.  $\dfrac{\mathrm{d}\left(\dfrac{u}{v}\right)}{\mathrm{d}x} =$

139.  $\dfrac{\mathrm{d}y}{\mathrm{d}x}$ when $y$ is a function of $u$ and $u$ is a function of $x$:

140.  $\dfrac{\mathrm{d}y}{\mathrm{d}x}$ when $x$ and $y$ are functions of $t$:

141.  $\dfrac{\mathrm{d}y}{\mathrm{d}x}$ in terms of $\dfrac{\mathrm{d}x}{\mathrm{d}y}$:

*Chapter 7*

Conditions for:

142.  a maximum point:

143.  a minimum point:

144.  Rate of change of $V$ (with respect to time) when $V$ is a function of $x$, and rate of change of $x$ is known:

145.  Small increase in $y$, $\delta y \approx$

146.  velocity, $v =$

147.  acceleration, $a =$

148.  angular velocity $=$

149.  Conditions for a point of inflexion:

## Integration and Differential Equations

*Chapter 9*

150.  $\displaystyle\int f'(x)\,\mathrm{d}x =$

151.  $\displaystyle\int_a^b f'(x)\,\mathrm{d}x =$

Give the integrals of:

152.  $x^n$

153.  $\dfrac{1}{x}$

154.  $e^x$

155.  $\cos x$

156.  $\sin x$

157.  $\tan x$

158.  $\dfrac{1}{1+x^2}$

159.  $\dfrac{1}{\sqrt{1-x^2}}$

160.  $\dfrac{f'(x)}{f(x)}$

161.  $\dfrac{1}{a^2+x^2}$

162.  $\dfrac{1}{\sqrt{a^2-x^2}}$

163.  Formula for integration by parts:

*Chapter 11*

164. $\displaystyle\text{limit}_{\delta x \to 0} \sum_{x=a}^{x=b} y\, \delta x =$

165. Area under curve, $A =$

166. Volume of revolution, $V =$

167. Mean value of $y =$

**Approximate Integration:**

168. Formula for trapezium rule:

169. Formula for Simpson's rule:

*Chapter 14*

**Laws of growth or decay:**

170. Equation for 'rate of growth of $x$ is proportional to $x$':

171. Solution of this equation:

172. Equation for 'rate of decay of $x$ is proportional to $x$':

173. Solution of this equation:

# Vectors

*Chapter 10*

Two vectors $\mathbf{a}$, $\mathbf{b}$:

174. Scalar product of $\mathbf{a}$, $\mathbf{b} =$

175. The angle between $\mathbf{a}$ and $\mathbf{b}$:

176. Condition for $\mathbf{a}$ and $\mathbf{b}$ to be perpendicular:

177. Condition for $\mathbf{a}$ and $\mathbf{b}$ to be parallel and in the same direction:

178. Condition for $\mathbf{a}$ and $\mathbf{b}$ to be parallel and in opposite directions:

179. The resolved part of $\mathbf{a}$ in direction $\mathbf{b} =$

If the position vectors of $A$ and $B$ are $\mathbf{a}$ and $\mathbf{b}$, then:

180. $\overrightarrow{AB} =$

181. $\overrightarrow{BA} =$

182. Position vector of the mid-point of $AB$:

183. Position vector of the point dividing $AB$ in the ratio $m : n$

If also the position vectors of $C$ and $D$ are $\mathbf{c}$ and $\mathbf{d}$, then conditions for:

184. $AB$ to be parallel to $CD$:

185. $A$, $B$, $C$ to lie on a straight line:

186. $AB$ to be perpendicular to $CD$:

187. $AB$ and $CD$ to be equal in length:

188. If $\mathbf{r} = x\mathbf{i} + y\mathbf{j} + z\mathbf{k}$ then $r =$

If $A$ is $(x_1, y_1, z_1)$ and $B$ is $(x_2, y_2, z_2)$,

189. $\overrightarrow{AB} =$

190. $AB =$

191. $\mathbf{i}^2 =$

192. $\mathbf{i} . \mathbf{j} =$

If $\mathbf{a} = x_1\mathbf{i} + y_1\mathbf{j} + z_1\mathbf{k}$ and $\mathbf{b} = x_2\mathbf{i} + y_2\mathbf{j} + z_2\mathbf{k}$, then:

193. $\mathbf{a} . \mathbf{b}$ in components $=$

194. The angle between $\mathbf{a}$ and $\mathbf{b}$:

195. Condition for $\mathbf{a}$ and $\mathbf{b}$ to be perpendicular:

196. Condition for $\mathbf{a}$ and $\mathbf{b}$ to be parallel:

197. The resolved part of $\mathbf{a}$ in the direction $\mathbf{b} =$

198. Condition for $\mathbf{a} = \mathbf{b}$:

Equation of a straight line:

199. through $A$ (position vector $\mathbf{a}$) in direction $\mathbf{b}$:

200. through 2 points with position vectors $\mathbf{a}$, $\mathbf{b}$:

2 lines with equations $\mathbf{r} = \mathbf{a}_1 + s\mathbf{b}_1$ and $\mathbf{r} = \mathbf{a}_2 + t\mathbf{b}_2$

201. The angle between the lines:

202. Condition for the lines to be perpendicular:

203. Condition for the lines to be parallel:

204. Equation used to find their point of intersection:

205. Equation used to find the point of intersection of the line $\mathbf{r} = \mathbf{a} + t\mathbf{b}$ with the plane $\mathbf{r} \cdot \mathbf{n} = d$:

206. The angle between planes $\mathbf{r} \cdot \mathbf{n}_1 = d_1$ and $\mathbf{r} \cdot \mathbf{n}_2 = d_2$:

## Complex Numbers

*Chapter 12*

207. $i =$

If $z = x + iy$:

208. Condition for $z$ to be zero:

209. $z^* =$           (conjugate of $z$)

If $z_1 = x_1 + iy_1$ and $z_2 = x_2 + iy_2$:

210. $z_1 + z_2 =$

211. $z_1 z_2 =$

212. $\dfrac{z_1}{z_2} =$

213. Condition for $z_1 = z_2$:

If $z = r(\cos\theta + i\sin\theta)$:

214. $|z| =$

215. $\arg z =$

216. $|z|$ in terms of $x$ and $y$

217. $\tan\theta$ in terms of $x$ and $y$

If $z_1 = r_1(\cos\theta_1 + i\sin\theta_1)$ and $z_2 = r_2(\cos\theta_2 + i\sin\theta)$:

218. $|z_1 z_2| =$

219. $\arg z_1 z_2 =$

220. $\left| \dfrac{z_1}{z_2} \right| =$

221. $\arg \dfrac{z_1}{z_2} =$

Locus of $z$ if:

222. $|z - z_1| = k$

223. $|z - z_1| = |z - z_2|$

224. $\arg(z - z_1) = \alpha$

## Coordinate Geometry

*Chapter 13*

2 points $A(x_1, y_1)$, $B(x_2, y_2)$:

225. Gradient of $AB =$

226. Distance $AB =$

227. Mid-point of $AB$:

228. Point dividing $AB$ in the ratio $m:n$

229. Equation of the line through $(x_1, y_1)$, gradient $m$:

230. Distance from $(h, k)$ to the line $ax + by + c = 0$:

2 lines, gradients $m_1$, $m_2$:

231. Angle between the lines:

232. Condition for the lines to be parallel:

233. Condition for the lines to be perpendicular:

234. General equation of a circle:

235. Condition for a quadratic equation to represent a circle:

236. Equation of a circle, centre $(a, b)$, radius $r$:

237. Parametric equations for this circle:

Transform into linear relations:

238. $y = ax^n$

239. $\dfrac{1}{x} + \dfrac{1}{y} = \dfrac{1}{a}$

*Chapter 6 and Chapter 15*

Type of curve, and parametric coordinates for

240. $y^2 = 4ax$

241. $xy = c^2$

242. $\dfrac{x^2}{a^2} + \dfrac{y^2}{b^2} = 1$

# Sketch Graph Checklist

Numbers 1–18 on the list are standard graphs and numbers 19–33 give some examples of certain functions. Most of these graphs are shown in earlier parts of this book.

You should show the general shape of the graph.
Include, where relevant and possible to find easily,
1  the behaviour of the graph as $x \to \pm\infty$
2  points where the graph cuts the $x$-axis and the $y$-axis
3  any asymptotes
4  any turning points on the curve.

A restricted graph showing plotted points for a few values of $x$ is not wanted.

A sketch graph can often be useful as an aid even if it is not required as part of an answer.

Sketch graphs of $f(x) =$

1.  $x^2$

2.  $x^3$

3.  $\dfrac{1}{x}$

4.  $\dfrac{1}{x^2}$

5.  $|x|$

6.  $e^x$

7.  $\ln x$

Sketch graphs of

8.  $ax + by = c$

9.  $y^2 = 4ax$

10.  $(x - a)^2 + (y - b)^2 = r^2$

11.  $\dfrac{x^2}{a^2} + \dfrac{y^2}{b^2} = 1$

12.  $y^2 = x^3$

Sketch graphs of $f(x) =$

13.  $\sin x, \ -\pi \leqslant x \leqslant 2\pi$

14.  $\cos x, \ -\pi \leqslant x \leqslant 2\pi$

15.  $\tan x, \ -\pi \leqslant x \leqslant 2\pi$

16.  $\sin^{-1} x$, range $-\pi/2$ to $\pi/2$

17.  $\cos^{-1} x$, range 0 to $\pi$

18.  $\tan^{-1} x$, range between $-\pi/2$ and $\pi/2$

19.  $x^2 + 8x + 20$

20.  $x^2 - 6x + 5$

21.  $-x^2 + 4x - 4$

22.  $(x + 1)(x - 2)(x - 3)$

23.  $(x + 1)(x - 2)^2$

24.  $\dfrac{3x - 2}{x + 1}$

25.  $\dfrac{x - 1}{x - 2}$

26.  $|2x - 3|$

27.  $e^{-x}$

28.  $2\cos\left(x-\dfrac{\pi}{3}\right)$

29.  $3\sin\left(x+\dfrac{\pi}{3}\right)$

Show on the same sketch:

30.  $y=\cos x,\ y=2\cos x$
     $(0\leqslant x\leqslant \pi)$

31.  $y=x^3,\ y=x^3+2$

32.  $y=x^2,\ y=(x-3)^2$

33.  $y=\sin x,\ y=\sin 2x$
     $(0\leqslant x\leqslant \pi)$

If $z_1$ and $z_2$ are complex numbers, show on the same sketch:

34.  $z_1,\ z_2,\ z_1+z_2$

35.  $z_1,\ z_2,\ z_1-z_2$

If **a** and **b** are vectors, show on the same sketch:

36.  **a, b, a+b**

37.  **a, b, a−b**

Sketch the curves with parametric equations:

38.  $x=a\cos t,\ y=b\sin t$

39.  $x=at^2,\ y=2at$

40.  $x=ct,\ y=\dfrac{c}{t}$

**To the student:**

# 6  During the Exam

Consider these instructions and if you think they are sensible for you then follow them. If you disagree then plan your own approach, on similar lines.

1    Make a note of the time the exam starts, with your watch, and the time it is due to end.

2    Check the instructions at the beginning of the paper so that you know how many questions you should answer, and note any other important points.

3    Read the first four or so questions carefully. This will take a few minutes. Do not rush. Decide on an easy or short question which you think you can answer. Read it again carefully and then answer it.
     (Advice is often given for you to read the whole paper before starting any question, but there are advantages in getting started on an easy question fairly quickly. However, you must decide what to do for yourself.)

4    After doing this question, and every other one, re-read the printed question. Have you done what you were asked to do? Have you answered all of it? Is the answer reasonable? Is the answer given in the form required, e.g. in terms of ln 2, or to 2 significant figures? If you can check your answer fairly quickly, for example by substituting in an original equation, then do so.

5    After finishing your first question, note the time, then read the next few questions on the paper and choose another easy or short one. The reason for choosing easy or short questions is that until you settle down into the exam you are more likely to make simple mistakes, so it is better to leave longer or harder questions until you are more relaxed.

6    After about 30–45 minutes (of a 3-hour exam) read the rest of the questions carefully and turn to some of the longer questions. Choose one you would like to attempt and decide how long you can spend on it so that you can do it calmly and thoroughly. Continue doing the longer questions for the next $1\frac{1}{2}$ hours.

7    When there is less than an hour to go, decide how to spend the remaining time so as to earn you most marks. You may prefer to return to the shorter questions hoping to get a few marks on each, or it may be better to keep to the longer questions which carry more marks. Try to work quickly, but carefully.

Here are a few more points:

8    If you are supplied with a formula sheet, then make use of it, so that you are using correct formulae.

9    If you start a question and get stuck, read the question again. Are you using all the information given? What are you trying to find? What is the topic? What

formulae do you know on this topic? What methods do you know on this topic? If there are several parts to a question then often the first part is a help to answering a later part. For example if in the first part you are asked to prove the formula $s = \dfrac{n}{2}(a + l)$ then this result could be needed in the next part. If you cannot do the first part of a question, you can still try the next part, using the quoted result of the first part. But if you really cannot get any further on any part of the question then abandon it and try a different one.

10    If the numbers in a question turn out to be complicated it is possible that you have made a simple numerical mistake. Check that you have copied down the equation correctly, and check the signs in your working. Simplify algebraic expressions as you go along, for example a gradient of $\dfrac{p^2 - q^2}{p - q}$ where $p \neq q$ would be much easier to use if simplified to $p + q$.

11    Keep your writing legible. Show all necessary working with the answer. Do all rough work near the answer and, if you wish, cross it out legibly. Draw careful diagrams but do not spend too much time on them. Do not waste time copying out the whole question. Just write down the equation or any important facts. Do not begin a question near the bottom of a right-hand page, because you may waste time and possibly make copying mistakes when turning over. It is better to leave the small space and begin at the top of the next page. Do not use white paint to blot out your mistakes. Some exam boards forbid its use, but even if it is permitted, it wastes time, and sometimes the damp paint soaks up the overwritten answer so the examiner cannot read it. Do not cross out work until you have replaced it with a better attempt.

Once the exam is over, forget it, until the results come out. We hope that your efforts have brought you the success you have worked for. **GOOD LUCK!**

# Answers

**Page 7**    **Exercise 1.1**

1.  1  $(4x-9)(x+2)$
    2  $2(3x+5)(x-1)$
    3  $4(x+5)(x-5)$
    4  $(x-2)(x^2+2x+4)$
    5  $(x+1)^2(x-1)$
    6  $(3x+5y)(x+3y)$
    7  $(3x-8y)(2x+y)$
    8  $(3x-5)(7y-4)$
    9  $(x^2+3)(x+2)(x-2)$
    10 $(3+y)(9-3y+y^2)$

2.  1  $x=0$ or $2\frac{3}{5}$    6  $x=3$
    2  $x=-7$ or $10$    7  $x=\pm2$ or $\pm3$
    3  $x=-3\frac{1}{2}$ or $2\frac{1}{2}$    8  $x=8$ or $20$
    4  $x=1\frac{1}{2}$ or $3$    9  $x=1$ or $5$
    5  $x=\pm2$    10  $x=12$

3.  1  $x^2-16x+64=(x-8)^2$
    2  $x^2+4xy+4y^2=(x+2y)^2$
    3  $2(x^2+10x+25)=2(x+5)^2$
    4  $3x^2-4x+\frac{4}{3}=3(x-\frac{2}{3})^2$
    5  $x^2-7x+12\frac{1}{4}=(x-3\frac{1}{2})^2$

4.  1  $x=-2.12$ or $6.12$
    2  $x=-2.62$ or $-0.382$
    3  $x=-1.39$ or $-0.360$
    4  $x=-0.303$ or $3.30$
    5  $x=-3.45$ or $1.45$

5.  1  $(x-2)^2+3$    4  $(x-2\frac{1}{2})^2-6\frac{1}{4}$
    2  $(x+4)^2-17$    5  $(x+\frac{1}{2})^2+\frac{3}{4}$
    3  $(x+5)^2+25$

6.  1  $2(x-3)^2+9$    4  $3(x-\frac{2}{3})^2+\frac{2}{3}$
    2  $3(x+2)^2-13$    5  $5(x+\frac{1}{5})^2-\frac{1}{5}$
    3  $2(x-\frac{1}{2})^2-3\frac{1}{2}$

7.  1  $x=-2a$ or $7a$    4  $x=-a-3$ or $a$
    2  $x=\frac{3}{2}a$ or $5a$    5  $x=-3a$ or $5a$
    3  $x=-a$ or $a-1$

8.  1  $k=4$ or $20$    2  $k=\frac{1}{7}$ or $7$

**Page 8**    **Exercise 1.2**

1.  1  $x=4$, $y=-3$    4  $x=2\frac{2}{5}$, $y=-12$
    2  $x=11$, $y=7$    5  $x=\frac{1}{7}$, $y=-1$
    3  $x=-4$, $y=0$

2.  1  $x^2-4x-5$    4  $x^2+ab-bc-ac$
    2  $14x-14$    5  $4ax+4bx$
    3  $4x-1$

3.  1  $3(2x-3)^2$
    2  $(x+6y)(x-7y)$
    3  $7(2xy+1)(2xy-1)$
    4  $(2x+1)(4x^2-2x+1)$
    5  $3x(x-1)^2$
    6  $(4x-5)(y-2z)$
    7  $(x+y)(x+y+1)(x+y-1)$
    8  $6(x^2+4)(x+2)(x-2)$
    9  $(x-8y)^2$
    10  $(x+1+a)(x+1-a)$

4.  1  $x=\dfrac{a}{b+c}$    6  $x=\dfrac{ac}{b-ad}$
    2  $x=\dfrac{b-d}{a-c}$    7  $x=\dfrac{(a-b)^2}{c^2}$
    3  $x=\dfrac{bc}{a-b}$    8  $x=a$ or $b$
    4  $x=\dfrac{ab}{b-a}$    9  $x=\dfrac{ac-b^2}{a+c-2b}$
    5  $x=\pm\sqrt{\dfrac{ac}{b}}$    10  $x=\dfrac{-a\pm\sqrt{a^2-4b}}{2}$

5.  1  $\dfrac{x^2+y^2}{(x+y)(x-y)}$    4  $\dfrac{1}{x+4}$
    2  $\dfrac{60-x}{12}$    5  $\dfrac{x}{(x-6)^2}$
    3  $-\dfrac{x+1}{(x-1)(x-2)}$

6.  1  $\dfrac{x+2}{y-x}$        4  $\dfrac{x}{x+3y}$

    2  $\dfrac{x(x^2-xy+y^2)}{x+2y}$        5  $\dfrac{y-x}{xy}$

    3  $\dfrac{x+1}{x-1}$

7.  1  $x=4$              6  $x=2$
    2  $x=-5$             7  $x=6$
    3  $x=-\frac{1}{2}$          8  $x=-1$
    4  $x=3$              9  $x=6$
    5  $x=5\frac{2}{3}$          10  $x=5$

8.  1  $2x^4-3x^3+7x^2-5x+1$
    2  $2x^4+x^3-10x^2+4x-8$
    3  $x^4-4x+3$
    4  $x^3+125$
    5  $x^5-1$

9.  1  $x^2-x+5$
    2  $x^2-3x-4$
    3  $x^2+3x+9$
    4  $x^3-7x^2+8x-9$
    5  $3x^2-x-2$

10. 1  $x=3,\ y=4,\ z=-1$
    2  $x=\frac{1}{2},\ y=1\frac{1}{2},\ z=-2\frac{1}{2}$
    3  $x=3,\ y=2,\ z=-2$
    4  $x=2,\ y=-1,\ z=5$
    5  $x=1,\ y=4,\ z=\frac{1}{2}$

## Page 11                Exercise 1.3

2.  $4\frac{1}{9}$, $9x^2-55x+50=0$
3.  $qx^2+p(q+1)x+(q+1)^2=0$
4.  $a^2x^2-(b^2-2ac)x+c^2=0$
5.  $2x^2-11x-4=0$
7.  2

## Page 11                Exercise 1.4

1.  $x=\frac{1}{2},\ y=-2$ or $x=18,\ y=12$
2.  $x=-1,\ y=-12$ or $x=3,\ y=4$
3.  $x=3,\ y=5$ or $x=5,\ y=3$
4.  $x=-3,\ y=2$ or $x=6,\ y=-7$
5.  $x=4,\ y=1$ or $x=16,\ y=19$
6.  $x=-20,\ y=-9$ or $x=1,\ y=-2$
7.  $x=-2,\ y=5$ or $x=0,\ y=1$
8.  $x=-1,\ y=-4$ or $x=3\frac{1}{5},\ y=-2\frac{3}{5}$
9.  $x=-3,\ y=-2$ or $x=\frac{1}{2},\ y=12$
10. $x=1\frac{1}{2},\ y=-6$ or $x=5\frac{1}{2},\ y=10$

## Page 11                Exercise 1.5

1.  1  $(x-1)(x-2)(x-3)$
    2  $(x+1)(x-2)(x-4)$
    3  $(x-1)(2x+1)(x+2)$
    4  $(x+3)(2x-3)(3x+2)$
    5  $(x-2)(x-3)(x-5)$

2.  $2x+1,\ x-6$
3.  $x-1,\ x-6$
4.  $(x-2)(x^2-4x+5)$
5.  $x+2,\ x-2;\ x=-3,-2,1$ or $2$
6.  $a=-11,\ x=-2$ or $3$

7.  1  $-12$        2  $12$        3  $46$

8.  $-6$
9.  $a=3,\ b=5$

## Page 14                Exercise 1.6

1.  $\dfrac{3}{x-1}+\dfrac{4}{x+2}$

2.  $\dfrac{2}{x+1}+\dfrac{1}{x-2}$

3.  $\dfrac{3}{x-3}-\dfrac{1}{x-1}$

4.  $\dfrac{5}{2(x+1)}+\dfrac{1}{2(x-3)}$

5.  $\dfrac{3}{x-5}-\dfrac{3}{x-3}$

6.  $\dfrac{1}{3(x-1)}-\dfrac{4}{3(x+2)}$

7.  $\dfrac{3}{2x-1}-\dfrac{1}{x-2}$

8.  $\dfrac{2}{2x+1}+\dfrac{3}{x-1}$

9.  $\dfrac{3}{x-2}+\dfrac{1}{x+1}-\dfrac{2}{x-1}$

10. $\dfrac{1}{x-1}-\dfrac{2}{x-2}+\dfrac{2}{2x-1}$

## Page 15                Exercise 1.7

1.  $\dfrac{2}{x-1}+\dfrac{3x+2}{x^2+1}$        2.  $\dfrac{4}{x-2}-\dfrac{2x-1}{x^2+2}$

3.  $\dfrac{3}{x+1} - \dfrac{2}{x-1} + \dfrac{1}{(x-1)^2}$

4.  $\dfrac{1}{x-3} + \dfrac{2}{x-1} + \dfrac{10}{(x-1)^2}$

5.  $1 - \dfrac{2}{x+1} + \dfrac{1}{x+2}$

6.  $2x - 3 + \dfrac{2}{5(2x-1)} - \dfrac{1}{5(x+2)}$

7.  $\dfrac{3}{x-3} - \dfrac{3}{x+2} + \dfrac{5}{(x+2)^2}$

8.  $2 - \dfrac{1}{x+1} - \dfrac{2}{x-2}$

9.  $\dfrac{3}{x+1} - \dfrac{3x-1}{x^2-x+1}$

10. $2 - \dfrac{3}{x} + \dfrac{1}{x+1} + \dfrac{2}{x-1}$

## Page 17            Exercise 1.8

1.  0
2.  $7 + 3\sqrt{6}$
3.  $2\sqrt{10} + 2\sqrt{3}$
4.  18
5.  11
6.  $x$
7.  $x + y + \sqrt{xy}$
8.  $\ln 2$
9.  $\frac{2}{3}$
10. 6

## Page 18           Exercise 1.9

1.  24
3.  $x = 7$
4.  $x = 9,\ y = -3$
5.  $-2$
6.  $x = 0$ or 1
7.  $x = 81$
9.  $x = -2$

## Page 18           Exercise 1.10

1.  $a + b$
2.  $x = 2$
3.  $x = -1$ or 0
4.  $x = \frac{1}{3}$
5.  $x = e^{-2}$ or $e^3$
6.  $x = 2e,\ y = 4e$ or $x = 4e,\ y = 2e$
7.  $x = 2,\ y = \pm\sqrt{6}$ or $x = -2,\ y = \pm 1/\sqrt{6}$
8.  $x = e,\ y = e^4$
9.  $x = \frac{1}{2}$
10. $20\frac{1}{4}$

## Page 27            Exercise 2.1

4.  $2 - \sqrt{3}$
5.  1
7.  $-9,\ \frac{1}{9}$
8.  $\cos(2\theta + 100°) + \cos 60°,\ 1\frac{1}{2},\ 130°$
9.  2
13. $2\cos^2 2\theta - 1$
16. $\operatorname{cosec} \theta$
18. $1 \quad \frac{5}{14}$
23. $2\sin P \cos Q$

## Page 28            Exercise 2.2

1.  0
2.  $\pi/2$
3.  $\pi/2$
4.  0
5.  $\pi/4$
6.  $-\pi/2$
7.  $\pi$
8.  $-\pi/4$
9.  $-\pi/6$
10. $\pi/3$
11. $\pi/3$
12. $5\pi/6$
13. $-\pi/4$
14. $2\pi/3$
15. $-\pi/6$
16. $\pi/6$
17. $\sqrt{3}/2$
18. $-\sqrt{3}$
19. $1/\sqrt{2}$
20. $\sqrt{5}$
21. $\theta = n\pi + (-1)^n \pi/8$
22. $\theta = 2n\pi \pm 2\pi/5$
23. $\theta = n\pi + \pi/3$
24. $\theta = n\pi + (-1)^n \pi/3$
25. $\theta = n\pi + \pi/4$

## Page 29            Exercise 2.3

1.  $\theta = 216.9°$ or $323.1°$
2.  $\theta = 70.5°$ or $289.5°$
3.  $\theta = 76.0°$ or $256.0°$
4.  $\theta = n\pi + (-1)^n \pi/6$
5.  $\theta = 2n\pi \pm 3\pi/4$
6.  $\theta = n\pi - \pi/4$
7.  $\theta = -30°$ or $90°$
8.  $\theta = -15°$ or $75°$
9.  $\theta = -156°,\ -126°,\ 24°$ or $54°$
10. $\theta = n\pi/4$
11. $\theta = 2n\pi \pm \pi/2$ or $2n\pi \pm 2\pi/3$
12. $\theta = (2n+1)\pi/4$ or $n\pi$
13. $\theta = 0°,\ 48.2°,\ 131.8°$ or $180°$
14. $\theta = 142.9°$ or $351.9°$
15. $\theta = 56.1°$ or $180°$

## Page 30            Exercise 2.4

1.  $\theta = 20.1°$ or $200.1°$
2.  $\theta = 18.4°$ or $198.4°$

3.  $\theta = 90°$ or $323.1°$
4.  $\theta = 80.5°, 180°$ or $260.5°$
5.  $\theta = 16.3°$ or $270°$
6.  $\theta = 71.6°, 135°, 251.6°$ or $315°$
7.  $\theta = \pi/2$ or $7\pi/6$
8.  $\theta = \pi/8, \pi/2, 5\pi/8, 9\pi/8, 3\pi/2$ or $13\pi/8$
9.  $\theta = \pi/3, \pi/2$ or $5\pi/3$
10. $\theta = 7\pi/12$ or $23\pi/12$
11. $\theta = 2\pi/5, 2\pi/3, 4\pi/5, 6\pi/5, 4\pi/3$ or $8\pi/5$
12. $\theta = n\pi/4$ or $2n\pi/3 \pm \pi/9$
13. $\theta = 2n\pi$ or $2n\pi \pm \pi/3$
14. $\theta = n\pi \pm \pi/4$ or $n\pi + (-1)^n \pi/6$
15. $\theta = n\pi/5 + \pi/10$

## Page 35            Exercise 3.1

1.  $-43$
2.  $39300$
3.  $650$
4.  $2107$
5.  $2\frac{1}{2}$
6.  $\frac{1}{2}n(3n+13)$, $24$
7.  $\frac{1}{4}n(n+2)$, $30$
8.  $3^{-5}$
9.  $-\frac{3}{5}(9^{10}-1)$
10. $-3(3^9+1)$
11. $\frac{9}{25}$
12. $6$
13. $\frac{2}{3}$

14.  
| 1 | 28 | 6 | $-4$ |
|---|---|---|---|
| 2 | 120 | 7 | 1 |
| 3 | 126 | 8 | $-\frac{1}{9}$ |
| 4 | 462 | 9 | $\frac{5}{81}$ |
| 5 | 3 | 10 | $-\frac{1}{16}$ |

15. $4860x^2$, $4320$
16. $-3$
17. $a = 89$, $b = 109$
18. $1 - 2x - 2x^2 - 4x^3$, $|x| < \frac{1}{4}$
19. $1 - 6x + 24x^2 - 80x^3$, $|x| < \frac{1}{2}$
20. $1 + 4x + 8x^2 + 16x^3$, $|x| < \frac{1}{2}$

## Page 36            Exercise 3.2

1.  $\dfrac{n(n+1)}{2} \ln a$
2.  $28000$
3.  $5, -1, -7, -13, \ldots$
4.  $10$

5.  $\dfrac{1}{-3 - 2\sqrt{2}}$
6.  $-\frac{1}{3}, 9\frac{1}{27}$
7.  $2, 10, 50, 250, \ldots$
8.  $18[(\frac{7}{6})^n - 1]$, $41$
9.  $\frac{1}{5}$
10. $4$
11. $4$
12. $2 \pm \sqrt{3}$
13. $-\frac{45}{4}$
14. $8$
15. $1 - \frac{5}{2}x^2$, $|x| < \frac{1}{3}$
17. $a = -6$, $b = 12$
18. $1 - x + 3x^2$
19. $\dfrac{1}{3(1-x)} + \dfrac{2}{3(1+2x)}$, $1 - x + 3x^2$,
    $\frac{1}{3}[1 + (-1)^r 2^{r+1}]x^r$, $|x| < \frac{1}{2}$
20. $\frac{107}{105}$

## Page 38            Exercise 3.3

1.  1  $3x - \frac{9}{2}x^2 + 9x^3 - \frac{81}{4}x^4$,
       $(-1)^{r+1}\dfrac{3^r}{r}x^r$, $-\frac{1}{3} < x \leq \frac{1}{3}$

    2  $-x - \dfrac{x^2}{2} - \dfrac{x^3}{3} - \dfrac{x^4}{4}$, $\dfrac{1}{r}x^r$, $-1 \leq x < 1$

    3  $1 + 2x + 2x^2 + \frac{4}{3}x^3$, $\dfrac{2^r}{r!}x^r$, all values

    4  $1 - 3x + \frac{9}{2}x^2 - \frac{9}{2}x^3$,
       $(-1)^{r+1}\dfrac{3^r}{r!}x^r$, all values

    5  $\ln 2 + \dfrac{x}{2} - \dfrac{x^2}{8} + \dfrac{x^3}{24}$, $(-1)^{r+1}\dfrac{1}{r \cdot 2^r}x^r$,
       $-2 < x \leq 2$

    6  $\ln 3 - \frac{2}{3}x - \frac{2}{9}x^2 - \frac{8}{81}x^3$, $-\dfrac{2^r}{r \cdot 3^r}x^r$,
       $-1\frac{1}{2} \leq x < 1\frac{1}{2}$

    7  $e\left(1 + x^2 + \dfrac{x^4}{2} + \dfrac{x^6}{6}\right)$, $\dfrac{ex^{2r}}{r!}$, all values

    8  $1 - \dfrac{x}{3} + \dfrac{x^2}{18} - \dfrac{x^3}{162}$, $(-1)^r \dfrac{1}{r!3^r}x^r$, all values

    9  $\dfrac{1}{x} - \dfrac{1}{2x^2} + \dfrac{1}{3x^3} - \dfrac{1}{4x^4}$,
       $(-1)^{r+1}\dfrac{1}{r \cdot x^r}$, $x < -1$ or $x \geq 1$

1. **10**  $\dfrac{1}{\ln 10}\left(x - \dfrac{x^2}{2} + \dfrac{x^3}{3} - \dfrac{x^4}{4}\right)$,

   $(-1)^{r+1}\dfrac{1}{r\ln 10}x^r$, $-1 < x \le 1$

2. **1**  $-x - \frac{5}{2}x^2 - \frac{7}{3}x^3$    **4**  $2x - 6x^2 + \frac{44}{3}x^3$

   **2**  $2x + \frac{4}{3}x^3 + \frac{4}{15}x^5$ ·    **5**  $1 - 2x + \frac{5}{2}x^2$

   **3**  $x - \frac{3}{2}x^2 + \frac{4}{3}x^3$

3. 2.7183

4. **1** $e^5$     **2** $e^{-1}$     **3** $e^{\frac{1}{2}}$

6. $2x - 2x^2 + \frac{8}{3}x^3$, $-3x - \frac{9}{2}x^2 - 9x^3$,

   $-\frac{1}{3} \le x < \frac{1}{3}$

8. $(1+x)(1-x+x^2)$,

   $-x + \dfrac{x^2}{2} + \dfrac{2x^3}{3} + \dfrac{x^4}{4} - \dfrac{x^5}{5} - \dfrac{x^6}{6}$

10. $-3x^2 - 10x^3 - \frac{57}{2}x^4$, $-\frac{1}{3} \le x < \frac{1}{3}$

11. $2x + \frac{2}{3}x^3 + \frac{2}{5}x^5$, 0.405

12. $-1$

13. 0.36

## Page 40     Exercise A1

1. $(x+2)(2x+1)(x-3)$, $x = -2, -\frac{1}{2}$ or 3
3. $x^2 - 3x - 28 = 0$
4. 0 or 5
5. $\dfrac{4}{x-1} - \dfrac{1}{x-3} + \dfrac{2}{(x-3)^2}$
6. $x = 0$ or 3
7. 0
8. $A = 1$, $B = \frac{1}{2}$, $C = 1\frac{1}{2}$
9. 5, 9, 13
10. $a = \frac{1}{6}$, $r = \frac{2}{3}$
11. 198
12. $1 + 3x + \frac{15}{2}x^2 + \frac{35}{2}x^3$, $|x| < \frac{1}{2}$
15. $\theta = 157.2°$ or $337.2°$
16. $\theta = 26.6°$ or $206.6°$
17. $\theta = 0, \dfrac{\pi}{3}, \dfrac{5\pi}{3}$ or $2\pi$
18. $\theta = \dfrac{\pi}{4}, \dfrac{\pi}{2}, \dfrac{3\pi}{4}, \dfrac{5\pi}{4}, \dfrac{3\pi}{2}$ or $\dfrac{7\pi}{4}$
19. $\theta = n\dfrac{\pi}{2}$
20. $25\cos(\theta - \alpha)$ where $\alpha = \tan^{-1}\frac{7}{24} \approx 16.3°$, $\theta = 87.6°$ or $304.9°$

## Page 41     Exercise A2

| | | |
|---|---|---|
| 1. A | 6. C | 11. A |
| 2. E | 7. B | 12. C |
| 3. E | 8. E | 13. B |
| 4. A | 9. A | 14. D |
| 5. B | 10. D | 15. E |

## Page 42     Exercise A3

2. $-270$
3. $\frac{1}{4}$
4. $4x^2 - 28x + 17 = 0$
5. $1$, $\theta = \pi/2$ or $3\pi/2$
6. $x = 0$ or 2
7. $\frac{3}{4}, -\frac{1}{4}$
9. $\theta = n\pi/4$
10. $x = \frac{1}{9}$ or 9
11. 30
12. $10\sin(\theta + \alpha)$ where $\alpha = \tan^{-1}\frac{4}{3} \approx 53.1°$, $\theta = 109.4°$ or $324.3°$
13. $-1 + 8x + \frac{56}{3}x^3$, $|x| < \frac{1}{6}$
14. $\dfrac{1}{x-1} - \dfrac{3}{x-2} + \dfrac{5}{x-3}$
15. $x = -1$ or $\pm 1/\sqrt{3}$, $\theta = \pi/6, 3\pi/4$ or $5\pi/6$

## Page 50     Exercise 4.1

In each answer, $\dfrac{dy}{dx} =$

1. $\dfrac{1}{4\sqrt{x}} - \dfrac{1}{x\sqrt{x}}$
2. $-\dfrac{9}{x^4} + \dfrac{8}{x^5}$
3. $-\dfrac{4}{3}\sin\dfrac{4x}{3}$
4. $\dfrac{2x+1}{x^2+x-2}$
5. $8x(x^2-2)^3$
6. $-3\operatorname{cosec}3x\cot 3x$
7. $\dfrac{2}{1+4x^2}$
8. $-\dfrac{4}{(4x-3)^2}$

9. $3 \cot 3x$

10. $-\dfrac{2}{(x-4)^3}$

11. $e^x(\cos x - \sin x)$

12. $\cos x - \operatorname{cosec}^2 x(1 - \cos x)$

13. $\dfrac{x}{\sqrt{x^2-1}}$

14. $\cos 3x \sec^2 x - 3 \tan x \sin 3x$

15. $x^2(1 + 3 \ln x)$

16. $2x \sin^{-1} x + \dfrac{x^2}{\sqrt{1-x^2}}$

17. $\dfrac{3x^2 + 6x + 2}{(x+1)^2}$

18. $\dfrac{x \sec^2 x - 2 \tan x}{x^3}$

19. $\dfrac{1}{(1-x)^2}$

20. $\dfrac{e^x(\sin x - \cos x)}{\sin^2 x}$

## Page 50　　　Exercise 4.2

1. $\dfrac{1}{t}$

2. $\dfrac{1-2t}{10t-4}$

3. $\dfrac{2-t^3}{t}$

4. $-\tan t$

5. $-\dfrac{1}{t^2}$

6. $-\dfrac{x}{9y}$

7. $-\dfrac{y}{2x}$

8. $\dfrac{x-y}{x+y}$

9. $-\dfrac{x^2}{y^2}$

10. $-\dfrac{\cos x}{\cos y}$

11. $4 - 6 \cos 2x$

12. $2(3x-5)(6x^2-5x+3)$

13. $-\dfrac{1}{\sqrt{4-x^2}}$

14. $3 \tan^2 x \sec^2 x$

15. $2x\, e^{x^2}$

16. $-\dfrac{\sin x}{2\sqrt{\cos x}}$

17. $e^{2x}(3 \sec^2 3x + 2 \tan 3x)$

18. $-2 \cot x \operatorname{cosec}^2 x$

19. $\cos x \cdot e^{\sin x}$

20. $-\dfrac{2}{1-x^2}$

## Page 51　　　Exercise 4.3

8. $\dfrac{\pi}{180} \cos \dfrac{\pi x}{180}$

9. $\dfrac{1}{x \ln 2}$

10. $3^x \ln 3$

In 11–18, $\dfrac{dy}{dx} =$

11. $\sqrt{2} \cos x$

12. $-\dfrac{x}{(x^2-4)^{\frac{3}{2}}}$

13. $x(2-3x)\, e^{-3x}$

14. $-1$

15. $\dfrac{2x^2+9}{\sqrt{x^2+9}}$

16. $\dfrac{1}{2\sqrt{x(1-x)}}$

17. $\dfrac{1}{(x^2+1)^{\frac{3}{2}}}$

18. $\dfrac{1}{\sqrt{x^2+4}}$

19. $-\sqrt{\dfrac{1-y^2}{1-x^2}}$

20. $\sqrt{\dfrac{y}{x}}$

## Page 58　　　Exercise 5.1

1. $(x+2)^2 + 6,\ 6,\ -2$
2. $2(x-\frac{5}{4})^2 - \frac{1}{8},\ -\frac{1}{8},\ -\frac{1}{8},\ 1\frac{1}{4}$
3. $-(x-5)^2 + 21,\ 21,\ 5$
4. $(x+\frac{1}{2}y)^2 + \frac{3}{4}y^2$
5. $(x-3)^2 + (y+2)^2 + 3,\ 3;\ x=3,\ y=-2$

15. **1** a, c, d, f, h, k
  **2** g, j, k
  **3** b, e, k

16. **1** $\pi$    **2** $4\pi$    **3** $\pi$

## Page 61　　　Exercise 5.2

1. $e^{2x+1}$
2. $\sin 2|x|\ (=|\sin 2x|)$
3. $\ln(x^2+1)$
4. $9x^2 + 6x + 3$
5. $\dfrac{1}{e^x + 3}$
6. all values, $\tan^{-1} x$, all $x$,
 $-\pi/2 < f^{-1}(x) < \pi/2$
7. all values $\neq \frac{1}{2}$, $\dfrac{1+x}{1-2x}$, all $x \neq \frac{1}{2}$,
 all values $\neq -\frac{1}{2}$
8. $f(x) > 0$, $-\ln x$, $x > 0$, all values
9. $f(x) \geqslant 2$, $\sqrt{x-2}$, $x \geqslant 2$, $f^{-1}(x) \geqslant 0$
10. $-1 \leqslant f(x) \leqslant 1$, $\frac{1}{2}\sin^{-1} x$,
 $-1 \leqslant x \leqslant 1$, $-\pi/4 \leqslant f^{-1}(x) \leqslant \pi/4$

11. all values, $10^x$, all $x$, $f^{-1}(x) > 0$

12. all values $\neq 0$, $\dfrac{4}{x}$, all $x \neq 0$, all values $\neq 0$

13. all values $\neq -1$, $\dfrac{4}{x+1}$, all $x \neq -1$,

 all values $\neq 0$

14. $0 \leqslant f(x) \leqslant 3$, $\sqrt{9-x^2}$, $0 \leqslant x \leqslant 3$,
 $0 \leqslant f^{-1}(x) \leqslant 3$

15. $f(x) \geqslant 0$, $\sqrt{x^2+1}$, $x \geqslant 0$, $f^{-1}(x) \geqslant 1$

16. $\sqrt[3]{x}$, all $x$, all values

17. $\sqrt{x}$, $x \geqslant 0$, $f^{-1}(x) \geqslant 0$

18. $\sin^{-1} x$, $-1 \leqslant x \leqslant 1$, $-\pi/2 \leqslant f^{-1}(x) \leqslant \pi/2$

19. $\log_2 x$, $x > 0$, all values

20. $\frac{1}{2}(x+5)$, all $x$, all values

11. $x < -2$ or $x > \frac{1}{2}$

12. no values of $x$

13. $x = 3$ only

14. $-1 \leqslant x \leqslant \frac{1}{3}$

15. all $x \neq 2$

16. $-1 < x < 1$

17. $-\frac{1}{2} \leqslant k \leqslant 3\frac{1}{2}$

18. $1 < k < 7$

21. $y \leqslant -\frac{2}{5}$ or $y \geqslant \frac{2}{5}$

22. $-\frac{1}{4} \leqslant y \leqslant 1$

## Page 68 Exercise 6.1

8. $\dfrac{x^2}{4} + y^2 = 1$

9. $y = 14 - 2x$

10. $9y^2 = x^3$

11. $y^2 = 24x$

12. $x^2 + (y+1)^2 = 1$

13. $xy = 16$

## Page 62 Exercise 5.3

1. $\dfrac{1}{x}$, $(x \neq 0)$

2. $\dfrac{4x+2}{x-3}$, all $x \neq 3$, all values $\neq 4$

3. $\sqrt{1-x^2}$, $(0 \leqslant x \leqslant 1)$

4. $\sqrt{2}\cos\left(x - \dfrac{\pi}{4}\right)$, $\dfrac{\pi}{4} + \cos^{-1}\dfrac{x}{\sqrt{2}}$, $0 \leqslant x \leqslant \sqrt{2}$

5. $x^2 - 4x + 3$, $x \geqslant 2$

6. $x \neq -\frac{1}{2}$, $\dfrac{4x-1}{2x+1}$, $x = \pm 1$

7. $\frac{1}{3}(x-2)$, $e^x$, $3 \ln x + 2$, $e^{(x-2)/3}$, $x > -\frac{2}{3}$

8. $-4x^2 - 12x - 5$, $11 - 2x^2$, $x = -4$ or $-2$

9. $e^{x^3}$, $\frac{1}{3} \ln x$, $x > 0$

10. $\dfrac{3x}{1+2x}$, all $x \neq -\frac{1}{2}$, all values $\neq 1\frac{1}{2}$

## Page 70 Exercise 6.2

11. $\dfrac{X^2}{9} + \dfrac{Y^2}{4} = 1$, ellipse

12. $Y^2 = 20X$, parabola

13. $Y = X^3$, cubic curve

14. $XY = 9$, rectangular hyperbola

15. $Y^2 = 8X^3$, (semi-cubical parabola)

## Page 72 Exercise B1

2. $r = \frac{1}{2}$ or 2, $s_\infty = 18$

3. $1 - 2x + 6x^2 - 20x^3$, $|x| < \frac{1}{4}$

4. $1 \leqslant k \leqslant 3$

5. $x = 1\frac{1}{2}$, $y = -2$

8. $\frac{21}{29}$

9. $\theta = 26.6°$ or $63.4°$

10. $17\cos(\theta + \alpha)$ where $\alpha = \tan^{-1}\frac{15}{8} \approx 61.9°$

11. $4x^3$

12. 1 $\dfrac{dy}{dx} = \dfrac{x \sec^2 x - 2\tan x}{x^3}$

 2 $\dfrac{dy}{dx} = \dfrac{x^3}{\sqrt{1-x^2}} + 3x^2 \sin^{-1} x$

13. 1 $\dfrac{dy}{dx} = 2x\,e^{x^2}$ 2 $\dfrac{dy}{dx} = \dfrac{2x}{x^2+3}$

14. 1 $-\dfrac{b}{a}\cot t$ 2 $-t$

15. 1 $-\dfrac{y}{x}$ 2 $-\dfrac{x}{3y}$

## Page 64 Exercise 5.4

1. $-1 \leqslant x \leqslant 2$ or $x \geqslant 4$

2. $x \leqslant -2$ or $-1 \leqslant x \leqslant 3$

3. $-3 < x < 0$

4. $-7 < x < 15$

5. $x < -4\frac{1}{2}$ or $x > 0$

6. $x > -1$

7. $x < 4$ or $x > 19$

8. $x < -\frac{1}{3}$ or $x > 1$

9. $-3 < x < \frac{1}{2}$

10. all $x$

**Page 73**         **Exercise B2**

1.  C          6.  A          11.  B
2.  E          7.  E          12.  A
3.  C          8.  E          13.  B
4.  C          9.  D          14.  B
5.  B          10.  A         15.  D

**Page 74**         **Exercise B3**

1.  $x = \pm\sqrt{5}$ or $\pm 3$
3.  $f^{-1}(x) = \ln x - 2$, $x > 0$, all values
4.  $x^2 + y^2 = r^2 \cos^2 \theta$, $x^2 + y^2 + z^2 = r^2$
5.  $x = 3$
6.  0.8, 0.6; $x = 45°$, $y = 8.1°$ or $x = 81.9°$, $y = 45°$
7.  $x^2 - 20x + 36 = 0$
9.  $x = -1 \pm \sqrt{1-a}$, $a \leq 1$
10. $k > 3$
11. $\theta = n\pi$ or $n\pi + \pi/6$
14. $XY = 25$, rectangular hyperbola
15. $\dfrac{2}{(x+4)^2} - \dfrac{1}{x+4} + \dfrac{3}{2x-1}$,

    $-\dfrac{4}{(x+4)^3} + \dfrac{1}{(x+4)^2} - \dfrac{6}{(2x-1)^2}$, $-6$

**Page 82**         **Exercise 7.1**

1.  $y \sin t = x(1 + \cos t) + t \sin t$
2.  minimum $(0, 0)$, maximum $(2, 4e^{-2})$
3.  $x + t^2 y = 2ct$, $ty = t^3 x + c - ct^4$
4.  140
6.  $ty = x + at^2$, $tx + y = 2at + at^3$
7.  maximum $(-3, -6)$, minimum $(3, 6)$
8.  $y = 4x + 2$
9.  $(\sqrt{3}/1200) \approx 0.0014$
10. maximum $(-3, 0)$, minimum $(1, -32)$
11. $y = 3tx - 2t^3$, $x + 3ty = 12t^4 + 2t^2$
12. $(\frac{1}{2}, \frac{15}{16})$, $(2, 0)$
13. $7, 1\frac{1}{2}$
14. $\pi/3$, $-3\sqrt{3}$
15. $(1, 32)$, $(5, 0)$; $(3, 16)$

**Page 83**         **Exercise 7.2**

1.  maximum $(\pi/4, 2\sqrt{2})$, minimum $(\pi/2, 2)$
2.  $-\frac{1}{7}$, $x + 7y = 6$
3.  $a = 2$, $b = -6$

4.  2%
5.  $(2x - 1) \ln x + x - 1$
6.  minimum $(\pm\sqrt{2}, -4)$, maximum $(0, 0)$
7.  1
8.  $\pi/3$ or $5\pi/3$
9.  $a = 1$, $b = -1$, $c = -1$; $(-\frac{1}{3}, \frac{5}{27})$
10. $1/(6\pi)$
11. $(e^{-\frac{1}{2}}, -\frac{1}{2}e^{-1})$, minimum
12. $\frac{1}{2}$
13. $(\pi/4, \pi/2)$, gradient 0; $(3\pi/4, 3\pi/2)$, gradient 4
14. $\pi/4$
15. $5 \tan^{-1} \frac{4}{3} \approx 4.6$, 0

**Page 87**         **Exercise 8.1**

2.  $\dfrac{ah}{bc}$            9.  $\sqrt{\dfrac{3\sqrt{3}}{\pi}} a$

5.  $30°$, $\dfrac{3\sqrt{3}+4}{10}$     10. $\sin^{-1} \frac{3}{4}$

7.  $\dfrac{\theta - \sin \theta}{\theta}$        12. $\dfrac{d \sin \beta \tan \theta}{\sin(\alpha + \beta)}$

8.  $\dfrac{r^2\theta}{4\pi}(\theta + 2\pi)$       13. $\tan^{-1} \dfrac{h}{r \cos \frac{1}{2}\theta}$

**Page 91**         **Exercise 8.2**

1.  1 $\frac{1}{4}$     2 4      3 2      4 $\frac{1}{2}$
2.  $\pm\frac{1}{21} \approx \pm 0.048$
3.  $\frac{1}{9}$
4.  5
5.  $\dfrac{2t}{1+t^2}$, $\dfrac{1-t^2}{1+t^2}$; $\theta = 0°$, 223.6° or 360°
6.  $\theta = 126.9°$
9.  $\pi/3 < |x| < 2\pi/3$
10. $\sqrt{2} \cos(x - \pi/4)$; $x = 0$, $\pi/2$ or $2\pi$

**Page 91**         **Exercise 8.3**

1.  $2r\left(\cot \dfrac{\theta}{2} + \theta\right)$

4.  $h = b \sin A = a \sin B$
5.  $a^2 = h^2 + (c - p)^2$, $h^2 = b^2 - p^2$, $a^2 = b^2 + c^2 - 2cp$, $p = b \cos A$
6.  angle $D$, 90°

7. $AB^2 = AM^2 + BM^2$
   $-2AM \cdot BM \cos \angle AMB, \ AC^2 =$
   $AM^2 + CM^2 - 2CM \cdot BM \cos \angle AMC$;
   $2\sqrt{3}$

9. $\dfrac{2(s-a)(s-b)}{ab}, \ 4\sqrt{6}$

10. $\theta = 36.9°$ or $110.6°$
11. $5 \sin(x + \alpha)$ where $\alpha = \tan^{-1} \frac{3}{4} \approx 36.9°$;
    $5, \ x = 53.1°; \ -5, \ x = 233.1°$
12. $|x| < \pi/4$ or $3\pi/4 < |x| < \pi$
15. $\frac{1}{2}r^2 \sin \theta, \ \frac{1}{2}r^2\theta, \ \frac{1}{2}r^2 \tan \theta$
17. $1 + t^2$

**Page 100**          **Exercise 9.1**

1. $\dfrac{2x^{\frac{3}{2}}}{3} + 2x^{\frac{1}{2}} + c$

2. $\sin^{-1} \dfrac{x}{5} + c$

3. $\dfrac{\tan^2 x}{2} + c$

4. $\dfrac{(x^2+3)^6}{12} + c$

5. $\sin x - \dfrac{\sin^3 x}{3} + c$

6. $\dfrac{\sqrt{4x^2+3}}{4} + c$

7. $\ln(x^2 + 5x + 7) + c$

8. $\ln \left| \dfrac{x+2}{x+3} \right| + c$

9. $2 \ln|x+3| + 3 \ln|x-1| + c$
10. $-x \cos x + \sin x + c$
11. $\frac{1}{2}(1 - e^{-1})$
12. $\pi/8$
13. $\frac{1}{3} \ln 2$
14. $\ln 2 - 3\pi/4$
15. $\ln \frac{3}{2}$
16. $\frac{1}{3} \ln 2$
17. $\frac{1}{12}(3\sqrt{3} - 1)$
18. $\pi/12 + \frac{1}{8}$
19. $3e^2 - 5$
20. $2 \ln 2 - \frac{3}{4}$

**Page 100**          **Exercise 9.2**

1. $2 \ln|x+2| + \dfrac{4}{x+2} + c$

2. $\frac{1}{3} \tan(3x - 2) + c$
3. $\frac{1}{4} e^{4x-3} + c$
4. $-\ln|1 - x| + c$

5. $\frac{1}{4} \tan^{-1} \dfrac{x}{4} + c$

6. $\frac{1}{2} \sin(2x + 3) + c$

7. $-\dfrac{1}{e^x + 3} + c$

8. $\sec x + c$

9. $\dfrac{x^3}{9}(3 \ln x - 1) + c$

10. $\ln \left| \dfrac{x-2}{x-1} \right| + c$

11. $\frac{15}{64}$
12. $\frac{1}{2}(\ln 2)^2$
13. $\frac{1}{3}$
14. $\frac{1}{4}(1 - 3e^{-2})$
15. $\frac{1}{2} \ln 2$
16. $\pi/6$
17. $1$
18. $\frac{1}{12}$
19. $-51\frac{1}{5}$
20. $\frac{1}{4} \ln \frac{5}{3}$

**Page 101**          **Exercise 9.3**

1. $\ln|(x^2 + 1)(x - 2)| + c$

2. $\frac{1}{4} \sin^{-1} \dfrac{4x}{3} + c$

3. 1  $\frac{1}{2} \ln(1 + x^2) + c$
   2  $x \tan^{-1} x - \frac{1}{2} \ln(1 + x^2) + c$

4. $\dfrac{1}{12(1-2x)^3} - \dfrac{1}{8(1-2x)^2} + c$

5. $\dfrac{1}{\sqrt{2}} \tan^{-1} \left( \dfrac{1}{\sqrt{2}} \tan \dfrac{x}{2} \right) + c$

6. $1$
7. $18\frac{2}{3}$
8. $\frac{1}{2} \ln \frac{9}{8}$
9. $\frac{1}{4} \ln 2$
10. $\pi^2/72$
11. $\frac{5}{24}$
14. $\tan x - x + c$
15. $\frac{1}{2} \ln 3$
16. $\ln \frac{4}{3}$

## Page 103  Exercise C1

1. $5\frac{1}{3}$
2. $(x-2)(x-1)(x+1)(x+3)$
3. $\dfrac{x+y}{2}$, $\sqrt{xy}$
4. $\dfrac{5}{x+1} - \dfrac{4}{x+2} + \dfrac{1}{(x+2)^2}$
6. $\theta = 19.5°$ or $160.5°$
7. $\theta = \dfrac{n\pi}{2} - \dfrac{\pi}{8}$
9. $2y = 9x - 16$
10. $(\ln 3, -27)$
11. $\dfrac{\sqrt{3}}{4} a^2$
12. $\dfrac{\sin 8x}{8} + \dfrac{\sin 2x}{2} + c$
13. $\pi/4$
14. $\pi/12$
15. $3 - e^2$

## Page 104  Exercise C2

| | | |
|---|---|---|
| 1.  C | 6.  B | 11.  D |
| 2.  C | 7.  B | 12.  E |
| 3.  E | 8.  B | 13.  D |
| 4.  A | 9.  E | 14.  A |
| 5.  D | 10.  D | 15.  A |

## Page 105  Exercise C3

1. 4
2. $\cot^2 x$, $-2 \cot x \operatorname{cosec}^2 x$
3. **1** $45\frac{5}{8}$
   **2** $57\frac{5}{8}$
4. $-\frac{1}{2}$
5. $x = -2\frac{1}{2}$, $y = -2$; $x < -2\frac{1}{2}$ or $x > 6\frac{1}{2}$
6. $\cos \theta$
7. $x = 2$, $s_n = 1 - 4^n$
8. $0.6\%$
9. $-4$, maximum; 3, minimum
10. $\ln \frac{10}{3}$
11. 13
12. $13 \cos(\theta + \alpha)$ where $\alpha = \tan^{-1} \frac{12}{5} \approx 67.4°$, $\theta = 292.6°$

13. $\pi r^2 - \dfrac{nr^2}{2} \sin \dfrac{2\pi}{n}$
14. $-\sqrt{1-x^2} + c$, $x \sin^{-1} x + \sqrt{1-x^2} + c$
15. $a = \frac{1}{2}$, $b = -\frac{1}{12}$; $-\frac{1}{24} x^4$

## Page 114  Exercise 10.1

1. 10
2. $2\mathbf{i} - \mathbf{j}$, $5\mathbf{i} - 5\mathbf{j}$
4. $\frac{16}{65}$
7. $\mathbf{r} = 4\mathbf{i} - \mathbf{j} + t(-3\mathbf{i} + 4\mathbf{j})$
8. $\mathbf{i} + 7\mathbf{j}$
9. $\frac{1}{2}\mathbf{i} + 3\frac{1}{2}\mathbf{j}$
10. $5\sqrt{2}$

## Page 115  Exercise 10.2

1. **1** $(0, 0, -5)$
   **2** $(5, -3, -1)$
4. $\sqrt{5}$, $\sqrt{14}$, $\sqrt{34}$, $\sqrt{19}$, $\sqrt{30}$
6. $\frac{16}{33}$
8. $\mathbf{r} = 2\mathbf{i} - 3\mathbf{j} + \mathbf{k} + t(-2\mathbf{i} + 4\mathbf{j} + \mathbf{k})$
9. Yes (at $-1\frac{1}{2}\mathbf{i} + \frac{1}{2}\mathbf{j} - 4\mathbf{k}$)
10. $(4, 1, 0)$, $\dfrac{2\sqrt{5}}{15}$
12. $\frac{2}{3}$
13. $\frac{2}{11}\mathbf{i} - \frac{6}{11}\mathbf{j} + \frac{9}{11}\mathbf{k}$

## Page 116  Exercise 10.3

2. $\mathbf{a} + \mathbf{c} - \mathbf{b}$
3. $-6\mathbf{i} - 6\mathbf{j} + 6\mathbf{k}$
5. $\frac{5}{3}\mathbf{a} + \frac{1}{3}\mathbf{b}$
6. $\frac{2}{3}\mathbf{b} + \frac{1}{3}\mathbf{c}$, $\frac{3}{5}\mathbf{a} + \frac{2}{5}\mathbf{c}$, $5:4$
7. $(-6, -6, 1)$
8. $\dfrac{\sqrt{13}}{13}$
9. 1
10. $(16, -2, 0)$

## Page 116  Exercise 10.4

2. $\sqrt{6}$
5. $\mathbf{r} = (2, -1, 1) + t(-5, 2, -1)$, $(7, -3, 2)$
6. $\mathbf{r} = (1, 6, 8) + t(-1, 2, -1)$, $(\frac{2}{3}, 6\frac{2}{3}, 7\frac{2}{3})$, $\sqrt{6}/3$
7. $(2\frac{1}{2}, 3\frac{1}{4}, 1\frac{1}{4})$
8. $a = 5$, $\sqrt{17}$

## Page 121  Exercise 11.1

1. $y = 2\sqrt{x+3} - 3$
2. $\pi/4 + 3$
3. $2 \ln 2 + 3$
4. $\ln \frac{5}{3}$
5. $\pi/6$
6. $4 \ln \frac{4}{3} - 1$
7. $36a^2$, $234\pi a^3$
8. $80\pi/3$
9. $40\pi(e^2 - 1)$ cm$^3$
10. $\frac{1}{2} + 2/\pi$

## Page 122 — Exercise 11.2

1. $1\frac{1}{8}$
2. $\frac{11}{24}$
3. $10\frac{2}{3}$
4. $\pi/6$
5. $5\pi/9$

6. $(1, 1)$
7. $8\pi$, $12\pi$
8. $e^2 + 1$, $\pi(5e^4 - 1)/4$
9. $2\frac{4}{45}$
10. $1\frac{1}{8} - \ln 2$

16. $z = -1$ or $\dfrac{1 \pm \sqrt{7}\,i}{2}$
17. $z = 1$ or $3 \pm 4i$
18. $p = 1$, $q = -3$
19. $p = 6$, $q = 20$
20. $p = 20$, $q = -12$

## Page 124 — Exercise 11.3

1. 1.34
2. 24.3
3. 0.7
4. 4.33
5. 0.234
6. 11.8
7. 0.777
8. 6
9. 0.740
10. 1.26

11. **1** 1.33, error 0.3%
    **2** 1.29, error 3.0%
    Exact: $\tan^{-1} 4 \approx 1.33$
12. 2.16, $\ln 8$, $\ln 2 \approx 0.718$
13. 1.74, $\sqrt{3}$, 0.5%
14. $\frac{1}{2}h(f_0 + 2f_1 + f_2)$
15. $\dfrac{2ah^3}{3} + 2ch$

## Page 132 — Exercise 12.1

1. **1** $2 + 3i$   **4** $-2 + 2i$
   **2** $11 - 10i$   **5** $2 + 3i$
   **3** $-3 - 4i$

2. **1** $3 - i$   **4** $8 - 19i$
   **2** $5 + 7i$   **5** $-\frac{16}{17} + \frac{13}{17}i$
   **3** 25

3. $2\cos 2\alpha$
6. $z = -10i$

7. **1** $z = -6 \pm 2i$
   **2** $z = -\frac{1}{2} \pm 3i$   **5** $z = -\frac{1}{2} \pm \dfrac{\sqrt{3}}{2}i$
   **3** $z = \frac{2}{3} \pm \frac{5}{3}i$
   **4** $z = \pm 3i$

8. **1** $(x + iy)(x - iy)$
   **2** $(x + iy)(x - iy)(x + y)(x - y)$

9. $5 - \sqrt{2}i$; $b = -10$, $c = 27$
10. $z = \pm(2 - i)$
11. $\dfrac{2 + x}{(2 + x)^2 + y^2} - i\dfrac{y}{(2 + x)^2 + y^2}$
12. **1** $x = -16$, $y = 30$
    **2** $x = \frac{1}{25}$, $y = \frac{11}{50}$
    **3** $x = \frac{3}{13}$, $y = -\frac{2}{13}$
13. $z = 1$ or $3 \pm i$
14. $z = 2$ or $-1 \pm \sqrt{5}i$
15. $z = 3$ or $\pm 2i$

## Page 134 — Exercise 12.2

4. $\sec\theta$, $\theta$
6. 26

7. $z_1 = \sqrt{2}\left(\cos\dfrac{\pi}{4} + i\sin\dfrac{\pi}{4}\right)$,

   $z_2 = 2\left(\cos\dfrac{\pi}{6} + i\sin\dfrac{\pi}{6}\right)$

   **1** $2\sqrt{2}$, $5\pi/12$   **3** $2$, $\pi/2$
   **2** $\sqrt{2}$, $-\pi/12$   **4** $1$, $\pi/3$

8. **1** 10   **2** 1

9. **1** $\pi/12$
   **2** $-7\pi/12$   **3** $\pi$

12. $2\sqrt{5}$
13. $\theta$

14. **1** $2$, $-2\pi/3$   **4** $\frac{2}{3}$, $\pi/2$
    **2** $3$, $5\pi/6$   **5** $4$, $2\pi/3$
    **3** $6$, $\pi/6$

## Page 136 — Exercise D1

1. $-84$
2. 20
5. $13\sin(\theta - \alpha)$ where $\alpha = \tan^{-1}\frac{12}{5} \approx 67.4°$, $\theta = 100.0°$ or $214.8°$
6. $\theta = 104.5°$ or $255.5°$
7. Circle, centre $\frac{1}{2} - \frac{1}{2}i$, radius $1/\sqrt{2}$, $(z \ne 1)$
8. $4\frac{1}{2} + 5\frac{1}{2}i$
9. $|z| = 1$, $\arg z = 2\pi/5$; $|z^5| = 1$, $\arg(z^5) = 0$
10. **2** $\dfrac{\pi}{12} - \dfrac{\sqrt{3}}{8}$

    **3** $\dfrac{\sqrt{3}}{8} - \dfrac{\pi}{24}$
11. $(0, 0)$, $(2, 8)$; $1\frac{1}{3}$
12. $256\pi$
13. 4
15. $B(6, 0, 15)$, $10\sqrt{3}$

**Page 137**          **Exercise D2**

1.  B
2.  D
3.  A
4.  D
5.  D

6.  B
7.  C
8.  E
9.  A
10. E

11. C
12. D
13. A
14. A
15. B

**Page 139**          **Exercise D3**

2.  3 or 15
3.  $8 - 6i$
5.  $3\theta$
6.  $(-3, 9), (3, 9); 72$
7.  $-1 < x < 2$ or $x > 3$
9.  $4/\pi, -8/\pi$
10. $5, 13, \frac{5}{13}, 4i + 2\frac{1}{2}j + 9k$

11. $\dfrac{\pi}{24}(4\pi - 3\sqrt{3})$

12. $\theta = 15°$ or $105°$

13. $\dfrac{1}{1+x} + \dfrac{3}{1-3x}$, $4 + 8x + 28x^2 + 80x^3$,
    $[3^{n+1} + (-1)^n]x^n$, $|x| < \frac{1}{3}$
14. $E\ (-17, -24, 7)$
15. 1 (gradient 0), 3 (gradient $-4e^{-3}$)
16. $a = 3, b = -3$

**Page 144**          **Exercise 13.1**

1.  $-\frac{3}{2}, -\frac{1}{4}, \frac{10}{11}$
2.  1  $5x + 2y = 19$
    2  $5y = 2x + 11$
    3  $6y = x + 9$
    4  $5y = 2x + 4$
3.  3
5.  $(5, 5)$, $C\ (7, 11)$, $D\ (2, 6)$, 40
6.  $\frac{16}{3}$
7.  $D\ (1, -2)$, $G\ (2, 1)$, $7y = 4x - 1$
8.  $(7, -\frac{1}{3})$
9.  $(15, 8), (8, 6), (23, 14), 17, 10$
10. $D\ (5, 7)$, $E\ (11, 7)$

**Page 147**          **Exercise 13.2**

1.  $x^2 + y^2 - 14x - 4y + 19 = 0$,
    $B\ (10, -3)$, $D\ (4, 7)$
3.  $4x^2 + 4y^2 - 20x - 8y + 25 = 0$
4.  $(-5, -4)$
5.  $(-5, -5), (0, 10)$

6.  $x + 2y = 5$
7.  $4y = 3x + 10$
8.  $x^2 + y^2 - 8x - 6y = 0$
9.  $x + y = 11$, $y = 7x - 57$, $(8\frac{1}{2}, 2\frac{1}{2})$
10. $2x + y = 30$, $(10, 10), (14, 2)$

**Page 148**          **Exercise 13.3**

1.  20
2.  6
3.  $(2\frac{1}{4}, 2\frac{3}{4})$
4.  $AB: 8x + y + 55 = 0$, $BC: 8y = x - 50$,
    $AC: 4x + 7y = 83$
5.  $(-7, -4)$, 165
8.  $3, 7$
9.  $x^2 + y^2 - 5x - 5y = 0$
10. $25, 20$
11. $(2, -2)$, radius 2; $(-2, 1)$, radius 3;
    $T(\frac{2}{5}, -\frac{4}{5})$; $3y = 4x - 4$

**Page 150**          **Exercise 13.4**

*There may be variations in your answers.*

1.  $a = 2.0, b = 3.0$
2.  $a = 1.2, b = 0.4$
3.  $a = 0.13$
4.  $a = 1.5, b = 3.0$
5.  $a = 5, b = 30$

**Page 154**          **Exercise 14.1**

1.  $y = \dfrac{(x + c)^2}{4}$, $(x \geq -c)$;

    $y = \dfrac{(x - 4)^2}{4}$, $(x \geq 4)$

2.  $y = a\,e^{-1/x}$, $y = e^{3 - 1/x}$
3.  $y = \tan(c - e^{-x})$, $y = \tan(1 - e^{-x})$
4.  $y = 1 + a\,e^{\cos x}$, $y = 1 - e^{\cos x}$
5.  $y = \sin^{-1}(c - \cos x)$, $y = \sin^{-1}(1 - \cos x)$
6.  $y = 2\sec x$

7.  $y = \dfrac{9}{(2x - 1)^2}$, $(x > \frac{1}{2})$

8.  $y = \dfrac{8 - x}{2 - x}$

9.  $y^2 = x^2 - 6x + 41$

10. $(y + 1)^2 = \dfrac{16(1 + x)}{1 - x}$

## Page 155            Exercise 14.2

1. $-1$
2. $e^{2-e}$
3. $\pm 2$
4. $y = 3e^{2x}$
5. $v = 2\tan(2t + \pi/4)$

6. $(2x, 0)$, $(0, 2y)$, $-\dfrac{y}{x}$, $\dfrac{dy}{dx} = -\dfrac{y}{x}$, $xy = 36$

7. $k = \frac{1}{20}\ln 2$, $t = \dfrac{20\ln 3}{\ln 2} = 31.7$

8. $\dfrac{dy}{dt} = -ky$, $y = a\,e^{-kt}$, $\frac{1}{27}y_0$

9. $\dfrac{d\theta}{dt} = -k\theta$, $\theta = a\,e^{-kt}$, $43°C$

10. $\dfrac{dp}{dt} = kp$, $p = p_0\,e^{-kt}$, $73$

## Page 160            Exercise 15.1

1. $\dfrac{2}{p+q}$

2. $(apq, a[p+q])$

4. $-\dfrac{1}{pq}$

12. $2y = 3tx - 8t^3$
13. $x\sin t + y\cos t = a\sin t\cos t$, $a$
14. $(\frac{2}{3}[p^2 + pq + q^2], pq[p+q])$
15. 
   1 $2y = 3x + 7$
   2 $8y = x^2 + 8$
   3 $(x-3)^2 + (y-2)^2 = 1$
   4 $y = x^2 + 3$
   5 $y = 3$
   6 $y^2 = x - 4$
   7 $2x^2 y = 25$
   8 $\dfrac{x^2}{16} + y^2 = 1$
   9 $y = \dfrac{3-x}{x-1}$
   10 $xy = 6$

## Page 162            Exercise 15.2

1. $pq + p^2 + 2 = 0$

3. $x\cos t + y\sin t = 7$, $\dfrac{x\cos t}{7} + \dfrac{y\sin t}{3} = 1$

4. $25y = 15x + 24$
5. $\pm 2ac$
7. $64y^2 = 81(4x - 9)$

10. $\dfrac{x\cos t}{5} + \dfrac{y\sin t}{4} = 1$,

   $(1 - \frac{3}{5}\cos t)\Big/\sqrt{\dfrac{\cos^2 t}{25} + \dfrac{\sin^2 t}{16}}$,

   $(1 + \frac{3}{5}\cos t)\Big/\sqrt{\dfrac{\cos^2 t}{25} + \dfrac{\sin^2 t}{16}}$,

   product $= 16$

13. $T\left(0, \dfrac{2c}{t}\right)$, $N\left(\dfrac{c(t^4 - 1)}{t^3}, 0\right)$

14. $(2, 1)$, $2$
16. $y = 3x - 1$
18. $x^2(1 - e^2) + y^2 = a^2(1 - e^2)$

## Page 165            Exercise E1

1. $x$
2. $x < -2$ or $x > \frac{2}{3}$
3. $\frac{1}{27} - \frac{1}{27}x + \frac{2}{81}x^2$
4. Domain, all $x \neq -2$, range, all $f(x) \neq 1$; $0$
5. $\tan A = -\tan(B + C)$
7. $\theta = 18.4°$ or $71.6°$
8. $2$
9. $y = 2x^2 - 1$, $(|x| \leq 1)$
10. $|z_1| = 2$, $|z_2| = 4$, $\arg z_1 = \alpha$,
    $\arg z_2 = 2\alpha$, $z_1 z_2 = 8(\cos 3\alpha + i\sin 3\alpha)$,
    $\dfrac{z_2}{z_1} = 2(\cos\alpha + i\sin\alpha)$
11. $\frac{23}{11}$
12. $(1\frac{1}{2}, 7\frac{1}{2})$
13. $1 : n$
15. $\dfrac{2\sec^2 2x}{\tan 2x}$
16. $4x + y = 14$
17. $\ln|e^x + 2x| + c$
18. $2$
19. $\mathbf{p} + 7\mathbf{q}$
20. $-\frac{26}{27}$

## Page 166            Exercise E2

| | | | |
|---|---|---|---|
| 1. C | 6. B | 11. E | 16. C |
| 2. E | 7. C | 12. A | 17. D |
| 3. B | 8. B | 13. A | 18. A |
| 4. C | 9. B | 14. D | 19. B |
| 5. E | 10. B | 15. D | 20. E |

**Page 168**          **Exercise E3**

| | | | |
|---|---|---|---|
| 1. | B | 11. | E |
| 2. | C | 12. | D |
| 3. | B | 13. | B |
| 4. | A | 14. | C |
| 5. | B | 15. | E |
| 6. | E | 16. | C |
| 7. | D | 17. | A |
| 8. | E | 18. | A |
| 9. | C | 19. | A |
| 10. | B | 20. | D |

**Page 171**          **Exercise E4**

1. $\frac{1}{2}\mathbf{a}+\frac{1}{2}\mathbf{b}$, $\frac{1}{2}\mathbf{c}+\frac{1}{2}\mathbf{d}$, $\frac{1}{4}\mathbf{a}+\frac{1}{4}\mathbf{b}+\frac{1}{4}\mathbf{c}+\frac{1}{4}\mathbf{d}$
2. $gf(x)=(\ln x)^2$, $(gf)^{-1}(x)=e^{\sqrt{x}}$
3. 3,5
4. $z=-1$ or $4\pm2i$
5. $y=2x+6$, $(-3,0)$
6. $\dfrac{|c|}{\sqrt{a^2+b^2}}$
7. $(2,0,6)$
8. $\theta=n\pi$ or $\dfrac{n\pi}{2}+(-1)^{n+1}\dfrac{\pi}{12}$
9. $8\pi a^2u$ cm$^3$/s
10. $14\ln 2-3$, $30(\ln 2)^2-14\ln 2+3$
13. $\dfrac{\pi}{6}-\dfrac{\sqrt{3}}{4}$
14. 2.1 minutes
15. $y=1+\dfrac{1}{x-3}+\dfrac{1}{x-1}$,

$\dfrac{dy}{dx}=-\dfrac{1}{(x-3)^2}-\dfrac{1}{(x-1)^2}$,

$\dfrac{d^2y}{dx^2}=\dfrac{2}{(x-3)^3}+\dfrac{2}{(x-1)^3}$, $2x+y=5$

**Page 172**          **Exercise E5**

1. 14
2. $\frac{2}{15}$
3. $1-x-\frac{1}{2}x^2-\frac{1}{2}x^3$, $|x|<\frac{1}{2}$, 1.4/4
4. Domain: all $x\neq3$, range: all $f(x)\neq1$,

$f^{-1}(x)=\dfrac{3x}{x-1}$, domain: all $x\neq1$,

range: all $f^{-1}(x)\neq3$; $x=0$ or 4
5. 10 cos $\theta$, 0.06
6. $x=5$
7. $1+\pi/2$
8. $5\sqrt{2}\cos(\theta-\alpha)$ where $\alpha=\tan^{-1}7\approx81.9°$; maximum $5\sqrt{2}$, minimum $-5\sqrt{2}$; $\theta=36.9°$ or $126.9°$
9. $x^2+y^2-6x-4y-112=0$
11. Maximum $(\pi/6,1)$, minimum $(-\pi/6,-1)$
12. $4\mathbf{j}+7\mathbf{k}$
13. 4
14. $y^2=\dfrac{5x-4}{3x}$, $y=\dfrac{4x}{2+3x}$, $\frac{2}{49}$
15. $\dfrac{x}{1+x^2}+\dfrac{2}{3-x}$

**Page 173**          **Exercise E6**

1. $\sin^{-1}\dfrac{1-x}{x}$, $x\geqslant\frac{1}{2}$
2. $\frac{1}{6}$
3. $x=\frac{1}{2}$ or $\pm\sqrt{3}/2$, $\theta=\pi/6$ or $\pm\pi/3$
4. $3x+y+20=0$, $-6-2i$
5. $30°$
6. 28.0, $9\pi$, 1.0%
8. $\dfrac{dy}{dx}=kxy$, $y=5\,e^{(x^2-4)/20}$
9. $P=a^nr^{\frac{1}{2}n(n-1)}$
10. $x^2+y^2-16x-12y=0$, $4x+3y=100$
11. $\dfrac{1}{1-3x}-\dfrac{1}{1-2x}$, $x+5x^2+19x^3$, $(3^r-2^r)x^r$, $|x|<\frac{1}{3}$
12. $y=8a$
13. $a=1.5$, $b=0.7$, $y=20$.
   (*There may be variations in your answers.*)
14.   1  $\dfrac{a}{1+a}$

      2  $1-\pi/4$

      3  $\pi/2-1$
15. $(4,2)$; $(2,0)$ and $(8,0)$, $30-32\ln 2$
16. $-\cos 2\theta-\dfrac{\cos^3 2\theta}{3}-\dfrac{\cos^5 2\theta}{5}$;

      0, $\pi/2$, $\pi$, $3\pi/2$ or $2\pi$

# Index